Universitext

Universitext

Universitext is a series of textbooks that presents material from a wide variety of mathematical disciplines at master's level and beyond. The books, often well class-tested by their author, may have an informal, personal, even experimental approach to their subject matter. Some of the most successful and established books in the series have evolved through several editions, always following the evolution of teaching curricula, into very polished texts.

Thus as research topics trickle down into graduate-level teaching, first textbooks written for new, cutting-edge courses may make their way into *Universitext*.

For further volumes:
www.springer.com/series/223

R.B. Bapat

Linear Algebra
and Linear Models

Third Edition

Prof. R.B. Bapat
Indian Statistical Institute
New Delhi
India

A co-publication with the Hindustan Book Agency, New Delhi, licensed for sale in all countries outside of India. Sold and distributed within India by the Hindustan Book Agency, P 19 Green Park Extn., New Delhi 110 016, India
© Hindustan Book Agency 2011
HBA ISBN 978-93-80250-28-1

ISSN 0172-5939   e-ISSN 2191-6675
Universitext
ISBN 978-1-4471-2738-3   e-ISBN 978-1-4471-2739-0
DOI 10.1007/978-1-4471-2739-0
Springer London Dordrecht Heidelberg New York

British Library Cataloguing in Publication Data
A catalogue record for this book is available from the British Library

Library of Congress Control Number: 2012931413

Mathematics Subject Classification: 15A03, 15A09, 15A18, 62J05, 62J10, 62K10

First edition: 1993 by Hindustan Book Agency, Delhi, India
Second edition: 2000 by Springer-Verlag New York, Inc., and Hindustan Book Agency
© Springer-Verlag London Limited 2012

Printed on acid-free paper

Springer is part of Springer Science+Business Media (www.springer.com)

Preface

The main purpose of the present monograph is to provide a rigorous introduction to the basic aspects of the theory of linear estimation and hypothesis testing. The necessary prerequisites in matrices, multivariate normal distribution, and distribution of quadratic forms are developed along the way. The monograph is primarily aimed at advanced undergraduate and first-year master's students taking courses in linear algebra, linear models, multivariate analysis, and design of experiments. It should also be of use to researchers as a source of several standard results and problems.

Some features in which we deviate from the standard textbooks on the subject are as follows.

We deal exclusively with real matrices, and this leads to some nonconventional proofs. One example is the proof of the fact that a symmetric matrix has real eigenvalues. We rely on ranks and determinants a bit more than is done usually. The development in the first two chapters is somewhat different from that in most texts.

It is not the intention to give an extensive introduction to matrix theory. Thus, several standard topics such as various canonical forms and similarity are not found here. We often derive only those results that are explicitly used later. The list of facts in matrix theory that are elementary, elegant, but not covered here is almost endless.

We put a great deal of emphasis on the generalized inverse and its applications. This amounts to avoiding the "geometric" or the "projections" approach that is favored by some authors and taking recourse to a more algebraic approach. Partly as a personal bias, I feel that the geometric approach works well in providing an understanding of why a result should be true but has limitations when it comes to proving the result rigorously.

The first three chapters are devoted to matrix theory, linear estimation, and tests of linear hypotheses, respectively. Chapter 4 collects several results on eigenvalues and singular values that are frequently required in statistics but usually are not proved in statistics texts. This chapter also includes sections on principal components and canonical correlations. Chapter 5 prepares the background for a course in designs, establishing the linear model as the underlying mathematical framework. The sections on optimality may be useful as motivation for further reading in this research area in which there is considerable activity at present. Similarly, the last chapter tries to provide a glimpse into the richness of a topic in generalized inverses (rank additivity) that has many interesting applications as well.

Several exercises are included, some of which are used in subsequent developments. Hints are provided for a few exercises, whereas reference to the original source is given in some other cases.

I am grateful to Professor Aloke Dey, H. Neudecker, K.P.S. Bhaskara Rao, and Dr. N. Eagambaram for their comments on various portions of the manuscript. Thanks are also due to B. Ganeshan for his help in getting the computer printouts at various stages.

About the Second Edition

This is a thoroughly revised and enlarged version of the first edition. Besides correcting the minor mathematical and typographical errors, the following additions have been made:

1. A few problems have been added at the end of each section in the first four chapters. All the chapters now contain some new exercises.
2. Complete solutions or hints are provided to several problems and exercises.
3. Two new sections, one on the "volume of a matrix" and the other on the "star order," have been added.

About the Third Edition

In this edition the material has been completely reorganized. The linear algebra part is dealt with in the first six chapters. These chapters constitute a first course in linear algebra, suitable for statistics students, or for those looking for a matrix approach to linear algebra.

We have added a chapter on linear mixed models. There is also a new chapter containing additional problems on rank. These problems are not covered in a traditional linear algebra course. However we believe that the elegance of the matrix theoretic approach to linear algebra is clearly brought out by problems on rank and generalized inverse like the ones covered in this chapter.

I thank the numerous individuals who made suggestions for improvement and pointed out corrections in the first two editions. I wish to particularly mention N. Eagambaram and Jeff Stuart for their meticulous comments. I also thank Aloke Dey for his comments on a preliminary version of Chap. 9.

New Delhi, India   Ravindra Bapat

Contents

Chapter 1
Vector Spaces and Subspaces

1.1 Preliminaries

In this chapter we first review certain basic concepts. We consider only real matrices. Although our treatment is self-contained, the reader is assumed to be familiar with the basic operations on matrices. We also assume knowledge of elementary properties of the determinant.

An $m \times n$ matrix consists of mn real numbers arranged in m rows and n columns. The entry in row i and column j of the matrix A is denoted by a_{ij}. An $m \times 1$ matrix is called a column vector of order m; similarly, a $1 \times n$ matrix is a row vector of order n. An $m \times n$ matrix is called a square matrix if $m = n$.

If A and B are $m \times n$ matrices, then $A + B$ is defined as the $m \times n$ matrix with (i, j)-entry $a_{ij} + b_{ij}$. If A is a matrix and c is a real number then cA is obtained by multiplying each element of A by c.

If A is $m \times p$ and B is $p \times n$, then their product $C = AB$ is an $m \times n$ matrix with (i, j)-entry given by

$$c_{ij} = \sum_{k=1}^{p} a_{ik}b_{kj}.$$

The following properties hold:

$$(AB)C = A(BC),$$
$$A(B + C) = AB + AC,$$
$$(A + B)C = AC + BC.$$

The *transpose* of the $m \times n$ matrix A, denoted by A', is the $n \times m$ matrix whose (i, j)-entry is a_{ji}. It can be verified that $(A')' = A$, $(A + B)' = A' + B'$ and $(AB)' = B'A'$.

A good understanding of the definition of matrix multiplication is quite useful. We note some simple facts which are often required. We assume that all products occurring here are defined in the sense that the orders of the matrices make them compatible for multiplication.

R.B. Bapat, *Linear Algebra and Linear Models*, Universitext,
DOI 10.1007/978-1-4471-2739-0_1, © Springer-Verlag London Limited 2012

(i) The j-th column of AB is the same as A multiplied by the j-th column of B.

(ii) The i-th row of AB is the same as the i-th row of A multiplied by B.

(iii) The (i, j)-entry of ABC is obtained as

$$(x_1, \ldots, x_p)B \begin{bmatrix} y_1 \\ \vdots \\ y_q \end{bmatrix}$$

where $(x_1, \ldots, x_p)$ is the i-th row of A and $(y_1, \ldots, y_q)'$ is the j-th column of C.

(iv) If $A = [a_1, \ldots, a_n]$ and

$$B = \begin{bmatrix} b'_1 \\ \vdots \\ b'_n \end{bmatrix}$$

where a_i denote columns of A and b'_j denote rows of B, then

$$AB = a_1 b'_1 + \cdots + a_n b'_n.$$

A *diagonal matrix* is a square matrix A such that $a_{ij} = 0$, $i \neq j$. We denote the diagonal matrix

$$\begin{bmatrix} \lambda_1 & 0 & \cdots & 0 \\ 0 & \lambda_2 & \cdots & 0 \\ \vdots & \vdots & \ddots & \vdots \\ 0 & 0 & \cdots & \lambda_n \end{bmatrix}$$

by $\mathrm{diag}(\lambda_1, \ldots, \lambda_n)$. When $\lambda_i = 1$ for all i, this matrix reduces to the *identity matrix* of order n, which we denote by I_n or often simply by I, if the order is clear from the context. Observe that for any square matrix A, we have $AI = IA = A$.

The entries $a_{11}, \ldots, a_{nn}$ are said to constitute the (main) diagonal entries of A. The *trace* of A is defined as

$$\mathrm{trace}\, A = a_{11} + \cdots + a_{nn}.$$

It follows from this definition that if A, B are matrices such that both AB and BA are defined, then

$$\mathrm{trace}\, AB = \mathrm{trace}\, BA.$$

The *determinant* of an $n \times n$ matrix A, denoted by $|A|$, is defined as

$$|A| = \sum_\sigma \varepsilon(\sigma) a_{1\sigma(1)} \cdots a_{n\sigma(n)}$$

where the summation is over all permutations $\{\sigma(1), \ldots, \sigma(n)\}$ of $\{1, \ldots, n\}$ and $\varepsilon(\sigma)$ is 1 or -1 according as σ is even or odd.

We state some basic properties of determinant without proof:

(i) The determinant can be evaluated by expansion along a row or a column. Thus, expanding along the first row,

$$|A| = \sum_{j=1}^{n}(-1)^{1+j}a_{1j}|A_{1j}|$$

where A_{1j} is the submatrix obtained by deleting the first row and the j-th column of A. We also note that

$$\sum_{j=1}^{n}(-1)^{1+j}a_{ij}|A_{1j}| = 0, \quad i = 2,\ldots,n.$$

(ii) The determinant changes sign if two rows (or columns) are interchanged.
(iii) The determinant is unchanged if a constant multiple of one row is added to another row. A similar property is true for columns.
(iv) The determinant is a linear function of any column (row) when all the other columns (rows) are held fixed.
(v) $|AB| = |A||B|$.

The matrix A is *upper triangular* if $a_{ij} = 0$, $i > j$. The transpose of an upper triangular matrix is *lower triangular*.

It will often be necessary to work with matrices in partitioned form. For example, let

$$A = \begin{bmatrix} A_{11} & A_{12} \\ A_{21} & A_{22} \end{bmatrix}, \qquad B = \begin{bmatrix} B_{11} & B_{12} \\ B_{21} & B_{22} \end{bmatrix},$$

be two matrices where each A_{ij}, B_{ij} is itself a matrix. If compatibility for matrix multiplication is assumed throughout then we can write

$$AB = \begin{bmatrix} A_{11}B_{11} + A_{12}B_{21} & A_{11}B_{12} + A_{12}B_{22} \\ A_{21}B_{11} + A_{22}B_{21} & A_{21}B_{12} + A_{22}B_{22} \end{bmatrix}.$$

1.2 Vector Spaces

A nonempty set S is called a *vector space* if it satisfies the following conditions:

(i) For any x, y in S, $x + y$ is defined and is in S. Further,

$$x + y = y + x \quad \text{(commutativity)},$$
$$x + (y + z) = (x + y) + z \quad \text{(associativity)}.$$

(ii) There exists an element in S, denoted by 0, such that $x + 0 = x$ for all x.
(iii) For any x in S there exists an element y in S such that $x + y = 0$.
(iv) For any x in S and any real number c, cx is defined and is in S; moreover, $1x = x$ for any x.

(v) For any x_1, x_2 in S and reals c_1, c_2, $c_1(x_1 + x_2) = c_1x_1 + c_1x_2$, $(c_1 + c_2)x_1 = c_1x_1 + c_2x_1$ and $c_1(c_2x_1) = (c_1c_2)x_1$.

Elements in S are called *vectors*. If x, y are vectors then the operation of taking their sum $x + y$ is referred to as vector addition. The vector in (ii) is called the *zero vector*. The operation in (iv) is called *scalar multiplication*. A vector space may be defined with reference to any field. We have taken the field to be the field of real numbers as this will be sufficient for our purpose.

The set of column vectors of order n (or $n \times 1$ matrices) is a vector space. So is the set of row vectors of order n. These two vector spaces are the ones we consider most of the time.

Let $\mathbb{R}^n$ denote the set $\mathbb{R} \times \mathbb{R} \times \cdots \times \mathbb{R}$, taken n times where $\mathbb{R}$ is the set of real numbers. We will write elements of $\mathbb{R}^n$ either as column vectors or as row vectors depending upon whichever is convenient in a given situation.

If S, T are vector spaces and $S \subset T$ then S is called a subspace of T.

Let us describe all possible subspaces of $\mathbb{R}^3$. Clearly $\mathbb{R}^3$ is a vector space and so is the space consisting of only the zero vector, i.e., the vector of all zeros. Let c_1, c_2, c_3 be real numbers. The set of all vectors $x \in \mathbb{R}^3$ which satisfy

$$c_1x_1 + c_2x_2 + c_3x_3 = 0$$

is a subspace of R^3 (here x_1, x_2, x_3 are the coordinates of x). Geometrically, this set represents a plane passing through the origin. Intersection of two distinct planes through the origin is a straight line through the origin and is also a subspace. These are the only possible subspaces of $\mathbb{R}^3$.

1.3 Basis and Dimension

The *linear span* of (or the space spanned by) the vectors $x_1, \ldots, x_m$ is defined to be the set of all linear combinations $c_1x_1 + \cdots + c_mx_m$ where $c_1, \ldots, c_m$ are real numbers. The linear span is a subspace; this follows from the definition.

A set of vectors $x_1, \ldots, x_m$ is said to be *linearly dependent* if there exist real numbers $c_1, \ldots, c_m$ such that at least one c_i is nonzero and $c_1x_1 + \cdots + c_mx_m = 0$. A set is *linearly independent* if it is not linearly dependent. Strictly speaking, we should refer to a *collection* (or a *multiset*) of vectors rather than a set of vectors in the two preceding definitions. Thus when we talk of vectors $x_1, \ldots, x_m$ being linearly dependent or independent, we allow for the possibility of the vectors not necessarily being distinct.

The following statements are easily proved.

(i) The set consisting of the zero vector alone is linearly dependent.
(ii) If $X \subset Y$ and if X is linearly dependent, then so is Y.
(iii) If $X \subset Y$ and if Y is linearly independent, then so is X.

A set of vectors is said to form a *basis* for the vector space S if it is linearly independent and its linear span equals S.

Let e_i be the i-th column of the $n \times n$ identity matrix. The set $e_1, \ldots, e_n$ forms a basis for $\mathbb{R}^n$, called the *standard basis*.

If $x_1, \ldots, x_m$ is a basis for S then any vector x in S admits a unique representation as a linear combination $c_1 x_1 + \cdots + c_m x_m$. For, if

$$x = c_1 x_1 + \cdots + c_m x_m = d_1 x_1 + \cdots + d_m x_m,$$

then

$$(c_1 - d_1)x_1 + \cdots + (c_m - d_m)x_m = 0$$

and since $x_1, \ldots, x_m$ are linearly independent, $c_i = d_i$ for each i.

A vector space is said to be *finite dimensional* if it has a basis consisting of finitely many vectors. The vector space containing only the zero vector is also finite dimensional. We will consider only finite dimensional vector spaces. Very often it will be implicitly assumed that the vector spaces under consideration are nontrivial, i.e. contain vectors other than the zero vector.

1.1 *Let S be a vector space. Then any two bases of S have the same cardinality.*

Proof Suppose $x_1, \ldots, x_p$ and $y_1, \ldots, y_q$ are bases for S and let, if possible, $p > q$. We can express every x_i as a linear combination of $y_1, \ldots, y_q$. Thus there exists a $p \times q$ matrix $A = (a_{ij})$ such that

$$x_i = \sum_{j=1}^{q} a_{ij} y_j, \quad i = 1, \ldots, p. \tag{1.1}$$

Similarly there exists a $q \times p$ matrix $B = (b_{ij})$ such that

$$y_j = \sum_{k=1}^{p} b_{jk} x_k, \quad j = 1, \ldots, q. \tag{1.2}$$

From (1.1), (1.2) we see that

$$x_i = \sum_{k=1}^{p} c_{ik} x_k, \quad i = 1, \ldots, p \tag{1.3}$$

where $C = AB$. It follows from (1.3) and the observation made preceding **1.1** that $AB = I$, the identity matrix of order p. Add $p - q$ zero columns to A to get the $p \times p$ matrix U. Similarly add $p - q$ zero rows to B to get the $p \times p$ matrix V. Then $UV = AB = I$. Therefore $|UV| = 1$. However $|U| = |V| = 0$, since U has a zero column and V has a zero row. Thus we have a contradiction and hence $p \leq q$. We can similarly prove that $q \leq p$ and it follows that $p = q$. ☐

In the process of proving **1.1** we have proved the following statement which will be useful. Let S be a vector space. Suppose $x_1, \ldots, x_p$ is a basis for S and suppose the set $y_1, \ldots, y_q$ spans S. Then $p \leq q$.

The *dimension* of the vector space S, denoted by $\dim(S)$, is defined to be the cardinality of a basis of S. By convention the dimension of the space containing only the zero vector is zero.

Let S, T be vector spaces. We say that S is *isomorphic* to T if there exists a one-to-one and onto map $f : S \longrightarrow T$ (called an isomorphism) such that f is *linear*, i.e., $f(x + y) = f(x) + f(y)$ and $f(cx) = cf(x)$ for all x, y in S and reals c.

1.2 *Let S and T be vector spaces. Then S, T are isomorphic if and only if $\dim(S) = \dim(T)$.*

Proof We first prove the *only if* part. Suppose $f : S \longrightarrow T$ is an isomorphism. If $x_1, \ldots, x_k$ is a basis for S then we will show that $f(x_1), \ldots, f(x_k)$ is a basis for T. First suppose $c_1 f(x_1) + \cdots + c_k f(x_k) = 0$. It follows from the definition of isomorphism that $f(c_1 x_1 + \cdots + c_k x_k) = 0$ and hence $c_1 x_1 + \cdots + c_k x_k = 0$. Since $x_1, \ldots, x_k$ are linearly independent, $c_1 = \cdots = c_k = 0$ and therefore $f(x_1), \ldots, f(x_k)$ are linearly independent. If $v \in T$ then there exists $u \in S$ such that $f(u) = v$. We can write $u = d_1 x_1 + \cdots + d_k x_k$ for some $d_1, \ldots, d_k$. Now $v = f(u) = d_1 f(x_1) + \cdots + d_k f(x_k)$. Thus $f(x_1), \ldots, f(x_k)$ span T and hence form a basis for T. It follows that $\dim(T) = k$.

To prove the converse, let $x_1, \ldots, x_k; y_1, \ldots, y_k$ be bases for S and T respectively. (Since $\dim(S) = \dim(T)$, the bases have the same cardinality.) Any x in S admits a unique representation

$$x = c_1 x_1 + \cdots + c_k x_k.$$

Define $f(x) = y$ where $y = c_1 y_1 + \cdots + c_k y_k$. It can be verified that f satisfies the definition of isomorphism.   □

1.3 *Let S be a vector space and suppose S is the linear span of the vectors $x_1, \ldots, x_m$. If some x_i is a linear combination of $x_1, \ldots, x_{i-1}, x_{i+1}, \ldots, x_m$, then these latter vectors also span S.*

The proof is easy.

1.4 *Let S be a vector space of dimension n and let $x_1, \ldots, x_m$ be linearly independent vectors in S. Then there exists a basis for S containing $x_1, \ldots, x_m$.*

Proof Let $y_1, \ldots, y_n$ be a basis for S. The set $x_1, \ldots, x_m, y_1, \ldots, y_n$ is linearly dependent and therefore there exists a linear combination

$$c_1 x_1 + \cdots + c_m x_m + d_1 y_1 + \cdots + d_n y_n = 0$$

where some c_i or d_i is nonzero. However, since $x_1, \ldots, x_m$ are linearly independent, it must be true that some d_i is nonzero. Therefore some y_i is a linear combination of the remaining vectors. By **1.3** the set

$$x_1, \ldots, x_m, y_1, \ldots, y_{i-1}, y_{i+1}, \ldots, y_n$$

also spans S. If the set is linearly independent then we have a basis as required. Otherwise we continue the process until we get a basis containing $x_1, \ldots, x_m$.   □

1.5 *Any set of $n + 1$ vectors in $\mathbb{R}^n$ is linearly dependent.*

Proof If the set is linearly independent then by **1.4** we can find a basis for $\mathbb{R}^n$ containing the set. This is a contradiction since every basis for $\mathbb{R}^n$ must contain precisely n vectors.   □

1.6 *Any subspace S of $\mathbb{R}^n$ admits a basis.*

Proof Choose vectors $x_1, \ldots, x_m$ in S successively so that at each stage they are linearly independent. At any stage if the vectors span S then we have a basis. Otherwise there exists a vector x_{m+1} in S which is not in the linear span of $x_1, \ldots, x_m$ and we arrive at the set $x_1, \ldots, x_m, x_{m+1}$ which is linearly independent. The process must terminate since by **1.5** any $n + 1$ vectors in $\mathbb{R}^n$ are linearly dependent.   □

1.7 *If S is a subspace of T then $\dim(S) \leq \dim(T)$. Furthermore, equality holds if and only if $S = T$.*

Proof Recall that we consider only finite dimensional vector spaces. Suppose $\dim(S) = p$, $\dim(T) = q$ and let $x_1, \ldots, x_p$ and $y_1, \ldots, y_q$ be bases for S and T respectively. Using a similar argument as in the proof of **1.6** we can show that any set of r vectors in T is linearly dependent if $r > q$. Since $x_1, \ldots, x_p$ is a linearly independent set of vectors in $S \subset T$, we have $p \leq q$. To prove the second part, suppose $p = q$ and suppose $S \neq T$. Then there exists a vector $z \in T$ which is not in the span of $x_1, \ldots, x_p$. Then the set $x_1, \ldots, x_p, z$ is linearly independent. This is a contradiction since by the remark made earlier, any $p + 1$ vectors in T must be linearly dependent. Therefore we have shown that if S is a subspace of T and if $\dim(S) = \dim(T)$, then $S = T$. Conversely, if $S = T$, then clearly $\dim(S) = \dim(T)$ and the proof is complete.   □

1.4 Exercises

1. Construct a 3×3 matrix A such that both A, A^2 are nonzero but $A^3 = 0$.
2. Decide whether the determinant of the following matrix A is even or odd, without evaluating it explicitly:

$$A = \begin{bmatrix} 387 & 456 & 589 & 238 \\ 488 & 455 & 677 & 382 \\ 440 & 982 & 654 & 651 \\ 892 & 564 & 786 & 442 \end{bmatrix}.$$

3. Let

$$A = \begin{bmatrix} 1 & 0 & 0 \\ 0 & 0 & 0 \\ 0 & 0 & 0 \end{bmatrix}.$$

Can you find 3×3 matrices X, Y such that $XY - YX = A$?

4. If A, B are $n \times n$ matrices, show that

$$\begin{vmatrix} A+B & A \\ A & A \end{vmatrix} = |A||B|.$$

5. Evaluate the determinant of the $n \times n$ matrix A, where $a_{ij} = ij$ if $i \neq j$ and $a_{ij} = 1 + ij$ if $i = j$.

6. Let A be an $n \times n$ matrix and suppose A has a zero submatrix of order $r \times s$ where $r + s = n + 1$. Show that $|A| = 0$.

7. Let A be an $n \times n$ matrix such that trace $AB = 0$ for every $n \times n$ matrix B. Can we conclude that A must be the zero matrix?

8. Which of the following sets are vector spaces (with the natural operations of addition and scalar multiplication)? (i) Vectors (a, b, c, d) such that $a + 2b = c - d$. (ii) $n \times n$ matrices A such that $A^2 = I$. (iii) 3×3 matrices A such that $a_{11} + a_{13} = a_{22} + a_{31}$.

9. If S and T are vector spaces, then are $S \cup T$ and $S \cap T$ vector spaces as well?

10. For any matrix A, show that $A = 0$ if and only if trace $A'A = 0$.

11. Let A be a square matrix. Prove that the following conditions are equivalent: (i) $A = A'$. (ii) $A^2 = AA'$. (iii) trace $A^2 = $ trace AA'. (iv) $A^2 = A'A$. (v) trace $A^2 = $ trace $A'A$.

12. Let A be a square matrix with all row sums equal to 1. If $AA' = A'A$, then show that the column sums of A are also equal to 1.

13. Verify that each of the following sets is a vector space and find its dimension: (i) Vectors (a, b, c, d) such that $a + b = c + d$. (ii) The set of solutions (x, y, z) to the system $2x - y = 0$, $2y + 3z = 0$.

14. If x, y, z is a basis for $\mathbb{R}^3$, which of the following are also bases for $\mathbb{R}^3$? (i) $x + 2y$, $y + 3z$, $x + 2z$. (ii) $x + y - 2z$, $x - 2y + z$, $-2x + y + z$. (iii) x, y, $x + y + z$.

15. If $\{x_1, x_2\}$ and $\{y_1, y_2\}$ are both bases of $\mathbb{R}^2$, show that at least one of the following statements is true: (i) $\{x_1, y_2\}$, $\{x_2, y_1\}$ are both bases of $\mathbb{R}^2$. (ii) $\{x_1, y_1\}$, $\{x_2, y_2\}$ are both bases of $\mathbb{R}^2$.

16. Consider the set of all vectors x in $\mathbb{R}^n$ such that $\sum_{i=1}^n x_i = 0$. Show that the set is a vector space and find a basis for the space.

17. Determine the dimension of the vector space of all $n \times n$ matrices A such that trace $A = 0$.

18. Let S, T be subspaces of $\mathbb{R}^n$. Define $S + T$ as the set of vectors of the form $x + y$ where $x \in S$, $y \in T$. Prove that $S + T$ is a subspace and that

$$\dim(S + T) = \dim(S) + \dim(T) - \dim(S \cap T).$$

19. Let S, T be subspaces of $\mathbb{R}^n$ such that $\dim(S) + \dim(T) > n$. Show that

$$\dim(S \cap T) \geq 1.$$

Chapter 2
Rank, Inner Product and Nonsingularity

2.1 Rank

Let A be an $m \times n$ matrix. The subspace of $\mathbb{R}^m$ spanned by the column vectors of A is called the *column space* or the *column span* of A and is denoted by $\mathscr{C}(A)$. Similarly the subspace of $\mathbb{R}^n$ spanned by the row vectors of A is called the *row space* of A, denoted by $\mathscr{R}(A)$. Clearly $\mathscr{R}(A)$ is isomorphic to $\mathscr{C}(A')$. The dimension of the column space is called the *column rank* whereas the dimension of the row space is called the *row rank* of the matrix. These two definitions turn out to be very short-lived in any linear algebra book since the two ranks are always equal as we show in the next result.

2.1 *The column rank of a matrix equals its row rank.*

Proof Let A be an $m \times n$ matrix with column rank r. Then $\mathscr{C}(A)$ has a basis of r vectors, say $b_1, \ldots, b_r$. Let B be the $m \times r$ matrix $[b_1, \ldots, b_r]$. Since every column of A is a linear combination of $b_1, \ldots, b_r$, we can write $A = BC$ for some $r \times n$ matrix C. Then every row of A is a linear combination of the rows of C and therefore $\mathscr{R}(A) \subset \mathscr{R}(C)$. It follows by **1.7** that the dimension of $\mathscr{R}(A)$, which is the row rank of A, is at most r. We can similarly show that the column rank does not exceed the row rank and therefore the two must be equal. $\qquad\square$

The common value of the column rank and the row rank of A will henceforth be called the *rank* of A and we will denote it by rank A. It is obvious that rank $A =$ rank A'. The rank of A is zero if and only if A is the zero matrix.

2.2 *Let A, B be matrices such that AB is defined. Then*

$$\text{rank}(AB) \leq \min\{\text{rank } A, \text{rank } B\}.$$

Proof A vector in $\mathscr{C}(AB)$ is of the form ABx for some vector x, and therefore it belongs to $\mathscr{C}(A)$. Thus $\mathscr{C}(AB) \subset \mathscr{C}(A)$ and hence by **1.7**,

R.B. Bapat, *Linear Algebra and Linear Models*, Universitext,   9
DOI 10.1007/978-1-4471-2739-0_2, © Springer-Verlag London Limited 2012

$$\text{rank}(AB) = \dim \mathscr{C}(AB) \leq \dim \mathscr{C}(A) = \text{rank}\, A.$$

Now using this fact we have

$$\text{rank}(AB) = \text{rank}\big(B'A'\big) \leq \text{rank}\, B' = \text{rank}\, B. \qquad \square$$

2.3 *Let A be an* $m \times n$ *matrix of rank* r, $r \neq 0$. *Then there exist matrices* B, C *of order* $m \times r$, $r \times n$ *respectively such that* $\text{rank}\, B = \text{rank}\, C = r$ *and* $A = BC$. *This decomposition is called a rank factorization of* A.

Proof The proof proceeds along the same lines as that of **2.1** so that we can write $A = BC$ where B is $m \times r$ and C is $r \times n$. Since the columns of B are linearly independent, $\text{rank}\, B = r$. Since C has r rows, $\text{rank}\, C \leq r$. However, by **2.2**, $r = \text{rank}\, A \leq \text{rank}\, C$ and hence $\text{rank}\, C = r$. $\qquad \square$

Throughout this monograph, whenever we talk of rank factorization of a matrix it is implicitly assumed that the matrix is nonzero.

2.4 *Let* A, B *be* $m \times n$ *matrices. Then* $\text{rank}(A + B) \leq \text{rank}\, A + \text{rank}\, B$.

Proof Let $A = XY$, $B = UV$ be rank factorizations of A, B. Then

$$A + B = XY + UV = [X, U]\begin{bmatrix} Y \\ V \end{bmatrix}.$$

Therefore, by **2.2**,

$$\text{rank}(A + B) \leq \text{rank}\,[X, U].$$

Let $x_1, \ldots, x_p$ and $u_1, \ldots, u_q$ be bases for $\mathscr{C}(X)$, $\mathscr{C}(U)$ respectively. Any vector in the column space of $[X, U]$ can be expressed as a linear combination of these $p + q$ vectors. Thus

$$\text{rank}\,[X, U] \leq \text{rank}\, X + \text{rank}\, U = \text{rank}\, A + \text{rank}\, B,$$

and the proof is complete. $\qquad \square$

The following operations performed on a matrix A are called *elementary column operations*.

  (i) Interchange two columns of A.
 (ii) Multiply a column of A by a nonzero scalar.
(iii) Add a scalar multiple of one column to another column.

These operations clearly leave $\mathscr{C}(A)$ unaffected and therefore they do not change the rank of the matrix. We may define elementary row operations similarly. The elementary row and column operations are particularly useful in computations. Thus to find the rank of a matrix we first reduce it to a matrix with several zeros by these operations and then compute the rank of the resulting matrix.

2.2 Inner Product

Let S be a vector space. A function which assigns a real number $\langle x, y \rangle$ to every pair of vectors x, y in S is said to be an *inner product* if it satisfies the following conditions:

(i) $\langle x, y \rangle = \langle y, x \rangle$
(ii) $\langle x, x \rangle \geq 0$ and equality holds if and only if $x = 0$
(iii) $\langle cx, y \rangle = c \langle x, y \rangle$
(iv) $\langle x + y, z \rangle = \langle x, z \rangle + \langle y, z \rangle$.

In $\mathbb{R}^n$, $\langle x, y \rangle = x'y = x_1 y_1 + \cdots + x_n y_n$ is easily seen to be an inner product. We will work with this inner product while dealing with $\mathbb{R}^n$ and its subspaces, unless indicated otherwise.

For a vector x, the positive square root of the inner product $\langle x, x \rangle$ is called the *norm* of x, denoted by $\|x\|$. Vectors x, y are said to be *orthogonal* or *perpendicular* if $\langle x, y \rangle = 0$, in which case we write $x \perp y$.

2.5 *If $x_1, \ldots, x_m$ are pairwise orthogonal nonzero vectors then they are linearly independent.*

Proof Suppose $c_1 x_1 + \cdots + c_m x_m = 0$. Then

$$\langle c_1 x_1 + \cdots + c_m x_m, x_1 \rangle = 0$$

and hence

$$\sum_{i=1}^{m} c_i \langle x_i, x_1 \rangle = 0.$$

Since the vectors $x_1, \ldots, x_m$ are pairwise orthogonal, it follows that $c_1 \langle x_1, x_1 \rangle = 0$ and since x_1 is nonzero, $c_1 = 0$. Similarly we can show that each c_i is zero. Therefore the vectors are linearly independent. $\quad\square$

A set of vectors $x_1, \ldots, x_m$ is said to form an *orthonormal basis* for the vector space S if the set is a basis for S and furthermore, $\langle x_i, x_j \rangle$ is 0 if $i \neq j$ and 1 if $i = j$.

We now describe the *Gram–Schmidt procedure* which produces an orthonormal basis starting with a given basis, $x_1, \ldots, x_n$.

Set $y_1 = x_1$. Having defined $y_1, \ldots, y_{i-1}$, we define

$$y_i = x_i - a_{i,i-1} y_{i-1} - \cdots - a_{i1} y_1$$

where $a_{i,i-1}, \ldots, a_{i1}$ are chosen so that y_i is orthogonal to $y_1, \ldots, y_{i-1}$. Thus we must solve $\langle y_i, y_j \rangle = 0$, $j = 1, \ldots, i - 1$. This leads to

$$\langle x_i - a_{i,i-1} y_{i-1} - \cdots - a_{i1} y_1, y_j \rangle = 0, \quad j = 1, \ldots, i - 1$$

which gives

$$\langle x_i, y_j \rangle - \sum_{k=1}^{i-1} a_{ik} \langle y_k, y_j \rangle = 0, \quad j = 1, \ldots, i - 1.$$

Now since $y_1, \ldots, y_{i-1}$, is an orthogonal set, we get

$$\langle x_i, y_j \rangle - a_{ij} \langle y_j, y_j \rangle = 0$$

and hence,

$$a_{ij} = \frac{\langle x_i, y_j \rangle}{\langle y_j, y_j \rangle}; \quad j = 1, \ldots, i - 1.$$

The process is continued to obtain the basis $y_1, \ldots, y_n$ of pairwise orthogonal vectors. Since $x_1, \ldots, x_n$ are linearly independent, each y_i is nonzero. Now if we set $z_i = \frac{y_i}{\|y_i\|}$, then $z_1, \ldots, z_n$ is an orthonormal basis. Note that the linear span of $z_1, \ldots, z_i$ equals the linear span of $x_1, \ldots, x_i$ for each i.

We remark that given a set of linearly independent vectors $x_1, \ldots, x_m$, the Gram–Schmidt procedure described above can be used to produce a pairwise orthogonal set $y_1, \ldots, y_m$, such that y_i is a linear combination of $x_1, \ldots, x_{i-1}, i = 1, \ldots, m$. This fact is used in the proof of the next result.

Let W be a set (not necessarily a subspace) of vectors in a vector space S. We define

$$W^\perp = \big\{ x : x \in S, \ \langle x, y \rangle = 0 \text{ for all } y \in W \big\}.$$

It follows from the definitions that $W^\perp$ is a subspace of S.

2.6 *Let S be a subspace of the vector space T and let $x \in T$. Then there exists a unique decomposition $x = u + v$ such that $u \in S$ and $v \in S^\perp$. The vector u is called the orthogonal projection of x on the vector space S.*

Proof If $x \in S$ then $x = x + 0$ is the required decomposition. Otherwise, let $x_1, \ldots, x_m$ be a basis for S. Use the Gram–Schmidt process on the set $x_1, \ldots, x_m, x$ to obtain the sequence $y_1, \ldots, y_m, v$ of pairwise orthogonal vectors. Since v is perpendicular to each y_i and since the linear span of $y_1, \ldots, y_m$ equals that of $x_1, \ldots, x_m$, then $v \in S^\perp$. Also, according to the Gram–Schmidt process, $x - v$ is a linear combination of $y_1, \ldots, y_m$ and hence $x - v \in S$. Now $x = (x - v) + v$ is the required decomposition. It remains to show the uniqueness.

If $x = u_1 + v_1 = u_2 + v_2$ are two decompositions satisfying $u_1 \in S, u_2 \in S, v_1 \in S^\perp, v_2 \in S^\perp$; then

$$(u_1 - u_2) + (v_1 - v_2) = 0.$$

Since $\langle u_1 - u_2, v_1 - v_2 \rangle = 0$, it follows from the preceding equation that $\langle u_1 - u_2, u_1 - u_2 \rangle = 0$. Then $u_1 - u_2 = 0$ and hence $u_1 = u_2$. It easily follows that $v_1 = v_2$. Thus the decomposition is unique.   □

2.7 *Let W be a subset of the vector space T and let S be the linear span of W. Then*

$$\dim(S) + \dim\big(W^\perp\big) = \dim(T).$$

Proof Suppose $\dim(S) = m$, $\dim(W^\perp) = n$ and $\dim(T) = p$. Let $x_1, \ldots, x_m$ and $y_1, \ldots, y_n$ be bases for S, $W^\perp$ respectively. Suppose

$$c_1 x_1 + \cdots + c_m x_m + d_1 y_1 + \cdots + d_n y_n = 0.$$

Let $u = c_1 x_1 + \cdots + c_m x_m$, $v = d_1 y_1 + \cdots + d_n y_n$. Since x_i, y_j are orthogonal for each i, j; u and v are orthogonal. However $u + v = 0$ and hence $u = v = 0$. It follows that $c_i = 0$, $d_j = 0$ for each i, j and hence $x_1, \ldots, x_m$, $y_1, \ldots, y_n$ is a linearly independent set. Therefore $m + n \leq p$. If $m + n < p$, then there exists a vector $z \in T$ such that $x_1, \ldots, x_m$, $y_1, \ldots, y_n, z$ is a linearly independent set. Let M be the linear span of $x_1, \ldots, x_m$, $y_1, \ldots, y_n$. By **2.6** there exists a decomposition $z = u + v$ such that $u \in M$, $v \in M^\perp$. Then v is orthogonal to x_i for every i and hence $v \in W^\perp$. Also, v is orthogonal to y_i for every i and hence $\langle v, v \rangle = 0$ and therefore $v = 0$. It follows that $z = u$. This contradicts the fact that z is linearly independent of $x_1, \ldots, x_m$, $y_1, \ldots, y_n$. Therefore $m + n = p$. $\square$

The proof of the next result is left as an exercise.

2.8 *If $S_1 \subset S_2 \subset T$ are vector spaces, then:* (i) $(S_2)^\perp \subset (S_1)^\perp$. (ii) $(S_1^\perp)^\perp = S_1$.

Let A be an $m \times n$ matrix. The set of all vectors $x \in \mathbb{R}^n$ such that $Ax = 0$ is easily seen to be a subspace of $\mathbb{R}^n$. This subspace is called the *null space* of A, and we denote it by $\mathcal{N}(A)$.

2.9 *Let A be an $m \times n$ matrix. Then $\mathcal{N}(A) = \mathcal{C}(A')^\perp$.*

Proof If $x \in \mathcal{N}(A)$ then $Ax = 0$ and hence $y'Ax = 0$ for all $y \in \mathbb{R}^m$. Thus x is orthogonal to any vector in $\mathcal{C}(A')$. Conversely, if $x \in \mathcal{C}(A')^\perp$, then x is orthogonal to every column of A' and therefore $Ax = 0$. $\square$

2.10 *Let A be an $m \times n$ matrix of rank r. Then $\dim(\mathcal{N}(A)) = n - r$.*

Proof We have

$$\dim(\mathcal{N}(A)) = \dim(\mathcal{C}(A')^\perp) \quad \text{by } \mathbf{5.5}$$
$$= n - \dim(\mathcal{C}(A')) \quad \text{by } \mathbf{2.7}$$
$$= n - r.$$

That completes the proof. $\square$

The dimension of the null space of A is called the *nullity* of A. Thus **2.10** says that *the rank plus the nullity equals the number of columns*. For this reason we will refer to **2.10** as the "rank plus nullity" theorem.

2.3 Nonsingularity

Suppose we have m linear equations in the n unknowns $x_1, \ldots, x_n$. The equations can conveniently be expressed as a single matrix equation $Ax = b$, where A is the $m \times n$ matrix of coefficients. The equation $Ax = b$ is said to be *consistent* if it has at least one solution, otherwise it is *inconsistent*. The equation is *homogeneous* if $b = 0$. The set of solutions of the homogeneous equation $Ax = 0$ is clearly the null space of A.

If the equation $Ax = b$ is consistent then we can write

$$b = x_1^0 a_1 + \cdots + x_n^0 a_n$$

for some $x_1^0, \ldots, x_n^0$ where $a_1, \ldots, a_n$ are the columns of A. Thus $b \in \mathscr{C}(A)$. Conversely, if $b \in \mathscr{C}(A)$ then $Ax = b$ must be consistent. If the equation is consistent and if x^0 is a solution of the equation then the set of all solutions of the equation is given by

$$\{x^0 + x : x \in \mathscr{N}(A)\}.$$

Clearly, the equation $Ax = b$ has either no solution, a unique solution or infinitely many solutions.

A matrix A of order $n \times n$ is said to be *nonsingular* if rank $A = n$, otherwise the matrix is *singular*.

2.11 *Let A be an $n \times n$ matrix. Then the following conditions are equivalent*:

 (i) *A is nonsingular, i.e., rank $A = n$.*
 (ii) *For any $b \in R^n$, $Ax = b$ has a unique solution.*
 (iii) *There exists a unique matrix B such that $AB = BA = I$.*

Proof (i) $\Rightarrow$ (ii). Since rank $A = n$ we have $\mathscr{C}(A) = \mathbb{R}^n$ and therefore $Ax = b$ has a solution. If $Ax = b$ and $Ay = b$ then $A(x - y) = 0$. By **2.10**, $\dim(\mathscr{N}(A)) = 0$ and therefore $x = y$. This proves the uniqueness.

(ii) $\Rightarrow$ (iii). By (ii), $Ax = e_i$ has a unique solution, say b_i, where e_i is the i-th column of the identity matrix. Then $B = (b_1, \ldots, b_n)$ is a unique matrix satisfying $AB = I$. Applying the same argument to A' we conclude the existence of a unique matrix C such that $CA = I$. Now $B = (CA)B = C(AB) = C$.

(iii) $\Rightarrow$ (i). Suppose (iii) holds. Then any $x \in \mathbb{R}^n$ can be expressed as $x = A(Bx)$ and hence $\mathscr{C}(A) = \mathbb{R}^n$. Thus rank A, which by definition is $\dim(\mathscr{C}(A))$ must be n. $\square$

The matrix B of (ii) of **2.11** is called the *inverse* of A and is denoted by A^{-1}.

If A, B are $n \times n$ matrices, then $(AB)(B^{-1}A^{-1}) = I$ and therefore $(AB)^{-1} = B^{-1}A^{-1}$. In particular, the product of two nonsingular matrices is nonsingular.

Let A be an $n \times n$ matrix. We will denote by A_{ij} the submatrix of A obtained by deleting row i and column j. The *cofactor* of a_{ij} is defined to be $(-1)^{i+j} |A_{ij}|$. The *adjoint* of A, denoted by adj A, is the $n \times n$ matrix whose (i, j)-entry is the cofactor of a_{ji}.

From the theory of determinants we have

$$\sum_{j=1}^{n} a_{ij}(-1)^{i+j}|A_{ij}| = |A|$$

and for $i \neq k$,

$$\sum_{j=1}^{n} a_{ij}(-1)^{i+k}|A_{kj}| = 0.$$

These equations can be interpreted as

$$A \operatorname{adj} A = |A|I.$$

Thus if $|A| \neq 0$, then A^{-1} exists and

$$A^{-1} = \frac{1}{|A|} \operatorname{adj} A.$$

Conversely if A is nonsingular, then from $AA^{-1} = I$, we conclude that $|AA^{-1}| = |A||A^{-1}| = 1$ and therefore $|A| \neq 0$. We have therefore proved the following result.

2.12 *A square matrix is nonsingular if and only if its determinant is nonzero.*

An $r \times r$ *minor* of a matrix is defined to be the determinant of an $r \times r$ submatrix of A.

Let A be an $m \times n$ matrix of rank r, let $s > r$, and consider an $s \times s$ minor of A, say the one formed by rows $i_1, \ldots, i_s$ and columns $j_1, \ldots, j_s$. Since the columns $j_1, \ldots, j_s$ must be linearly dependent then by **2.12** the minor must be zero.

Conversely, if A is of rank r then A has r linearly independent rows, say the rows $i_1, \ldots, i_r$. Let B be the submatrix formed by these r rows. Then B has rank r and hence B has column rank r. Thus there is an $r \times r$ submatrix C of B, and hence of A, of rank r. By **2.12**, C has a nonzero determinant.

We therefore have the following definition of rank in terms of minors: The rank of the matrix A is r if (i) there is a nonzero $r \times r$ minor and (ii) every $s \times s$ minor, $s > r$, is zero. As remarked earlier, the rank is zero if and only if A is the zero matrix.

2.4 Frobenius Inequality

2.13 *Let B be an $m \times r$ matrix of rank r. Then there exists a matrix X (called the left inverse of B), such that $XB = I$.*

Proof If $m = r$ then B is nonsingular and admits an inverse. So suppose $r < m$. The columns of B are linearly independent. Thus we can find a set of $m - r$ columns, which, together with the columns of B, form a basis for $\mathbb{R}^m$. In other words, we can find a matrix U of order $m \times (m - r)$ such that $[B, U]$ is nonsingular. Let the inverse of $[B, U]$ be partitioned as $\left[\begin{smallmatrix} X \\ V \end{smallmatrix} \right]$ where X is $r \times m$. Since

$$\begin{bmatrix} X \\ V \end{bmatrix} [B, U] = I,$$

we have $XB = I$. $\square$

We can similarly show that an $r \times n$ matrix C of rank r has a *right inverse*, i.e., a matrix Y such that $CY = I$. Note that a left inverse or a right inverse is not unique, unless the matrix is square and nonsingular.

2.14 *Let B be an $m \times r$ matrix of rank r. Then there exists a nonsingular matrix P such that*

$$PB = \begin{bmatrix} I \\ 0 \end{bmatrix}.$$

Proof The proof is the same as that of **2.13**. If we set $P = \left[\begin{smallmatrix} X \\ V \end{smallmatrix} \right]$ then P satisfies the required condition. $\square$

Similarly, if C is $r \times n$ of rank r then there exists a nonsingular matrix Q such that $CQ = [I, 0]$. These two results and the rank factorization (see **2.3**) immediately lead to the following.

2.15 *Let A be an $m \times n$ matrix of rank r. Then there exist nonsingular matrices P, Q such that*

$$PAQ = \begin{bmatrix} I_r & 0 \\ 0 & 0 \end{bmatrix}.$$

Rank is not affected upon multiplying by a nonsingular matrix. For, if A is $m \times n$ and P is nonsingular of order m then

$$\begin{aligned} \operatorname{rank} A &= \operatorname{rank}\left(P^{-1}PA\right) \\ &\leq \operatorname{rank}(PA) \\ &\leq \operatorname{rank} A. \end{aligned}$$

Hence $\operatorname{rank}(PA) = \operatorname{rank} A$. A similar result holds for post-multiplication by a nonsingular matrix.

2.16 *If A is an $n \times n$ matrix of rank r then there exists an $n \times n$ matrix Z of rank $n - r$ such that $A + Z$ is nonsingular.*

Proof By **2.15** there exist nonsingular matrices P, Q such that

$$PAQ = \begin{bmatrix} I_r & 0 \\ 0 & 0 \end{bmatrix}.$$

Set

$$Z = P^{-1} \begin{bmatrix} 0 & 0 \\ 0 & I_{n-r} \end{bmatrix} Q^{-1}.$$

Then $A + Z = P^{-1}Q^{-1}$ which is nonsingular. □

Observe that **2.16** may also be proved using rank factorization; we leave this as an exercise.

2.17 The Frobenius Inequality *Let* A, B *be* $n \times n$ *matrices. Then*

$$\text{rank}(AB) \geq \text{rank } A + \text{rank } B - n.$$

Proof By **2.16** there exists a matrix Z of rank $n - \text{rank } A$ such that $A + Z$ is nonsingular. We have

$$\begin{aligned}
\text{rank } B &= \text{rank}\big((A+Z)B\big) \\
&= \text{rank}(AB + ZB) \\
&\leq \text{rank}(AB) + \text{rank}(ZB) \quad \text{by } \mathbf{2.4} \\
&\leq \text{rank}(AB) + \text{rank}(Z) \\
&= \text{rank}(AB) + n - \text{rank } A.
\end{aligned}$$

Hence $\text{rank}(AB) \geq \text{rank } A + \text{rank } B - n$. □

2.5 Exercises

1. Find the rank of the following matrix for each real number α:

$$\begin{bmatrix} 1 & 4 & \alpha & 4 \\ 2 & -6 & 7 & 1 \\ 3 & 2 & -6 & 7 \\ 2 & 2 & -5 & 5 \end{bmatrix}.$$

2. Let $\{x_1, \ldots, x_p\}$, $\{y_1, \ldots, y_q\}$ be linearly independent sets in $\mathbb{R}^n$, where $p < q \leq n$. Show that there exists $i \in \{1, \ldots, q\}$ such that $\{x_1, \ldots, x_p, y_i\}$ is linearly independent.

3. Let $X = \{x_1, \ldots, x_n\}$, $Y = \{y_1, \ldots, y_n\}$ be bases for $\mathbb{R}^n$ and let $S \subset X$ be a set of cardinality r, $1 \leq r \leq n$. Show that there exists $T \subset Y$ of cardinality r such that $(X \setminus S) \cup T$ is a basis for $\mathbb{R}^n$.

4. Let A be an $m \times n$ matrix and let B be obtained by changing any k entries of A. Show that

$$\text{rank } A - k \leq \text{rank } B \leq \text{rank } A + k.$$

5. Let A, B, C be $n \times n$ matrices. Is it always true that $\text{rank}(ABC) \leq \text{rank}(AC)$?

6. Find two different rank factorizations of the matrix

$$\begin{bmatrix} 1 & 1 & 2 & 0 \\ 2 & -3 & 1 & 1 \\ 3 & -2 & 3 & 1 \\ 5 & -5 & 4 & 2 \end{bmatrix}.$$

7. Let A, B, C, D be $n \times n$ matrices such that the matrix

$$\begin{bmatrix} A & B \\ C & D \end{bmatrix}$$

has rank n. Show that $|AD| = |BC|$.

8. Which of the following functions define an inner product on R^3?
   (i) $f(x, y) = x_1 y_1 + x_2 y_2 + x_3 y_3 + 1$
   (ii) $f(x, y) = 2x_1 y_1 + 3x_2 y_2 + x_3 y_3 - x_1 y_2 - x_2 y_1$
   (iii) $f(x, y) = x_1 y_1 + 2x_2 y_2 + x_3 y_3 + 2x_1 y_2 + 2x_2 y_1$
   (iv) $f(x, y) = x_1 y_1 + x_2 y_2$
   (v) $f(x, y) = x_1^3 y_1^3 + x_2^3 y_2^3 + x_3^3 y_3^3$.

9. Find the orthogonal projection of $[2, 1, 0]$ on the space spanned by $[1, -1, 1]$, $[0, 1, 1]$.

10. The following vectors form a basis for $\mathbb{R}^3$. Use the Gram–Schmidt procedure to convert it into an orthonormal basis.

$$x = \begin{bmatrix} 2 & 3 & -1 \end{bmatrix}, \qquad y = \begin{bmatrix} 3 & 1 & 0 \end{bmatrix}, \qquad z = \begin{bmatrix} 4 & -1 & 2 \end{bmatrix}.$$

11. Let A be an $n \times n$ matrix. Show that A is nonsingular if and only if $Ax = 0$ has no nonzero solution.

12. Let A be a nonsingular matrix, let $B = A^{-1}$, and suppose A, B are conformally partitioned as

$$A = \begin{bmatrix} A_{11} & A_{12} \\ A_{21} & A_{22} \end{bmatrix}, \qquad B = \begin{bmatrix} B_{11} & B_{12} \\ B_{21} & B_{22} \end{bmatrix}.$$

Then assuming the inverses exist, show that

$$B_{11} = \left(A_{11} - A_{12} A_{22}^{-1} A_{21} \right)^{-1} = A_{11}^{-1} + A_{11}^{-1} A_{12} B_{22} A_{21} A_{11}^{-1},$$

$$B_{22} = \left(A_{22} - A_{21} A_{11}^{-1} A_{12} \right)^{-1} = A_{22}^{-1} + A_{22}^{-1} A_{21} B_{11} A_{12} A_{22}^{-1},$$

$$B_{12} = -A_{11}^{-1} A_{12} B_{22} = -B_{11} A_{12} A_{22}^{-1}.$$

13. Let A be an $n \times n$ matrix and let $b \in \mathbb{R}^n$. Show that A is nonsingular if and only if $Ax = b$ has a unique solution.

14. Let A be an $n \times n$ matrix with only integer entries. Show that A^{-1} exists and has only integer entries if and only if $|A| = \pm 1$.

15. Compute the inverses of the following matrices:
   (i) $\begin{bmatrix} a & b \\ c & d \end{bmatrix}$, where $ad - bc \neq 0$

   (ii) $\begin{bmatrix} 2 & -1 & 0 \\ 2 & 1 & -1 \\ 1 & 0 & 4 \end{bmatrix}$.

16. Let A, B be matrices of order 9×7 and 4×3 respectively. Show that there exists a nonzero 7×4 matrix X such that $AXB = 0$.

17. Let A, X, B be $n \times n$ matrices. Prove the following generalization of the Frobenius Inequality:

$$\operatorname{rank}(AXB) \geq \operatorname{rank}(AX) + \operatorname{rank}(XB) - \operatorname{rank}(X).$$

18. Let A, B, C, D be $n \times n$ matrices such that A is nonsingular and suppose $AC = CA$. Then show that

$$\begin{vmatrix} A & B \\ C & D \end{vmatrix} = |AD - CB|.$$

19. Let P be an orthogonal matrix and let Q be obtained by deleting the first row and column of P. Show that p_{11} and $|Q|$ are equal in absolute value.

Chapter 3
Eigenvalues and Positive Definite Matrices

3.1 Preliminaries

Let A be an $n \times n$ matrix. The determinant $|A - \lambda I|$ is a polynomial in the (complex) variable λ of degree n and is called the *characteristic polynomial* of A. The equation

$$|A - \lambda I| = 0$$

is called the *characteristic equation* of A. By the Fundamental Theorem of Algebra the equation has n roots and these roots are called the *eigenvalues* of A.

The eigenvalues may not all be distinct. The number of times an eigenvalue occurs as a root of the characteristic equation is called the *algebraic multiplicity* of the eigenvalue.

We factor the characteristic polynomial as

$$|A - \lambda I| = (\lambda_1 - \lambda) \cdots (\lambda_n - \lambda). \tag{3.1}$$

If we set $\lambda = 0$ in (3.1) then we see that $|A|$ is just the product of the eigenvalues of A. Similarly by equating the coefficient of λ^{n-1} on either side of (3.1) we see that the trace of A equals the sum of the eigenvalues.

A *principal submatrix* of a square matrix is a submatrix formed by a set of rows and the corresponding set of columns. A *principal minor* of A is the determinant of a principal submatrix.

A square matrix A is called *symmetric* if $A = A'$. An $n \times n$ matrix A is said to be *positive definite* if it is symmetric and if for any nonzero vector x, $x'Ax > 0$. A symmetric $n \times n$ matrix A is said to be *positive semidefinite* if $x'Ax \geq 0$ for all $x \in \mathbb{R}^n$.

The identity matrix is clearly positive definite and so is a diagonal matrix with only positive entries along the diagonal.

3.1 *If A is positive definite then it is nonsingular.*

Proof If $Ax = 0$, then $x'Ax = 0$ and since A is positive definite, $x = 0$. Therefore A must be nonsingular. □

R.B. Bapat, *Linear Algebra and Linear Models*, Universitext,
DOI 10.1007/978-1-4471-2739-0_3, © Springer-Verlag London Limited 2012

The next result is obvious from the definition.

3.2 *If A, B are positive definite and if $\alpha \geq 0$, $\beta \geq 0$, with $\alpha + \beta > 0$, then $\alpha A + \beta B$ is positive definite.*

3.3 *If A is positive definite then $|A| > 0$.*

Proof For $0 \leq \alpha \leq 1$, define

$$f(\alpha) = |\alpha A + (1 - \alpha)I|.$$

By **3.2**, $\alpha A + (1 - \alpha)I$ is positive definite and therefore by **3.1**, $f(\alpha) \neq 0, 0 \leq \alpha \leq 1$. Clearly, $f(0) = 1$ and since f is continuous, $f(1) = |A| > 0$.   □

3.4 *If A is positive definite then any principal submatrix of A is positive definite.*

Proof Since A is positive definite, $x'Ax > 0$ for all $x \neq 0$. Apply this condition to the set of vectors which have zeros in coordinates $j_1, \ldots, j_s$. For such a vector x, $x'Ax$ reduces to an expression of the type $y'By$ where B is the principal submatrix of A formed by deleting rows and columns $j_1, \ldots, j_s$ from A. It follows that B, and similarly any principal submatrix of A, is positive definite.   □

3.2 The Spectral Theorem

3.5 *If A is a symmetric matrix then the eigenvalues of A are all real.*

Proof Suppose μ is an eigenvalue of A and let $\mu = \alpha + i\beta$, where α, β are real and $i = \sqrt{-1}$. Since $|A - \mu I| = 0$, we have

$$|(A - \alpha I) - i\beta I| = 0.$$

Taking the complex conjugate of the above determinant and multiplying the two we get

$$|(A - \alpha I) - i\beta I||(A - \alpha I) + i\beta I| = 0. \tag{3.2}$$

Thus

$$|(A - \alpha I)^2 + \beta^2 I| = 0.$$

Since A (and hence $A - \alpha I$) is symmetric, it is true that $(A - \alpha I)^2$ is positive semidefinite (this follows from the definition). Thus if $\beta \neq 0$ then $(A - \alpha I)^2 + \beta^2 I$ is positive definite and then by **3.1**, (3.2) cannot hold. Thus $\beta = 0$ and μ must be real.   □

If A is a symmetric $n \times n$ matrix, we will denote the eigenvalues of A by $\lambda_1(A) \geq \cdots \geq \lambda_n(A)$ and occasionally by $\lambda_1 \geq \cdots \geq \lambda_n$ if there is no possibility of confusion.

Let A be a symmetric $n \times n$ matrix. Then for any i, $|A - \lambda_i I| = 0$ and therefore $A - \lambda_i I$ is singular. Thus the null space of $A - \lambda_i I$ has dimension at least one. This null space is called the *eigenspace* of A corresponding to λ_i and any nonzero vector in the eigenspace is called an *eigenvector* of A corresponding to λ_i. The dimension of the null space is called the *geometric multiplicity* of λ_i.

3.6 *Let A be a symmetric $n \times n$ matrix, let $\lambda \neq \mu$ be eigenvalues of A with x, y as corresponding eigenvectors respectively. Then $x'y = 0$.*

Proof We have $Ax = \lambda x$ and $Ay = \mu y$. Therefore $y'Ax = y'(Ax) = \lambda y'x$. Also, $y'Ax = (y'A)x = \mu y'x$. Thus $\lambda y'x = \mu y'x$. Since $\lambda \neq \mu$, it follows that $x'y = 0$. □

A square matrix P is said to be *orthogonal* if $P^{-1} = P'$; that is to say, if $PP' = P'P = I$. Thus an $n \times n$ matrix is orthogonal if its rows (as well as columns) form an orthonormal basis for $\mathbb{R}^n$.

The identity matrix is clearly orthogonal. A matrix obtained from the identity matrix by permuting its rows (and/or columns) is called a *permutation matrix* and is orthogonal as well. The product of orthogonal matrices is easily seen to be orthogonal.

3.7 The Spectral Theorem *Let A be a symmetric $n \times n$ matrix. Then there exists an orthogonal matrix P such that*

$$P'AP = \operatorname{diag}(\lambda_1, \ldots, \lambda_n). \tag{3.3}$$

Proof The result is obvious for $n = 1$. Assume the result for matrices of order $n - 1$ and proceed by induction. Let x be an eigenvector corresponding to λ_1 with $\|x\| = 1$. Let Q be an orthogonal matrix with x as the first column (such a Q exists; first extend x to a basis for $\mathbb{R}^n$ and then apply the Gram–Schmidt process). Then

$$Q'AQ = \begin{bmatrix} \lambda_1 & 0 & \cdots & 0 \\ 0 & & & \\ \vdots & & B & \\ 0 & & & \end{bmatrix}.$$

The eigenvalues of $Q'AQ$ are also $\lambda_1, \ldots, \lambda_n$ and hence the eigenvalues of B are $\lambda_2, \ldots, \lambda_n$. Clearly, B is symmetric since $Q'AQ$ is so. By the induction assumption there exists an orthogonal matrix R such that

$$R'BR = \operatorname{diag}(\lambda_2, \ldots, \lambda_n).$$

Now set

$$P = Q \begin{bmatrix} 1 & 0 & \cdots & 0 \\ 0 & & & \\ \vdots & & R & \\ 0 & & & \end{bmatrix}.$$

Then $P'AP = \operatorname{diag}(\lambda_1, \ldots, \lambda_n)$. □

Suppose the matrix P in **3.7** has columns $x_1, \ldots, x_n$. Then, since

$$AP = P \operatorname{diag}(\lambda_1, \ldots, \lambda_n),$$

we have $Ax_i = \lambda_i x_i$. In other words, x_i is an eigenvector of A corresponding to λ_i. Another way of writing (3.3) is

$$A = \lambda_1 x_1 x_1' + \cdots + \lambda_n x_n x_n'.$$

This is known as the *spectral decomposition* of A.

3.8 *Let A be a symmetric $n \times n$ matrix. Then A is positive definite if and only if the eigenvalues of A are all positive.*

Proof By the Spectral Theorem, $P'AP = \operatorname{diag}(\lambda_1, \ldots, \lambda_n)$ for an orthogonal matrix P. The result follows from the fact that A is positive definite if and only if $P'AP$ is so. □

Similarly, a symmetric matrix is positive semidefinite if and only if its eigenvalues are all nonnegative.

3.9 *If A is positive semidefinite then there exists a unique positive semidefinite matrix B such that $B^2 = A$. The matrix B is called the square root of A and is denoted by $A^{1/2}$.*

Proof There exists an orthogonal matrix P such that (3.3) holds. Since A is positive semidefinite, $\lambda_i \geq 0$, $i = 1, \ldots, n$. Set

$$B = P \operatorname{diag}\left(\lambda_1^{\frac{1}{2}}, \ldots, \lambda_n^{\frac{1}{2}}\right) P'.$$

Then $B^2 = A$.

To prove the uniqueness we must show that if B, C are positive semidefinite matrices satisfying $A = B^2 = C^2$, then $B = C$. Let $D = B - C$. By the Spectral Theorem, there exists an orthogonal matrix Q such that $Z = QDQ'$ is a diagonal matrix. Let $E = QBQ'$, $F = QCQ'$ and it will be sufficient to show that $E = F$. Since $Z = E - F$ is a diagonal matrix, $e_{ij} = f_{ij}$, $i \neq j$. Also,

$$EZ + ZF = E(E - F) + (E - F)F = E^2 - F^2 = Q(B^2 - C^2)Q' = 0$$

and therefore,

$$(e_{ii} + f_{ii})z_{ii} = 0, \quad i = 1, \ldots, n.$$

If $z_{ii} = 0$ then $e_{ii} = f_{ii}$. If $z_{ii} \neq 0$ then $e_{ii} + f_{ii} = 0$. However, since E, F are positive semidefinite, $e_{ii} \geq 0$, $f_{ii} \geq 0$ and it follows that $e_{ii} = f_{ii} = 0$. Thus $e_{ii} = f_{ii}$, $i = 1, \ldots, n$ and the proof is complete. □

A square matrix A is said to be *idempotent* if $A^2 = A$.

3.10 *If A is idempotent then each eigenvalue of A is either 0 or 1.*

Proof Let $\lambda_1, \ldots, \lambda_n$ be the eigenvalues of A. Then $\lambda_1^2, \ldots, \lambda_n^2$ are the eigenvalues of A^2 (see Exercise 7). Since $A = A^2$, $\{\lambda_1^2, \ldots, \lambda_n^2\} = \{\lambda_1, \ldots, \lambda_n\}$ and it follows that $\lambda_i = 0$ or 1 for each i. □

Conversely, if A is symmetric and if each eigenvalue of A is 0 or 1 then A is idempotent. This follows by an application of the Spectral Theorem.

We say that a matrix has *full row (or column) rank* if its rank equals the number of rows (or columns).

3.11 *If A is idempotent then* rank $A =$ trace A.

Proof Let $A = BC$ be a rank factorization. Since B has full column rank, it admits a left inverse by **2.13**. Similarly, C admits a right inverse. Let B_ℓ^-, C_r^- be a left inverse and a right inverse of B, C respectively. Then $A^2 = A$ implies

$$B_\ell^- BCBCC_r^- = B_\ell^- BCC_r^- = I$$

and hence $CB = bI$, where the order of the identity matrix is the same as rank A. Thus trace $A =$ trace $BC =$ trace $CB =$ rank A. □

3.3 Schur Complement

If A is positive definite then all principal submatrices of A are positive definite and therefore all principal minors of A are positive. We now prove the converse. The following result will be used whose proof follows by expanding the determinant along a column several times.

3.12 *Let A be an $n \times n$ matrix. Then for any μ,*

$$|A + \mu I| = \sum_{i=0}^{n} \mu^{n-i} s_i, \tag{3.4}$$

where s_i is the sum of all $i \times i$ principal minors of A. We set $s_0 = 1$. Note that $s_n = |A|$.

If A is a symmetric $n \times n$ matrix and if all principal minors of A are positive, then by **3.12**, $|A + \mu I| > 0$ for any $\mu \geq 0$ (when $\mu = 0$ use the fact that $|A| > 0$). Thus A cannot have a nonpositive eigenvalue and therefore A is positive definite. Combining this observation with **3.3**, **3.4** we get the following:

3.13 *Let A be a symmetric $n \times n$ matrix. Then A is positive definite if and only if all the principal minors of A are positive.*

Similarly, a symmetric matrix is positive semidefinite if and only if all its principal minors are nonnegative.

Let A be a symmetric matrix which is partitioned as

$$\begin{bmatrix} B & C \\ C' & D \end{bmatrix},$$ (3.5)

where B, D are square matrices. If B is nonsingular, then the *Schur complement* of B in A is defined to be the matrix $D - C'B^{-1}C$. Similarly, if D is nonsingular, then the Schur complement of D in A is $B - CD^{-1}C'$.

Let B in (3.5) be nonsingular and let $X = -C'B^{-1}$. The following identity can be verified by simple matrix multiplication.

$$\begin{bmatrix} I & 0 \\ X & I \end{bmatrix}\begin{bmatrix} B & C \\ C' & D \end{bmatrix}\begin{bmatrix} I & X' \\ 0 & I \end{bmatrix} = \begin{bmatrix} B & 0 \\ 0 & D - C'B^{-1}C \end{bmatrix}.$$ (3.6)

Several useful facts can be proved using (3.6).

3.14 *The following assertions are true*:

(i) *If A is positive definite then $D - C'B^{-1}C$ is positive definite.*
(ii) *Let A be symmetric. If a principal submatrix of A and its Schur complement in A are positive definite then A is positive definite.*
(iii) $|A| = |B| |D - C'B^{-1}C|$.

Proof (i) Clearly if A is positive definite then SAS' is positive definite for any nonsingular S. If

$$S = \begin{bmatrix} I & 0 \\ X & I \end{bmatrix},$$

where, as before, $X = -C'B^{-1}$, then $|S| = 1$ and hence S is nonsingular. Thus SAS' is positive definite (see (3.6)) and since $D - C'B^{-1}C$ is a principal submatrix of S, it is positive definite.

(ii) Suppose A is partitioned as in (3.5) and suppose B and $D - C'B^{-1}C$ are positive definite. Then the right-hand side of (3.6) is positive definite and it follows that A is positive definite since S defined in (i) is nonsingular.

(iii) This is immediate by taking the determinant of both sides in (3.6). $\square$

In (3.5), suppose A is $n \times n$ and B is $(n - 1) \times (n - 1)$. Then C is a column vector and D is 1×1. Let us rewrite (3.5) as

$$\begin{bmatrix} B & c \\ c' & d \end{bmatrix}.$$ (3.7)

The Schur complement of B in A is $d - c'B^{-1}c$ which is a scalar. By (iii), **3.14**,

$$d - c'B^{-1}c = \frac{|A|}{|B|}.$$ (3.8)

A principal submatrix formed by rows $1, \ldots, k$ and columns $1, \ldots, k$ for any k is called a *leading principal submatrix* and its determinant is a *leading principal minor*. We are ready to obtain yet another characterization of positive definite matrices.

3.15 *Let A be a symmetric $n \times n$ matrix. Then A is positive definite if and only if all leading principal minors of A are positive.*

Proof Clearly if A is positive definite then all its leading principal minors are positive. We prove the converse by induction. The result is obvious for $n = 1$. Assume the result for $(n - 1) \times (n - 1)$ matrices. Let A be partitioned as in (3.7). Since any leading principal minor of B must be positive, by the induction assumption, B is positive definite. Also, $|A| > 0$ and therefore by (3.8), the Schur complement of B in A, $d - c'B^{-1}c$ is positive. Thus by (iii), **3.14**, A is positive definite and the proof is complete.   □

Let A, B be $n \times n$ matrices. We write $A \geq B$ to denote the fact that A, B and $A - B$ are all positive semidefinite matrices. We write $A \leq B$ if it is true that $B \geq A$.

3.16 *Let A, B be positive definite matrices such that $A \geq B$. Then $A^{-1} \leq B^{-1}$.*

Proof First suppose $B = I$. Then $A \geq I$ implies that $A - I$ is positive semidefinite. Thus each eigenvalue of A is greater than or equal to 1. Therefore each eigenvalue of A^{-1} is less than or equal to 1 and $A^{-1} \leq I$. In general, $A \geq B$ implies that

$$B^{-1/2}AB^{-1/2} \geq I$$

and now the first part can be used to complete the proof.   □

3.4 Exercises

1. Let A be a symmetric $n \times n$ matrix such that the sum of the entries in any row of A is α. Show that α is an eigenvalue of A. Let $\alpha_2, \ldots, \alpha_n$ be the remaining eigenvalues. What are the eigenvalues of $A + \beta J$, where β is a real number and J is a matrix of all ones?
2. Find the eigenvalues of the $n \times n$ matrix with all diagonal entries equal to a and all off-diagonal entries equal to b.
3. If A is a symmetric matrix, then show that the algebraic multiplicity of any eigenvalue of A equals its geometric multiplicity.
4. Let A be a symmetric, nonsingular matrix. Show that A is positive definite if and only if A^{-1} is positive definite.
5. Let A be an $n \times n$ positive definite matrix and let $x \in \mathbb{R}^n$ with $\|x\| = 1$. Show that

$$(x'Ax)(x'A^{-1}x) \geq 1.$$

6. Let A be a symmetric matrix. If every leading principal minor of A is nonnegative, can we conclude that A is positive semidefinite?
7. If A has eigenvalues $\lambda_1, \ldots, \lambda_n$ then show that A^2 has eigenvalues $\lambda_1^2, \ldots, \lambda_n^2$.
8. If A, B are $n \times n$ matrices, then show that AB and BA have the same eigenvalues.
9. Let A, B be matrices of order $m \times n$, $n \times m$ respectively. Consider the identity

$$\begin{bmatrix} I_m - AB & A \\ 0 & I_n \end{bmatrix} \begin{bmatrix} I_m & 0 \\ B & I_n \end{bmatrix} = \begin{bmatrix} I_m & 0 \\ B & I_n \end{bmatrix} \begin{bmatrix} I_m & A \\ 0 & I_n - BA \end{bmatrix}$$

and show that

$$|I_m - AB| = |I_n - BA|.$$

Now obtain a relationship between the characteristic polynomials of AB and BA. Conclude that the nonzero eigenvalues of AB and BA are the same.
10. If S is a nonsingular matrix then show that A and $S^{-1}AS$ have the same eigenvalues.
11. Suppose A is an $n \times n$ matrix and let

$$|A - \lambda I| = c_0 - c_1\lambda + c_2\lambda^2 - \cdots + c_n(-1)^n\lambda^n$$

be the characteristic polynomial of A. The Cayley–Hamilton Theorem asserts that A satisfies its characteristic equation, i.e.,

$$c_0 I - c_1 A + c_2 A^2 - \cdots + c_n(-1)^n A^n = 0.$$

Prove the theorem for a diagonal matrix. Then prove the theorem for any symmetric matrix.
12. Prove the following: If $A = B'B$ for some matrix B then A is positive semidefinite. Further, A is positive definite if B has full column rank.
13. If A is positive semidefinite, prove the following: (i) $|A| \geq 0$. (ii) All principal minors of A are nonnegative. (iii) A is positive definite if and only if it is nonsingular.
14. Let A be a square matrix such that $A + A'$ is positive definite. Then prove that A is nonsingular.
15. If A is symmetric then show that rank A equals the number of nonzero eigenvalues of A, counting multiplicity.
16. Let A have eigenvalues $\lambda_1, \ldots, \lambda_n$ and let $1 \leq k \leq n$. Show that

$$\sum_{i_1 < \cdots < i_k} \lambda_{i_1} \cdots \lambda_{i_k}$$

equals the sum of the $k \times k$ principal minors of A.
17. Let A, B be $n \times n$ matrices such that A is positive definite and B is symmetric. Show that there exists a nonsingular matrix E such that $E'AE = I$ and $E'BE$ is diagonal. Conclude that if A is positive definite then there exists a nonsingular matrix E such that $E'AE = I$.
18. Let A, B be $n \times n$ matrices where A is symmetric and B is positive semidefinite. Show that AB has only real eigenvalues. If A is positive semidefinite then show that AB has only nonnegative eigenvalues.

19. Suppose A is a symmetric $n \times n$ matrix. Show that A is positive semidefinite if and only if trace$(AB) \geq 0$ for every positive semidefinite matrix B.

20. If A is a symmetric matrix, what would be a natural way to define matrices $\sin A$ and $\cos A$? Does your definition respect the identity $(\sin A)^2 + (\cos A)^2 = I$?

21. Let $\theta_1, \ldots, \theta_n \in [-\pi, \pi]$ and let A be the $n \times n$ matrix with its (i, j)-entry given by $\cos(\theta_i - \theta_j)$ for all i, j. Show that A is positive semidefinite. What can you say about the rank of A?

22. Let A be an $n \times n$ positive definite matrix, $n > 1$, and suppose $a_{ij} \leq 0$ for all $i \neq j$. Let B be the Schur complement of a_{11} in A. Show that $b_{ij} \leq 0$ for all $i \neq j$.

23. Let A be an $n \times n$ matrix, not necessarily symmetric, and suppose all principal minors of A are positive. Show that any real eigenvalue of A must be positive.

24. Let A, B be $n \times n$ positive semidefinite matrices and let C be the matrix with its (i, j)-entry given by $c_{ij} = a_{ij}b_{ij}$, $i, j = 1, \ldots, n$. Show that C is positive semidefinite.

25. Let $x_1, \ldots, x_n$ be positive numbers. Show that the $n \times n$ matrix with its (i, j)-entry $\frac{1}{x_i + x_j}$, $i, j = 1, \ldots, n$ is positive semidefinite.

26. Let X, Y be $n \times n$ symmetric matrices such that X is positive definite and $XY + YX$ is positive semidefinite. Show that Y must be positive semidefinite.

27. Let A, B be $n \times n$ matrices such that $A \geq B$. Show that $A^{\frac{1}{2}} \geq B^{\frac{1}{2}}$.

Chapter 4
Generalized Inverses

4.1 Preliminaries

Let A be an $m \times n$ matrix. A matrix G of order $n \times m$ is said to be a *generalized inverse* (or a *g-inverse*) of A if $AGA = A$.

If A is square and nonsingular, then A^{-1} is the unique g-inverse of A. Otherwise A has infinitely many g-inverses as we will see shortly.

4.1 *Let A, G be matrices of order $m \times n$ and $n \times m$ respectively. Then the following conditions are equivalent*:

(i) *G is a g-inverse of A.*
(ii) *For any $y \in \mathscr{C}(A)$, $x = Gy$ is a solution of $Ax = y$.*

Proof (i) $\Rightarrow$ (ii). Any $y \in \mathscr{C}(A)$ is of the form $y = Az$ for some z. Then $A(Gy) = AGAy = Az = y$.

(ii) $\Rightarrow$ (i). Since $AGy = y$ for any $y \in \mathscr{C}(A)$, we have $AGAz = Az$ for all z. In particular, if we let z be the i-th column of the identity matrix then we see that the i-th columns of AGA and A are identical. Therefore $AGA = A$. $\square$

Let $A = BC$ be a rank factorization. We have seen that B admits a left inverse B_ℓ^-, and C admits a right inverse C_r^-. Then $G = C_r^- B_\ell^-$ is a g-inverse of A, since

$$AGA = BC(C_r^- B_\ell^-)BC = BC = A.$$

Alternatively, if A has rank r, then by **2.15** there exist nonsingular matrices P, Q such that

$$A = P \begin{bmatrix} I_r & 0 \\ 0 & 0 \end{bmatrix} Q.$$

It can be verified that for any U, V, W of appropriate dimensions,

$$\begin{bmatrix} I_r & U \\ V & W \end{bmatrix} Q$$

R.B. Bapat, *Linear Algebra and Linear Models*, Universitext,
DOI 10.1007/978-1-4471-2739-0_4, © Springer-Verlag London Limited 2012

is a g-inverse of

$$\begin{bmatrix} I_r & 0 \\ 0 & 0 \end{bmatrix}.$$

Then

$$G = Q^{-1} \begin{bmatrix} I_r & U \\ V & W \end{bmatrix} P^{-1}$$

is a g-inverse of A. This also shows that any matrix which is not a square, nonsingular matrix admits infinitely many g-inverses.

Another method which is particularly suitable for computing a g-inverse is as follows. Let A be of rank r. Choose any $r \times r$ nonsingular submatrix of A. For convenience let us assume

$$A = \begin{bmatrix} A_{11} & A_{12} \\ A_{21} & A_{22} \end{bmatrix}$$

where A_{11} is $r \times r$ and nonsingular. Since A has rank r, there exists a matrix X such that $A_{12} = A_{11}X$, $A_{22} = A_{21}X$. Now it can be verified that the $n \times m$ matrix G defined as

$$G = \begin{bmatrix} A_{11}^{-1} & 0 \\ 0 & 0 \end{bmatrix}$$

is a g-inverse of A. (Just multiply AGA out.) We will often use the notation A^- to denote a g-inverse of A.

4.2 *If G is a g-inverse of A, then* rank $A = \text{rank}(AG) = \text{rank}(GA)$.

Proof We have rank $A = \text{rank}(AGA) \le \text{rank}(AG) \le \text{rank } A$, and hence rank $A = \text{rank}(AG)$. The second part follows similarly.   □

A g-inverse of A is called a *reflexive g-inverse* if it also satisfies $GAG = G$. Observe that if G is any g-inverse of A, then GAG is a reflexive g-inverse of A.

4.3 *Let G be a g-inverse of A. Then* rank $A \le \text{rank } G$. *Furthermore, equality holds if and only if G is reflexive.*

Proof For any g-inverse G we have rank $A = \text{rank}(AGA) \le \text{rank } G$. If G is reflexive, then rank $G = \text{rank}(GAG) \le \text{rank } A$ and hence rank $A = \text{rank } G$.

Conversely, suppose rank $A = \text{rank } G$. First observe that $\mathscr{C}(GA) \subset \mathscr{C}(G)$. By **4.2**, rank $G = \text{rank}(GA)$ and hence $\mathscr{C}(G) = \mathscr{C}(GA)$. Therefore $G = GAX$ for some X. Now

$$GAG = GAGAX = GAX = G$$

and G is reflexive.   □

4.2 Minimum Norm and Least Squares g-Inverse

4.4 *Let A be an $m \times n$ matrix, let G be a g-inverse of A, and let $y \in \mathscr{C}(A)$. Then the class of solutions of $Ax = y$ is given by $Gy + (I - GA)z$, where z is arbitrary.*

Proof Since $y \in \mathscr{C}(A)$, then $y = Av$ for some v. Now for any z,

$$A\{Gy + (I - GA)z\} = AGy = AGAv = Av = y$$

and hence $Gy + (I - GA)z$ is a solution. Conversely, if u is a solution of $Ax = y$, then set $z = u - Gy$ and verify that

$$Gy + (I - GA)z = u.$$

That completes the proof. $\square$

A g-inverse G of A is said to be a *minimum norm g-inverse* if, in addition to $AGA = A$, it satisfies $(GA)' = GA$. The reason for this terminology will be clear from the next result.

4.5 *Let A be an $m \times n$ matrix. Then the following conditions are equivalent:*

 (i) *G is a minimum norm g-inverse of A.*
(ii) *For any $y \in \mathscr{C}(A)$, $x = Gy$ is a solution of $Ax = y$ with minimum norm.*

Proof (i) $\Rightarrow$ (ii). In view of **4.4** we must show that

$$\|Gy\| \le \|Gy + (I - GA)z\| \tag{4.1}$$

for any $y \in \mathscr{C}(A)$ and for any z.
   We have

$$\|Gy + (I - GA)z\|^2 = \|Gy\|^2 + \|(I - GA)z\|^2 + 2y'G'(I - GA)z. \tag{4.2}$$

Since $y \in \mathscr{C}(A)$, then $y = Au$ for some u. Hence

$$\begin{aligned}
y'G'(I - GA)z &= u'A'G'(I - GA)z \\
&= u'G'A(I - GA)z \\
&= 0.
\end{aligned}$$

Inserting this in (4.2) we get (4.1).
   (ii) $\Rightarrow$ (i). Since for any $y \in \mathscr{C}(A)$, $x = Gy$ is a solution of $Ax = y$, by **4.1**, G is a g-inverse of A. Now we have (4.1) for all z and therefore for all u, a,

$$0 \le \|(I - GA)z\|^2 + 2u'A'G'(I - GA)z. \tag{4.3}$$

Replace u by αu in (4.3). If $u'A'G'(I - GA)z < 0$, then choosing α large and positive we get a contradiction in (4.3). Similarly if $u'A'G'(I - GA)z > 0$, then choosing α large and negative we get a contradiction. We therefore conclude that

$$u'A'G'(I - GA)z = 0$$

for all u, z and hence $A'G'(I - GA)z = 0$. Thus $A'G'$ equals $(GA)'GA$, which is symmetric.   □

A g-inverse G of A is said to be a least squares g-inverse of A if, in addition to $AGA = A$, it satisfies $(AG)' = AG$.

4.6 *Let A be an m × n matrix. Then the following conditions are equivalent:*

 (i) *G is a least squares norm g-inverse of A.*
(ii) *For any x, y, $\|AGy - y\| \leq \|Ax - y\|$.*

Proof (i) $\Rightarrow$ (ii). Let $x - Gy = w$. Then we must show

$$\|AGy - y\| \leq \|AGy - y + Aw\|. \tag{4.4}$$

We have

$$\|AGy - y + Aw\|^2 = \left\|(AG - I)y\right\|^2 + \|Aw\|^2 + 2w'A'(AG - I)y. \tag{4.5}$$

But

$$w'A'(AG - I)y = w'\left(A'G'A' - A'\right)y = 0, \tag{4.6}$$

since $(AG)' = AG$. Inserting (4.6) in (4.5) we get (4.4).

(ii) $\Rightarrow$ (i). For any vector x, set $y = Ax$ in (ii). Then we see that

$$\|AGAx - Ax\| \leq \|Ax - Ax\| = 0$$

and hence $AGAx = Ax$. Since x is arbitrary, $AGA = A$ and therefore G is a g-inverse of A. The remaining part of the proof parallels that of (ii) $\Rightarrow$ (i) in **4.5** and is left as an exercise.   □

Suppose we have the equation $Ax = y$ which is not necessarily consistent and suppose we wish to find a solution x such that $\|Ax - y\|$ is minimized. Then according to **4.6** this is achieved by taking $x = Gy$ for any least squares g-inverse G of A.

4.3 Moore–Penrose Inverse

If G is a reflexive g-inverse of A which is both minimum norm and least squares then it is called a Moore–Penrose inverse of A. In other words, G is a Moore–Penrose inverse of A if it satisfies

$$AGA = A, \qquad GAG = G, \qquad (AG)' = AG, \qquad (GA)' = GA. \tag{4.7}$$

We will show that such a G exists and is, in fact, unique. We first show uniqueness. Suppose G_1, G_2 both satisfy (4.6). Then we must show $G_1 = G_2$. Each of the following steps follows by applying (4.6). The terms which are underlined are to be reinterpreted to get the next step each time.

$$G_1 = G_1 \underline{AG_1}$$
$$= G_1 G_1' \underline{A'}$$
$$= G_1 G_1' A' \underline{G_2' A'}$$
$$= G_1 \underline{G_1' A'} AG_2$$
$$= G_1 \underline{AG_1 A} G_2$$
$$= G_1 \underline{A} G_2$$
$$= G_1 A \underline{G_2 A} G_2$$
$$= \underline{G_1 A} A' G_2' G_2$$
$$= A' \underline{G_1' A'} G_2' G_2$$
$$= \underline{A' G_2' G_2}$$
$$= G_2 A G_2$$
$$= G_2.$$

We will denote the Moore–Penrose inverse of A by A^+. We now show the existence. Let $A = BC$ be a rank factorization. Then it can be easily verified that

$$B^+ = \left(B'B\right)^{-1} B', \qquad C^+ = C'\left(CC'\right)^{-1}$$

and then

$$A^+ = C^+ B^+.$$

4.4 Exercises

1. Find two different g-inverses of

$$\begin{bmatrix} 1 & 0 & -1 & 2 \\ 2 & 0 & -2 & 4 \\ -1 & 1 & 1 & 3 \\ -2 & 2 & 2 & 6 \end{bmatrix}.$$

2. Find a g-inverse of the following matrix such that it does not contain any zero entry.

$$\begin{bmatrix} 1 & 2 & 1 \\ 0 & 1 & 1 \\ 1 & 3 & 2 \end{bmatrix}.$$

3. Let A be a matrix and let G be a g-inverse of A. Show that the class of all g-inverses of A is given by

$$G + (I - GA)U + V(I - AG),$$

where U, V are arbitrary.

4. Show that the class of g-inverses of $\left[\begin{smallmatrix} 1 & -1 \\ -1 & 1 \end{smallmatrix}\right]$ is given by

$$\begin{bmatrix} 1+a+c & a+d \\ b+c & b+d \end{bmatrix}$$

where a, b, c, d are arbitrary.

5. Let A be an $m \times n$ matrix, let rank $A = r$, and let $r \leq k \leq \min\{m, n\}$. Show that A has a g-inverse of rank k. In particular, show that any square matrix has a nonsingular g-inverse.

6. Find the minimum norm solution of the system of equations:

$$2x + y - z = 1,$$
$$x - 2y + z = -2,$$
$$x + 3y - 2z = 3.$$

7. Find the Moore–Penrose inverse of

$$\begin{bmatrix} 2 & 4 \\ 3 & 6 \end{bmatrix}.$$

8. Let x be an $n \times 1$ vector. Find the g-inverse of x which is closest to the origin.

9. Let X be an $n \times m$ matrix and let $y \in \mathbb{R}^n$. Show that the orthogonal projection of y onto $\mathscr{C}(X)$ is given by $X(X'X)^- X'y$ for any choice of the g-inverse.

10. For any matrix X, show that $X^+ = (X'X)^+ X'$ and $X(X'X)^- X' = XX^+$.

11. Let A be an $m \times n$ matrix and let P, Q be matrices of order $r \times m$. Show that $PA = QA$ if and only if $PAA' = QAA'$.

12. Let A, G be matrices of order $m \times n$, $n \times m$ respectively. Show that G is a minimum norm g-inverse of A if and only if $GAA' = A'$.

13. Let A be an $m \times n$ matrix of rank r and suppose A is partitioned as

$$\begin{bmatrix} A_{11} & A_{12} \\ A_{21} & A_{22} \end{bmatrix}$$

where A_{11} is $r \times r$. Show that

$$A \begin{bmatrix} \operatorname{adj} A_{11} & 0 \\ 0 & 0 \end{bmatrix} A = |A_{11}|A.$$

14. Let A be an $m \times n$ matrix of rank r with only integer entries. If there exists an integer linear combination of the $r \times r$ minors of A which equals 1, then show that A admits a g-inverse with only integer entries.

Chapter 5
Inequalities for Eigenvalues and Singular Values

5.1 Eigenvalues of a Symmetric Matrix

We begin by providing a representation for the largest eigenvalue of a symmetric matrix.

5.1 *Let A be a symmetric $n \times n$ matrix. Then*

$$\max_{x \neq 0} \frac{x'Ax}{x'x} = \lambda_1$$

and the maximum is attained at any eigenvector of A corresponding to λ_1.

Proof Write $A = P' \operatorname{diag}(\lambda_1, \ldots, \lambda_n) P$, where P is orthogonal and where, as usual, $\lambda_1 \geq \cdots \geq \lambda_n$ are the eigenvalues of A. Then for $x \neq 0$,

$$\frac{x'Ax}{x'x} = \frac{y' \operatorname{diag}(\lambda_1, \ldots, \lambda_n) y}{y'y}, \quad y = Px$$

$$= \frac{\lambda_1 y_1^2 + \cdots + \lambda_n y_n^2}{y_1^2 + \cdots + y_n^2}$$

$$\leq \frac{\lambda_1 y_1^2 + \cdots + \lambda_1 y_n^2}{y_1^2 + \cdots + y_n^2}$$

$$= \lambda_1.$$

Therefore

$$\max_{x \neq 0} \frac{x'Ax}{x'x} \leq \lambda_1.$$

Clearly, if x is an eigenvector corresponding to λ_1, then

$$\frac{x'Ax}{x'x} = \lambda_1,$$

and the result is proved. $\qquad \square$

R.B. Bapat, *Linear Algebra and Linear Models*, Universitext,
DOI 10.1007/978-1-4471-2739-0_5, © Springer-Verlag London Limited 2012

5.2 *Let A, B be n × n matrices where A is symmetric and B is positive definite. Then*

$$\max_{x \neq 0} \frac{x'Ax}{x'Bx} \leq \mu,$$

where μ is the largest eigenvalue of AB^{-1}.

Proof We have

$$\max_{x \neq 0} \frac{x'Ax}{x'Bx} = \max_{x \neq 0} \frac{x'Ax}{(x'B^{1/2})(B^{1/2}x)},$$

$$B^{-1/2}yy'B^{-1/2} = \max_{y \neq 0} \frac{y'B^{-1/2}AB^{-1/2}y}{y'y}.$$

By **5.1** this last expression equals the maximum eigenvalue of $B^{-1/2}AB^{-1/2}$. However, $B^{-1/2}AB^{-1/2}$ and AB^{-1} have the same eigenvalues and the proof is complete. $\square$

In **5.2** the maximum is attained at $B^{1/2}y$ where y is any eigenvector of $B^{-1/2}AB^{-1/2}$ corresponding to the eigenvalue μ.

5.3 *Let B be a positive definite n × n matrix and let $y \in R^n$. Then*

$$\max_{x \neq 0} \frac{(x'y)^2}{x'Bx} = y'B^{-1}y.$$

Proof We have

$$\max_{x \neq 0} \frac{(x'y)^2}{x'Bx} = \max_{x \neq 0} \frac{x'yy'x}{x'Bx},$$

which is the largest eigenvalue of $yy'B^{-1}$ by **5.2**. Again the eigenvalues of $yy'B^{-1}$ and $B^{-1/2}yy'B^{-1/2}$ are equal. Since the latter matrix is symmetric and has rank 1, it has only one nonzero eigenvalue, counting multiplicity. The eigenvalue equals

$$\text{trace } B^{-1/2}yy'B^{-1/2} = \text{trace } y'B^{-1}y = y'B^{-1}y,$$

and the proof is complete. $\square$

We may rewrite **5.3** as

$$(x'y)^2 \leq (x'Bx)(y'B^{-1}y) \tag{5.1}$$

for any positive definite matrix B. An alternative proof of (5.1) can be given using the Cauchy–Schwarz inequality:

$$\left(\sum u_i v_i\right)^2 \leq \left(\sum u_i^2\right)\left(\sum v_i^2\right).$$

5.2 Singular Values

Let A be an $n \times n$ matrix. The *singular values* of A are defined to be the eigenvalues of $(AA')^{\frac{1}{2}}$. Since $A'A$ is positive semidefinite, the singular values are nonnegative and we denote them by

$$\sigma_1(A) \geq \cdots \geq \sigma_n(A).$$

If there is no possibility of confusion then we will denote the singular values of A simply by $\sigma_1 \geq \cdots \geq \sigma_n$.

The singular values of a rectangular matrix are defined as follows. Suppose A is an $m \times n$ matrix with $m < n$. Augment A by $n - m$ zero rows to get a square matrix, say B. Then the singular values of A are defined to be the singular values of B. If $m > n$, then a similar definition can be given by augmenting A by zero columns, instead of zero rows. For convenience we will limit our discussion mostly to singular values of square matrices. The general case can be handled by making minor modifications.

The following assertions are easily verified. We omit the proof.

(i) The singular values of A and PAQ are identical for any orthogonal matrices P, Q.

(ii) The rank of a matrix equals the number of nonzero singular values of the matrix.

(iii) If A is symmetric then the singular values of A are the absolute values of its eigenvalues. If A is positive semidefinite then the singular values are the same as eigenvalues.

5.4 The Singular Value Decomposition *Let A be an $n \times n$ matrix. Then there exist orthogonal matrices P, Q such that*

$$PAQ = \begin{bmatrix} \sigma_1 & 0 & \cdots & 0 \\ 0 & \sigma_2 & & 0 \\ \vdots & & \ddots & 0 \\ 0 & 0 & \cdots & \sigma_n \end{bmatrix}, \tag{5.2}$$

where $\sigma_1 \geq \cdots \geq \sigma_n$ are the singular values of A.

Proof If $A = 0$, then the result is trivial, so we assume $A \neq 0$. Let x be an eigenvector of AA' corresponding to the eigenvalue σ_1^2, such that $\|x\| = 1$. Thus

$$AA'x = \sigma_1^2 x$$

and hence $x'AA'x = \sigma_1^2$. If we set

$$y = \frac{1}{\|A'x\|} A'x,$$

then it follows that $x'Ay = \sigma_1$. We can construct orthogonal matrices U, V such that the first row of U is x' and the first column of V is y. Then

$$UAV = \begin{bmatrix} \sigma_1 & 0 & \cdots & 0 \\ 0 & & & \\ \vdots & & B & \\ 0 & & & \end{bmatrix}.$$

Now we use induction as in the proof of the Spectral Theorem (3.7) and get the result.   □

In (5.2), let $y_1, \ldots, y_n$ denote the columns of Q and let $x_1, \ldots, x_n$ denote the columns of P'. Then y_i is an eigenvector of $A'A$ and x_i is an eigenvector of AA' corresponding to the same eigenvalue. These vectors are called the *singular vectors* of A.

5.5 *Let A be an $n \times n$ matrix. Then*

$$\max_{\|u\|=1, \|v\|=1} |u'Av| = \sigma_1.$$

Proof We make use of (5.2). For any u, v of norm 1,

$$
\begin{aligned}
|u'Av| &= |u'P \operatorname{diag}(\sigma_1, \ldots, \sigma_n)Q'v| \\
&= |w' \operatorname{diag}(\sigma_1, \ldots, \sigma_n)z| \quad (w = Pu, \; z = Q'v) \\
&= |\sigma_1 w_1 z_1 + \cdots + \sigma_n w_n z_n| \\
&\leq \sigma_1 (|w_1 z_1| + \cdots + |w_n z_n|) \\
&\leq \sigma_1 \|w\| \|z\|, \quad \text{by the Cauchy–Schwarz inequality} \\
&= \sigma_1.
\end{aligned}
$$

$$(5.3)$$

$$(5.4)$$

Therefore

$$\max_{\|u\|=1, \|v\|=1} |u'Av| \leq \sigma_1. \tag{5.5}$$

Also, following the notation of the proof of **5.2**, $|x_1' A y_1| = \sigma_1$ and hence equality is attained in (5.5).   □

5.6 *Let A be an $n \times n$ matrix. Let P, Q be orthogonal matrices such that (5.2) holds. Let $y_1, \ldots, y_n$ denote the columns of Q and let $x_1, \ldots, x_n$ denote the columns of P'. Then for $2 \leq k \leq n$,*

$$\max |u'Av| = \sigma_k,$$

where the maximum is taken over the set

$$\{u, v : \|u\| = \|v\| = 1, \; u \perp x_i, \; v \perp y_i; \; i = 1, \ldots, k-1\}.$$

Proof The proof proceeds along similar lines as that of **5.5**. Only observe that in (5.3), the first $k - 1$ terms reduce to zero.   □

5.3 Minimax Principle and Interlacing

If **5.5, 5.6** are applied to a positive semidefinite matrix then we get a representation for the eigenvalues. This is known as a *Rayleigh quotient* expression and is given in the next result.

5.7 *Let A be a positive semidefinite $n \times n$ matrix. Then*

(i) $\max_{\|u\|=1} u' Au = \lambda_1$.

(ii) *Let $\{x_1, \ldots, x_n\}$ be a set of orthonormal eigenvectors of A corresponding to $\lambda_1, \ldots, \lambda_n$ respectively. Then*

$$\max u' Au = \lambda_k, \quad k = 2, \ldots, n;$$

where the maximum is taken over the set

$$\big\{ u : \|u\| = 1, \ u \perp x_1, \ldots, x_{k-1} \big\}.$$

Proof Since A is positive semidefinite,

$$\big| u' Av \big| \le \left(u' Au \right)^{\frac{1}{2}} \left(v' Av \right)^{\frac{1}{2}}.$$

This fact and **5.5, 5.6** give the result. $\square$

Note that **5.7** holds for any symmetric matrix as well. This can be seen as follows. If A is symmetric then we may choose $\delta > 0$ sufficiently large so that $A + \delta I$ is positive semidefinite and then apply **5.7**.

The next result is known as the *Courant–Fischer Minimax Theorem*. It is an important result with several interesting consequences.

5.8 *Let A be a symmetric $n \times n$ matrix. Then for $k = 2, \ldots, n$;*

$$\lambda_k(A) = \min_{w_1, \ldots, w_{k-1}} \ \max_{u \perp w_1, \ldots, w_{k-1}, \, \|u\|=1} u' Au.$$

Proof It is sufficient to show that

$$\lambda_k(A) \le \min_{w_1, \ldots, w_{k-1}} \ \max_{u \perp w_1, \ldots, w_{k-1}, \, \|u\|=1} u' Au,$$

since by **5.7**, equality is attained when $w_i = x_i$. Let P be orthogonal with $PAP' = \mathrm{diag}(\lambda_1, \ldots, \lambda_n)$. Then

$$u' Au = \sum_{i=1}^{n} \lambda_i z_i^2,$$

where $z = Pu$.

Consider the vector spaces

$$T_1 = \big\{ z \in \mathbb{R}^n : z \perp Pw_1, \ldots, Pw_{k-1} \big\}$$

and

$$T_2 = \{z \in \mathbb{R}^n : z_{k+1} = \cdots = z_n = 0\}.$$

Then $\dim(T_1) \geq n - k + 1$ and $\dim(T_2) = k$. Thus (see Exercise 19 in Chap. 1) there exists a vector z of norm 1 in $T_1 \cap T_2$. For this z,

$$\sum_{i=1}^{n} \lambda_i z_i^2 = \sum_{i=1}^{k} \lambda_i z_i^2 \geq \lambda_k.$$

Thus for any $w_1, \ldots, w_{k-1}$,

$$\max_{u \perp w_1, \ldots, w_{k-1}, \|u\|=1} u' A u = \max_{z \perp P w_1, \ldots, P w_{k-1}, \|z\|=1} \sum_{i=1}^{n} \lambda_i z_i^2 \geq \lambda_k,$$

and the proof is complete.   □

5.9 Cauchy Interlacing Principle *Let A be a symmetric $n \times n$ matrix, and let B be a principal submatrix of A of order $(n-1) \times (n-1)$. Then*

$$\lambda_k(A) \geq \lambda_k(B) \geq \lambda_{k+1}(A), \quad k = 1, \ldots, n-1.$$

Proof We assume, without loss of generality, that B is obtained by deleting the first row and column of A. By **5.7**,

$$\lambda_1(A) = \max_{\|u\|=1} u' A u$$

$$\geq \max_{\|u\|=1, u_1=0} u' A u$$

$$= \lambda_1(B).$$

Similarly, for $k = 2, \ldots, n-1$, by **5.8**,

$$\lambda_k(A) = \min_{w_1, \ldots, w_{k-1}} \max_{u \perp w_1, \ldots, w_{k-1}, \|u\|=1} u' A u$$

$$\geq \min_{w_1, \ldots, w_{k-1}} \max_{u \perp w_1, \ldots, w_{k-1}, \|u\|=1, u_1=0} u' A u$$

$$= \lambda_k(B).$$

Now

$$\lambda_k(B) = -\lambda_{n-k}(-B)$$

$$\geq -\lambda_{n-k}(-A) \quad \text{by the first part}$$

$$= \lambda_{k+1}(A),$$

$k = 2, \ldots, n-1$.   □

5.10 *Let A, B be $n \times n$ matrices such that $A \geq B$. Then*

$$\lambda_k(A) \geq \lambda_k(B), \quad k = 1, \ldots, n.$$

Proof Recall that the notation $A \geq B$ means that A, B and $A - B$ are all (symmetric) positive semidefinite matrices. It is possible to derive the result using **5.8**. However we give another proof. Let $u_1, \ldots, u_n$ be orthonormal eigenvectors of A corresponding to $\lambda_1(A), \ldots, \lambda_n(A)$, respectively. Similarly, let $v_1, \ldots, v_n$ be orthonormal eigenvectors of B corresponding to $\lambda_1(B), \ldots, \lambda_n(B)$, respectively. Fix $k \in \{1, \ldots, n\}$ and let

$$T_1 = \operatorname{span}\{u_k, \ldots, u_n\}$$

and

$$T_2 = \operatorname{span}\{v_1, \ldots, v_k\}.$$

Then $\dim(T_1) = n - k + 1$, $\dim(T_2) = k$ and therefore there exists a unit vector $z \in T_1 \cap T_2$. Consider

$$z'Az = z'\big(\lambda_1(A)u_1u_1' + \cdots + \lambda_n(A)u_nu_n'\big)z.$$

Since $z \in T_1$, it is orthogonal to $\{u_1, \ldots, u_{k-1}\}$ and hence we have

$$z'Az = z'\big(\lambda_k(A)u_ku_k' + \cdots + \lambda_n(A)u_nu_n'\big)z.$$

Now, using the fact that $\lambda_k(A) \geq \lambda_i(A)$, $i \geq k$ and that

$$z'\big(u_ku_k' + \cdots + u_nu_n'\big)z \leq z'\big(u_1u_1' + \cdots + u_nu_n'\big)z = 1,$$

we get $z'Az \leq \lambda_k(A)$. A similar argument, using $z \in T_2$, gives

$$\begin{aligned}
z'Bz &= z'\big(\lambda_1(B)v_1v_1' + \cdots + \lambda_n(B)v_nv_n'\big)z \\
&= z'\big(\lambda_1(B)v_1v_1' + \cdots + \lambda_k(B)v_kv_k'\big)z \\
&\geq \lambda_k(B).
\end{aligned}$$

The result now follows since for any z, $z'Az \geq z'Bz$. $\qquad\square$

5.4 Majorization

If $x \in \mathbb{R}^n$, then we denote by

$$x_{[1]} \geq \cdots \geq x_{[n]}$$

the components of x arranged in nonincreasing order. If $x, y \in \mathbb{R}^n$, then x is said to be *majorized* by y, denoted $x \prec y$, if

$$\sum_{i=1}^k x_{[i]} \leq \sum_{i=1}^k y_{[i]}, \quad k = 1, \ldots, n-1$$

and

$$\sum_{i=1}^n x_i = \sum_{i=1}^n y_i.$$

Intuitively, $x \prec y$ if the components of y are more "spread out" than the components of x. The concept finds applications in several areas in mathematics, statistics and economics.

5.11 *Let $A = (a_{ij})$ be a symmetric $n \times n$ matrix. Then*

$$(a_{11}, \ldots, a_{nn}) \prec (\lambda_1, \ldots, \lambda_n).$$

Proof The result is obvious for $n = 1$. Assume the result to be true for matrices of order $n - 1$ and proceed by induction. Let A be a symmetric $n \times n$ matrix. By a permutation of rows and an identical permutation of columns we can arrange the diagonal entries in nonincreasing order and this operation does not change the eigenvalues. Therefore we assume, without loss of generality, that

$$a_{11} \geq \cdots \geq a_{nn}.$$

Let B be the submatrix obtained by deleting the last row and column of A. Then for $k = 1, \ldots, n - 1$;

$$\sum_{i=1}^{k} \lambda_i(A) \geq \sum_{i=1}^{k} \lambda_i(B) \geq \sum_{i=1}^{k} a_{ii},$$

where the first inequality follows by **5.9** and the second by the induction assumption. Also,

$$\sum_{i=1}^{n} \lambda_i(A) = \text{trace } A = \sum_{i=1}^{k} a_{ii},$$

and the proof is complete.   □

5.12 *Let $A = (a_{ij})$ be a symmetric $n \times n$ matrix. Then for $k = 1, \ldots, n$;*

$$\sum_{i=1}^{k} \lambda_i = \max \text{trace } R'AR$$

where the maximum is taken over all $n \times k$ matrices R with orthonormal columns.

Proof Let R be an $n \times k$ matrix with orthonormal columns. Complete R into an $n \times n$ orthogonal matrix P. Then trace $R'AR$ is the sum of the first k diagonal entries of $P'AP$. Since $P'AP$ has the same eigenvalues as A, it follows by **5.11** that

$$\sum_{i=1}^{k} \lambda_i \geq \text{trace } R'AR. \tag{5.6}$$

If the columns of R are chosen to form an orthonormal set of eigenvectors corresponding to $\lambda_1, \ldots, \lambda_k$ then equality holds in (5.6) and the result is proved.   □

5.13 *Let A, B be symmetric $n \times n$ matrices. Then*

$$\big(\lambda_1(A+B), \ldots, \lambda_n(A+B)\big)$$

is majorized by

$$\big(\lambda_1(A) + \lambda_1(B), \ldots, \lambda_n(A) + \lambda_n(B)\big).$$

Proof We use **5.12**. The maximum in the following argument is over $n \times k$ matrices R with orthonormal columns. We have

$$\sum_{i=1}^{k} \lambda_i(A+B) = \max \operatorname{trace} R'(A+B)R$$

$$\leq \max \operatorname{trace} R'AR + \max \operatorname{trace} R'BR$$

$$= \sum_{i=1}^{k} \lambda_i(A) + \sum_{i=1}^{k} \lambda_i(B)$$

and the proof is complete.   □

5.14 *Let A be a symmetric $n \times n$ matrix and let $P_1, \ldots, P_m$ be $n \times n$ orthogonal matrices. Then the eigenvalues of*

$$\frac{1}{m} \sum_{i=1}^{m} P_i' A P_i$$

are majorized by the eigenvalues of A.

Proof The result follows by a simple application of **5.13**.   □

5.5 Volume of a Matrix

Let A be an $m \times n$ matrix and let $1 \leq k \leq \min\{m, n\}$. We denote by $Q_{k,n}$, the set of increasing sequences of k elements from $\{1, \ldots, n\}$. For indices $I \subset \{1, \ldots, m\}$, $J \subset \{1, \ldots, n\}$, A_{IJ} will denote the corresponding submatrix of A. The k-th *compound* of A, denoted by $C_k(A)$, is an $\binom{m}{k} \times \binom{n}{k}$ matrix defined as follows. The rows and the columns of $C_k(A)$ are indexed by $Q_{k,m}$, $Q_{k,n}$, respectively, where the ordering is arbitrary but fixed. If $I \in Q_{k,m}$, $J \in Q_{k,n}$, then the (I, J)-entry of $C_k(A)$ is set to be $|A_{IJ}|$.

The next result generalizes the familiar fact that for $n \times n$ matrices A, B, $|AB| = |A||B|$.

5.15 Cauchy–Binet Formula *Let A, B be matrices of order $m \times n$, $n \times m$ respectively, where $m \leq n$. Let $S = \{1, \ldots, m\}$. Then*

$$|AB| = \sum_{I \in Q_{m,n}} |A_{SI}||B_{IS}|. \tag{5.7}$$

Proof We only sketch a proof. By elementary row operations it can be verified that

$$\begin{vmatrix} -I_n & B \\ A & 0 \end{vmatrix} = \begin{vmatrix} -I_n & B \\ 0 & AB \end{vmatrix}.$$

The determinant on the right-hand side in the equation above is clearly $(-1)^n |AB|$. It can be seen, by expanding along the first n columns, that the determinant on the left equals

$$(-1)^n \sum_{I \in Q_{m,n}} |A_{SI}||B_{IS}|,$$

and the result is proved. □

The next result follows immediately from **5.15**.

5.16 *Let A, B be matrices of order $m \times n$, $n \times m$ respectively and let $1 \le k \le \min\{m, n, p\}$. Then $C_k(AB) = C_k(A)C_k(B)$.*

If A is an $n \times n$ matrix, then as usual, $\sigma_1(A) \ge \cdots \ge \sigma_n(A)$ will denote the singular values of A. We will often write σ_i instead of $\sigma_i(A)$.

5.17 *Let A be an $n \times n$ matrix and let $1 \le k \le n$. Then the singular values of $C_k(A)$ are given by*

$$\left\{ \prod_{i \in I} \sigma_i(A) : I \in Q_{k,n} \right\}. \tag{5.8}$$

Proof By **5.4**, there exist orthogonal matrices P, Q such that

$$A = P \begin{bmatrix} \sigma_1 & 0 & \cdots & 0 \\ 0 & \sigma_2 & \cdots & 0 \\ \vdots & & \ddots & \\ 0 & 0 & \cdots & \sigma_k \end{bmatrix} Q.$$

Then by **5.16**,

$$C_k(A) = C_k(P)C_k \begin{bmatrix} \sigma_1 & 0 & \cdots & 0 \\ 0 & \sigma_2 & \cdots & 0 \\ \vdots & & \ddots & \\ 0 & 0 & \cdots & \sigma_k \end{bmatrix} C_k(Q).$$

Since P, Q are orthogonal, it follows by **5.16** that $C_k(P)$, $C_k(Q)$ are also orthogonal. Then the singular values of $C_k(A)$ are given by the diagonal elements of $C_k(\text{diag}(\sigma_1 \ldots, \sigma_n))$, which are precisely as in (5.8). □

Let A be an $n \times n$ matrix. The *k-volume* of A, denoted by $\text{vol}_k(A)$ is defined as

$$\text{vol}_k(A) = \left(\sum_{I, J \in Q_{k,n}} |A_{IJ}|^2 \right)^{\frac{1}{2}} = \left(\text{trace}\, C_k(AA') \right)^{\frac{1}{2}}.$$

Note that $\text{vol}_k(A) = 0$ if $k > \text{rank } A$. Also, it follows from **5.17** that

$$\text{vol}_k(A) = \left\{ \sum_{I \in Q_{k,n}} \prod_{i \in I} \sigma_i^2 \right\}^{\frac{1}{2}}.$$

In particular, if $k = r = \text{rank } A$, then

$$\text{vol}_r(A) = \sigma_1 \cdots \sigma_r.$$

We call the r-volume of A simply the *volume* of A and denote it by $\text{vol}(A)$.

The term "volume" can be justified as follows. There is a close connection between determinant and (geometrical) volume. Suppose A is an $n \times n$ matrix and let C be the unit cube in $\mathbb{R}^n$. Consider the linear transformation $x \to Ax$ from $\mathbb{R}^n$ to $\mathbb{R}^n$ and let $A(C)$ be the image of C under this transformation. Then it turns out that the volume of $A(C)$ is precisely $|A|$. More generally, suppose A is an $n \times n$ matrix of rank r and let $\tilde{C}$ be the unit cube in the column space of A'. Then the volume of the image of $\tilde{C}$ under the linear transformation $x \to Ax$ is $\text{vol}(A)$.

We now obtain some characterizations of the Moore–Penrose inverse in terms of volume. For example, we will show that if A is an $n \times n$ matrix then A^+ is a g-inverse of A with minimum volume. First we prove some preliminary results. It is easily seen (sec Exercise 14) that A^+ can be determined from the singular value decomposition of A. A more general result is proved next.

5.18 *Let A be an $n \times n$ matrix of rank r and let*

$$A = P \begin{bmatrix} \Sigma & 0 \\ 0 & 0 \end{bmatrix} Q$$

be the singular value decomposition of A, where P, Q are orthogonal and $\Sigma = \text{diag}(\sigma_1, \ldots, \sigma_r)$. Then the class of g-inverses of A is given by

$$G = Q' \begin{bmatrix} \Sigma^{-1} & X \\ Y & Z \end{bmatrix} P' \tag{5.9}$$

where X, Y, Z are arbitrary matrices of appropriate dimension. The class of reflexive g-inverses G of A is given by (5.9) with the additional condition that $Z = Y\Sigma X$. The class of least squares g-inverses G of A is given by (5.9) with $X = 0$. The class of minimum norm g-inverses G of A is given by (5.9) with $Y = 0$. Finally, the Moore–Penrose inverse of A is given by (5.9) with X, Y, Z all being zero.

Proof Let $B = \begin{bmatrix} \Sigma & 0 \\ 0 & 0 \end{bmatrix}$ and suppose $H = \begin{bmatrix} U & X \\ Y & Z \end{bmatrix}$ is a g-inverse of B. Then $BHB = B$ leads to

$$\begin{bmatrix} \Sigma U \Sigma & 0 \\ 0 & 0 \end{bmatrix} = \begin{bmatrix} \Sigma & 0 \\ 0 & 0 \end{bmatrix}.$$

Thus with $U = \Sigma^{-1}$ and with arbitrary X, Y, Z; H is a g-inverse of B. Since the class of g-inverses of A is given by

$$\left\{ Q' \begin{bmatrix} \Sigma & 0 \\ 0 & 0 \end{bmatrix}^{-} P' \right\},$$

we have proved the first assertion. The remaining assertions are proved easily. For example, imposing both the conditions $BHB = B$ and $HBH = H$ we see that $U = \Sigma^{-1}$ and $Z = Y\Sigma X$. That completes the proof. $\qquad\square$

We now show that the Moore–Penrose inverse enjoys a certain minimality property with respect to the singular values in the class of all g-inverses of a given matrix.

5.19 *Let A be an $n \times n$ matrix of rank r with singular values*

$$\sigma_1 \geq \cdots \geq \sigma_r > \sigma_{r+1} = \cdots = \sigma_n = 0.$$

Let G be a g-inverse of A with rank s and with singular values

$$\sigma_1(G) \geq \cdots \geq \sigma_s(G) > \sigma_{s+1}(G) = \cdots = \sigma_n(G) = 0.$$

Then

$$\sigma_i(G) \geq \sigma_i(A^+), \quad i = 1, \ldots, n.$$

Proof We assume, without loss of generality, that $A = \begin{bmatrix} \Sigma & 0 \\ 0 & 0 \end{bmatrix}$, where $\Sigma = \text{diag}(\sigma_1, \ldots, \sigma_r)$. By **5.18**, $G = \begin{bmatrix} \Sigma^{-1} & X \\ Y & Z \end{bmatrix}$ for some X, Y, Z. Then

$$GG' = \begin{bmatrix} \Sigma^{-1} & X \\ Y & Z \end{bmatrix} \begin{bmatrix} \Sigma^{-1} & Y' \\ X' & Z' \end{bmatrix} = \begin{bmatrix} \Sigma^{-2} + XX' & ? \\ ? & ? \end{bmatrix},$$

where ? denotes a matrix not needed explicitly in the proof. Using **5.9**, **5.10**, we get

$$\begin{aligned} \sigma_i^2(G) &= \lambda_i(GG') \\ &\geq \lambda_i(\Sigma^{-2} + XX') \\ &\geq \lambda_i(\Sigma^{-2}) \\ &= \sigma_i^2(A^+), \quad i = 1, \ldots, r. \end{aligned}$$

If $i > r$, then $\sigma_i = 0$ and the proof is complete. $\qquad\square$

5.20 *Let A be an $m \times n$ matrix of rank r and let $1 \leq k \leq r$. Then for any g-inverse G of A, $\text{vol}_k(G) \geq \text{vol}_k(A^+)$.*

Proof Recall that the square of $\text{vol}_k(G)$ equals the sum of squares of the singular values of $C_k(G)$. Now the result follows using (5.8) and **5.19**. $\qquad\square$

5.6 Exercises

1. Let A be an $n \times n$ symmetric matrix. Show that the largest eigenvalue of A cannot be less than $\frac{1}{n}\sum_{i,j=1}^{n} a_{ij}$.

2. Show that

$$\max_{(x_1,x_2)\neq(0,0)} \frac{(x_1 - x_2)^2}{5x_1^2 - 4x_1x_2 + x_2^2} = 4.$$

3. Find the singular values and the singular vectors of the following matrices:

$$\begin{bmatrix} 2 & 0 & 0 \\ -1 & 0 & 0 \\ 2 & 0 & 0 \end{bmatrix}, \quad \begin{bmatrix} 1 & 1 & 0 \\ 1 & 1 & 0 \\ 1 & 1 & 0 \end{bmatrix}.$$

4. Let A be an $n \times n$ matrix with $\frac{n^2}{2}$ entries equal to 2 and the remaining entries equal to 4. Show that the sum of the squares of the singular values of A is $10n^2$.

5. For $1 \leq i < j \leq v$, let e^{ij} denote the $v \times 1$ column vector with 1 and -1 at coordinates i and j respectively, and zeros elsewhere. Let A be the matrix with n rows and with $\frac{n(n-1)}{2}$ columns given by e^{ij}, $1 \leq i < j \leq n$. Show that the only nonzero singular value of A is $\sqrt{n}$ with multiplicity $n - 1$.

6. Let A be an $n \times n$ matrix with singular values $\sigma_1 \geq \cdots \geq \sigma_n$. Show that

$$\max_{i,j} |a_{ij}| \leq \sigma_1.$$

7. Let A, B be $n \times n$ positive semidefinite matrices such that $\lambda_k(A) \geq \lambda_k(B)$, $k = 1, \ldots, n$. Does it follow that $A \geq B$?

8. Let A be a symmetric $n \times n$ matrix with eigenvalues $\lambda_1 \geq \cdots \geq \lambda_n$ such that only λ_n is negative. Suppose all the diagonal entries of A are negative. Show that any principal submatrix of A also has exactly one negative eigenvalue.

9. Show that the vector $(x_1, \ldots, x_p)$ majorizes the vector $(\bar{x}, \ldots, \bar{x})$, where $\bar{x}$ appears p times.

10. There are n players participating in a chess tournament. Each player plays a game against every other player. The winner gets 1 point and the loser gets zero. In case of a draw each player is awarded half a point. Let s_i denote the score of player i, $i = 1, \ldots, n$. Show that the vector $(s_1, \ldots, s_n)$ is majorized by $(0, 1, \ldots, n - 1)$.

11. Let A be a symmetric $n \times n$ matrix with eigenvalues $\lambda_1, \ldots, \lambda_n$. By the Spectral Theorem there exists an orthogonal matrix P such that $A = PDP'$, where $D = \text{diag}(\lambda_1, \ldots, \lambda_n)$. Let $S = (s_{ij})$ be the $n \times n$ matrix where $s_{ij} = p_{ij}^2$, $i, j = 1, \ldots, n$. Show that

$$\begin{bmatrix} a_{11} \\ \vdots \\ a_{nn} \end{bmatrix} = S \begin{bmatrix} \lambda_1 \\ \vdots \\ \lambda_n \end{bmatrix}.$$

Also show that S has row and column sums equal to one. (Thus S is *doubly stochastic* and it follows by a well-known result of Hardy, Littlewood and Polya that

$$(a_{11}, \ldots, a_{nn}) \prec (\lambda_1, \ldots, \lambda_n)$$

leading to another proof of **5.11**.)

12. The *Frobenius norm* of a matrix A, denoted by $\|A\|_F$, is defined as $(\sum_{i,j} a_{ij}^2)^{\frac{1}{2}}$.
    Show that if A is an $n \times n$ matrix, then for any g-inverse G of A, $\|G\|_F \geq \|A\|_F$
    and that equality holds if and only if $G = A^+$.

13. Consider the matrix

$$A = \begin{bmatrix} 1 & 1 & 0 \\ 0 & -1 & 0 \\ 1 & 2 & 0 \end{bmatrix}.$$

Let C be the unit square with vertices

$$\begin{bmatrix} 0 \\ 0 \\ 0 \end{bmatrix}, \quad \begin{bmatrix} 1 \\ 0 \\ 0 \end{bmatrix}, \quad \begin{bmatrix} 0 \\ 1 \\ 0 \end{bmatrix}, \quad \begin{bmatrix} 0 \\ 0 \\ 1 \end{bmatrix}.$$

Find the area of the image of C under the transformation $x \rightarrow Ax$. Verify that
the area equals $\mathrm{vol}(A)$.

14. Let A be an $n \times n$ matrix of rank r with singular value decomposition

$$PAQ = \mathrm{diag}(\sigma_1, \ldots, \sigma_r, 0, \ldots, 0),$$

where P and Q are orthogonal. Show that

$$A^+ = Q \, \mathrm{diag}(\sigma_1^{-1}, \ldots, \sigma_r^{-1}, 0, \ldots, 0) \, P.$$

15. Let A, B be positive definite matrices of order $m \times m$, $n \times n$ respectively, and
    let C be $m \times n$. Prove that the matrix

$$\begin{bmatrix} A & C \\ C' & B \end{bmatrix}$$

is positive definite if and only if the largest singular value of $A^{-\frac{1}{2}} C B^{-\frac{1}{2}}$ is less
than 1.

16. Let A be a symmetric $n \times n$ matrix. Show that

$$\lambda_n = \min_{\|x\|=1} x'Ax.$$

Obtain a similar expression for λ_1. Also obtain a max-min version of the
Courant–Fischer Theorem.

17. Let A be a symmetric $n \times n$ matrix with $|A| = 0$. Show that the $(n-1) \times (n-1)$
    principal minors of A are either all nonnegative or all nonpositive.

Chapter 6
Rank Additivity and Matrix Partial Orders

6.1 Characterizations of Rank Additivity

If A, B are $m \times n$ matrices then, since $B = A + (B - A)$, we have

$$\text{rank}\, B \leq \text{rank}\, A + \text{rank}(B - A). \tag{6.1}$$

When does equality hold in (6.1)? It turns out that there exist a number of different equivalent necessary and sufficient conditions for this to happen. In this chapter we first study several such conditions and their interrelationships. An application to generalized linear models will be illustrated in a later chapter.

6.1 *Let A, B be nonzero matrices. Then $AC^- B$ is invariant under the choice of the g-inverse if and only if $\mathscr{C}(B) \subset \mathscr{C}(C)$ and $\mathscr{R}(A) \subset \mathscr{R}(C)$.*

Proof If $\mathscr{C}(B) \subset \mathscr{C}(C)$ and $\mathscr{R}(A) \subset \mathscr{R}(C)$, then $B = CX$ and $A = YC$ for some matrices X, Y. Then $AC^- B = YCC^- CX = YCX$ is clearly invariant under the choice of the g-inverse.

Conversely, suppose $AC^- B$ is invariant under the choice of the g-inverse, and suppose that $\mathscr{C}(B)$ is not contained in $\mathscr{C}(C)$. Then

$$D = (I - CC^-)B$$

is a nonzero matrix. Let $A = XY$, $D = PQ$ be rank factorizations. Let

$$C^= = C^- + Y_\ell^- P_\ell^- (I - CC^-)$$

where Y_ℓ^-, P_ℓ^- are respectively, a right inverse of Y, and a left inverse of P. Clearly $C^=$ is also a g-inverse of C and

$$AC^= B = AC^- B + AY_\ell^- P_\ell^- D = AC^- B + XQ.$$

Since X admits a left inverse and Q admits a right inverse, XQ is a nonzero matrix and we get a contradiction. Thus $\mathscr{C}(B) \subset \mathscr{C}(C)$. Similarly we can show that $\mathscr{R}(A) \subset \mathscr{R}(C)$. $\qquad \square$

R.B. Bapat, *Linear Algebra and Linear Models*, Universitext,
DOI 10.1007/978-1-4471-2739-0_6, © Springer-Verlag London Limited 2012

Suppose A, B are $n \times n$ positive definite matrices. In the context of parallel connections of two electrical networks, the following sum, called the *parallel sum* of A, B is defined.

$$P(A, B) = (A^{-1} + B^{-1})^{-1}.$$

Note that

$$(A^{-1} + B^{-1})^{-1} = A(A + B)^{-1}B$$

and this suggests the following definition. Call matrices A, B (not necessarily positive definite) *parallel summable* if

$$A(A + B)^{-}B \tag{6.2}$$

is invariant under the choice of g-inverse, in which case we call (6.2) the *parallel sum* of A, B, denoted by $P(A, B)$. As we shall see, the concept of parallel sum is closely linked with rank additivity.

As usual, A^{-} will denote an arbitrary g-inverse of A. We say that two vector spaces are *virtually disjoint* if they have only the zero vector in common.

6.2 *Let A, B be $m \times n$ matrices. Then the following conditions are equivalent:*

  (i) rank B = rank A + rank($B - A$)
 (ii) $\mathscr{C}(A) \cap \mathscr{C}(B - A) = \{0\}$, $\mathscr{R}(A) \cap \mathscr{R}(B - A) = \{0\}$
(iii) *every B^{-} is a g-inverse of A*
 (iv) *there exists A^{-} such that $A^{-}A = A^{-}B$, $AA^{-} = BA^{-}$*
  (v) *there exists A^{-} such that $AA^{-}B = BA^{-}A = A$*
 (vi) *A, $B - A$ are parallel summable and $P(A, B - A) = 0$*
(vii) *$\mathscr{C}(A) \subset \mathscr{C}(B)$ and there exists A^{-} such that $A^{-}B = A^{-}A$*
(viii) *$\mathscr{R}(A) \subset \mathscr{R}(B)$ and there exists A^{-} such that $BA^{-} = AA^{-}$*
 (ix) *there exist g-inverses $B^{-}, \hat{B}, \tilde{B}$ such that $A = BB^{-}A = A\hat{B}B = A\tilde{B}A$*
  (x) *for any B^{-}, $A = BB^{-}A = AB^{-}B = AB^{-}A$*
 (xi) *there exist K, L, at least one of which is idempotent, such that $A = KB = BL$*
(xii) *there exists a B^{-} which is a g-inverse of both A and $B - A$*
(xiii) *every B^{-} is a g-inverse of both A and $B - A$*
(xiv) *there exist nonsingular matrices P, Q such that*

$$PAQ = \begin{bmatrix} X & 0 \\ 0 & 0 \end{bmatrix}, \qquad P(B - A)Q = \begin{bmatrix} 0 & 0 \\ 0 & Y \end{bmatrix}$$

 (xv) *there exist g-inverses $A^{-}, A^{=}$ such that $A^{-}A = A^{-}B$, $AA^{=} = BA^{=}$*
(xvi) *there exist g-inverses $A^{-}, A^{=}$ such that $A^{-}AB = BA^{=}A = A$.*

Proof We will assume that both A and $B - A$ are nonzero matrices, for otherwise, the result is trivial. Let $A = XY$, $B - A = UV$ be rank factorizations.

   (i) $\Rightarrow$ (iii). We have

$$B = A + (B - A) = \begin{bmatrix} X & U \end{bmatrix} \begin{bmatrix} Y \\ V \end{bmatrix}. \tag{6.3}$$

Since (i) holds, (6.3) is a rank factorization of B. Now for any B^-,

$$[X \quad U] \begin{bmatrix} Y \\ V \end{bmatrix} B^- [X \quad U] \begin{bmatrix} Y \\ V \end{bmatrix} = [X \quad U] \begin{bmatrix} Y \\ V \end{bmatrix}.$$

Hence

$$\begin{bmatrix} Y \\ V \end{bmatrix} B^- [X \quad U] = I_r,$$

where rank $B = r$.

Then

$$\begin{bmatrix} YB^-X & YB^-U \\ VB^-X & VB^-U \end{bmatrix} = I_r,$$

and therefore

$$YB^-X = I, \qquad YB^-U = 0, \qquad VB^-X = 0.$$

Since $A = XY$, it follows that $AB^-A = A$. We also conclude that

$$(B - A)B^-A = 0 \quad \text{and} \quad AB^-(B - A) = 0$$

and thus (i) $\Rightarrow$ (ix),(x). Furthermore,

$$(B - A)B^-(B - A) = (B - A)B^-B = B - A$$

and therefore (i) $\Rightarrow$ (xii),(xiii) as well.

(iii) $\Rightarrow$ (ii). For any B^-, $AB^-A = A$ and thus AB^-A is invariant under the choice of g-inverse. Thus by **6.1**, $\mathscr{C}(A) \subset \mathscr{C}(B)$, $\mathscr{R}(A) \subset \mathscr{R}(B)$. In particular, $A = UB$ for some U and therefore $AB^-B = A$. Suppose

$$x \in \mathscr{C}(A) \cap \mathscr{C}(B - A). \tag{6.4}$$

Then

$$x = Ay = (B - A)z \tag{6.5}$$

for some y, z. Then

$$x = Ay = AB^-Ay = AB^-(B - A)z$$
$$= AB^-Bz - AB^-Az = Az - Az = 0.$$

Thus $\mathscr{C}(A) \cap \mathscr{C}(B - A) = \{0\}$. Similarly it can be shown that the row spaces of A and $B - A$ are also virtually disjoint.

(ii) $\Rightarrow$ (i). We make use of (6.3). Since (ii) holds, $[X \; U]$ must have full column rank and $\begin{bmatrix} Y \\ V \end{bmatrix}$ must have full row rank. It follows that the rank of B must equal the number of columns in $[X \; U]$ and hence (i) is true.

(i) $\Rightarrow$ (iv). Since (i) $\Rightarrow$ (iii),(x), for any B^-, we have $AB^-B = AB^-A = A$. Since B^-AB^- is a g-inverse of A as well, setting $A^- = B^-AB^-$ we see that $A^-B = A^-A$. Similarly using $(B - A)B^-A = 0$ it follows that $AA^- = BA^-$.

The proof of (i) $\Rightarrow$ (v) is similar.

(iv) $\Rightarrow$ (ii). Suppose (6.4) holds. Then (6.5) is true for some y, z. Now

$$x = Ay = AA^- Ay = AA^-(B - A)z$$
$$= A^- Bz - Az = AA^- Az - Az = 0.$$

Thus $\mathscr{C}(A) \cap \mathscr{C}(B - A) = \{0\}$. Similarly it can be shown that the row spaces of A and $B - A$ are also virtually disjoint.

The proof of (v) $\Rightarrow$ (ii) is similar.

(i) $\Rightarrow$ (vi). This follows since (i) $\Rightarrow$ (x).

(vi) $\Rightarrow$ (iii). By **6.1**, $\mathscr{R}(A) \subset \mathscr{R}(B)$. Thus for any B^-, $AB^- B = A$. Now $AB^-(B - A) = 0$ implies that $AB^- A = A$ and thus (iii) holds.

(iv) $\Rightarrow$ (vii). We must only show that $\mathscr{C}(A) \subset \mathscr{C}(B)$. Let $y \in \mathscr{C}(A)$ so that $y = Ax$ for some x. Then $y = AA^- Ax = BA^- Ax \in \mathscr{C}(B)$.

(vii) $\Rightarrow$ (iii). Since $\mathscr{C}(A) \subset \mathscr{C}(B)$, then $BB^- A = A$. Now for any B^-,

$$AB^- A = AA^- AB^- A = AA^- BB^- A = AA^- A = A.$$

The proof of (iv) $\Rightarrow$ (viii) and of (viii) $\Rightarrow$ (iii) is similar. We have already seen that (i) $\Rightarrow$ (ix),(x).

(ix) $\Rightarrow$ (ii). Suppose (6.2) holds. Then (6.5) is true for some y, z. Now

$$x = Ay = AB^= Ay = AB^=(B - A)z$$
$$= AB^= Bz - AB^= Az = A\hat{B}BB^= Bz - Az$$
$$= A\hat{B}Bz - Az = Az - Az = 0.$$

Thus $\mathscr{C}(A) \cap \mathscr{C}(B - A) = \{0\}$. Similarly it can be shown that the row spaces of A and $B - A$ are also virtually disjoint.

Clearly, (x) $\Rightarrow$ (ix).

(x) $\Rightarrow$ (xi). Set $K = AB^-$, $L = B^- A$ for some B^-.

(xi) $\Rightarrow$ (x). Suppose L is idempotent. We have

$$BB^- A = BB^- BL = BL = A,$$
$$AB^- B = KBB^- B = KB = A$$

and

$$AB^- A = KBB^- BL = KBL = AL$$
$$= BLL = BL = A.$$

If K is idempotent then the proof is similar.

We have already seen that (i) $\Rightarrow$ (xii),(xiii).

(xii) $\Rightarrow$ (i). Since BB^-, AB^-, $(B - A)B^-$ are idempotent,

$$\text{rank } B = \text{rank}(BB^-)$$
$$= \text{trace } BB^-$$
$$= \text{trace } AB^- + \text{trace}(B - A)B^-$$
$$= \text{rank}(AB^-) + \text{rank}((B - A)B^-)$$
$$= \text{rank } A + \text{rank}(B - A).$$

Clearly, (xiii) $\Rightarrow$ (xii).

The proof of (xiv) $\Rightarrow$ (i) is easy. We now prove (ii) $\Rightarrow$ (xiv). We may assume, without loss of generality, that

$$A = \begin{bmatrix} I_r & 0 \\ 0 & 0 \end{bmatrix},$$

where r is the rank of A. Let rank$(B - A) = s$ and let

$$B - A = UV = \begin{bmatrix} U_1 \\ U_2 \end{bmatrix} \begin{bmatrix} V_1 & V_2 \end{bmatrix}$$

be a rank factorization of $B - A$, where U_1 is $r \times s$ and V_1 is $s \times r$. We first claim that rank $U_2 = s$. Suppose rank $U_2 < s$. Then the null space of U_2 contains a nonzero vector, say x. If $U_1 x \neq 0$, then

$$\begin{bmatrix} U_1 \\ U_2 \end{bmatrix} x = \begin{bmatrix} U_1 x \\ 0 \end{bmatrix}$$

is a nonzero vector in $\mathscr{C}(A) \cap \mathscr{C}(B - A)$, which is not possible. Thus $U_1 x = 0$. Then $Ux = 0$, which contradicts the fact that U has full column rank. Thus the claim is proved. It follows that $U_1 = M U_2$ for some M. Similarly, $V_1 = V_2 N$ for some N. Set

$$P = \begin{bmatrix} I_r & -M \\ 0 & I_{s-r} \end{bmatrix}, \quad Q = \begin{bmatrix} I_r & 0 \\ -N & I_{s-r} \end{bmatrix}.$$

Then $PAQ = A$ and

$$P(B - A)Q = P \begin{bmatrix} U_1 \\ U_2 \end{bmatrix} \begin{bmatrix} V_1 & V_2 \end{bmatrix} Q$$

$$= \begin{bmatrix} 0 & 0 \\ 0 & U_2 V_2 \end{bmatrix}.$$

This proves (ii) $\Rightarrow$ (xiv).

The treatment of cases (xv), (xvi) is similar to that of (iv), (v) respectively.

We have thus proved the following implications (or a hint is provided towards the proof). It is left to the reader to verify that all the other implications then follow.

- (i) $\Rightarrow$ (iii)–(vi),(ix),(x),(xii),(xiii),(xv),(xvi)
- (ii) $\Rightarrow$ (i),(xiv); (iii) $\Rightarrow$ (ii)
- (iv) $\Rightarrow$ (ii),(vii),(viii); (v) $\Rightarrow$ (ii) (vi) $\Rightarrow$ (iii)
- (vii) $\Rightarrow$ (iii); (viii) $\Rightarrow$ (iii); (ix) $\Rightarrow$ (ii)
- (x) $\Rightarrow$ (ix),(xi); (xi) $\Rightarrow$ (x); (xii) $\Rightarrow$ (i)
- (xiii) $\Rightarrow$ (xii); (xiv) $\Rightarrow$ (i); (xv) $\Rightarrow$ (vii); (xvi) $\Rightarrow$ (ii).

That completes the proof. $\square$

6.2 The Star Order

Let $M_{m \times n}$ denote the set of $m \times n$ matrices. A binary relation $\prec$ on $M_{m \times n}$ is said to be a *partial order* if it satisfies the following conditions:

(i) $A \prec A$ for every A (reflexivity)
(ii) $A \prec B$, $B \prec A \Rightarrow A = B$ (antisymmetry)
(iii) $A \prec B$, $B \prec C \Rightarrow A \prec C$ (transitivity)

Note that not every pair of matrices is necessarily comparable. Thus there exist pairs A, B for which neither $A \prec B$ nor $B \prec A$ is true.

The *minus partial order*, denoted by $<^-$, is defined as follows. If A, B are $m \times n$ matrices, then $A <^- B$ if $\operatorname{rank} B = \operatorname{rank} A + \operatorname{rank}(B - A)$. The fact that this is a partial order can be seen as follows.

Clearly, $<^-$ is reflexive. If $A <^- B$ and $B <^- A$, then $\operatorname{rank}(B - A) = 0$ and hence $A = B$. Thus $<^-$ is antisymmetric. Finally, by (iii) of **6.2**, $A <^- B$ if and only if every g-inverse of B is a g-inverse of A, and hence it follows that $<^-$ is transitive. Thus $<^-$ is a partial order.

The *star order* can be viewed as a refinement of the minus order, although historically the star order was introduced earlier. The definition is as follows. If A, B are $m \times n$ matrices, then A is dominated by B under the star order, denoted $A <^* B$, if $(B - A)A' = 0$ and $A'(B - A) = 0$. Note that for complex matrices these conditions would be reformulated as $(B - A)A^* = 0$ and $A^*(B - A) = 0$, where A^* denotes the complex conjugate of A, and this explains the term "star order".

The star order is closely related to the Moore–Penrose inverse. This is mainly due to the following property of the Moore–Penrose inverse.

6.3 *Let A be an $m \times n$ matrix. Then $\mathscr{C}(A^+) = \mathscr{C}(A')$ and $\mathscr{R}(A^+) = \mathscr{R}(A')$.*

Proof We have $A^+ = A^+ A A^+ = A'(A^+)' A^+$ and thus $\mathscr{C}(A^+) \subset \mathscr{C}(A')$. However rank $A^+ = \operatorname{rank} A$ and hence the two spaces must be equal. The second part is proved similarly.   □

We now provide some alternative definitions of the star order.

6.4 *Let A, B be $m \times n$ matrices. Then the following conditions are equivalent:*

(i) $A <^* B$, *i.e.*, $(B - A)A' = 0$, $A'(B - A) = 0$
(ii) $(B - A)A^+ = 0$, $A^+(B - A) = 0$
(iii) $\mathscr{C}(A) \perp \mathscr{C}(B - A)$, $\mathscr{R}(A) \perp \mathscr{R}(B - A)$.

Proof The equivalence of (i) and (ii) follows from **6.3**, while the equivalence of (i) and (iii) is trivial.   □

As observed in **6.2**, $A <^- B$ if and only if every g-inverse of B is a g-inverse of A. We wish to obtain an analogous statement for the star order. We first prove some preliminary results. The next result explains our earlier remark that the star order can be viewed as a refinement of the minus order.

6.5 *Let A, B be $m \times n$ matrices and suppose $A <^* B$. Then $A <^- B$.*

Proof If $A <^* B$, then by **6.4**, $(B - A)A^+ = 0$, $A^+(B - A) = 0$. It follows by (iv) of **6.2** that $A <^- B$.   □

6.6 *Let A, B be $m \times n$ matrices and suppose $A <^* B$. Then $B^+ = A^+ + (B - A)^+$.*

Proof If $A <^* B$, then clearly $(B - A) <^* B$. Now using **6.4**, we have

$$B\big(A^+ + (B - A)^+\big) = AA^+ + (B - A)(B - A)^+,$$

and

$$\big(A^+ + (B - A)^+\big)B = A^+A + (B - A)^+(B - A).$$

Thus both $B(A^+ + (B - A)^+)$ and $(A^+ + (B - A)^+)B$ are symmetric. Also

$$B\big(A^+ + (B - A)^+\big)B = AA^+A + (B - A)(B - A)^+(B - A).$$

Thus $A^+ + (B - A)^+$ is a least squares, minimum norm g-inverse of B. To show that it is also reflexive, it is sufficient to show that it has the same rank as B. This is seen as follows. We have

$$\begin{aligned}
\operatorname{rank} B &\leq \operatorname{rank}\big(A^+ + (B - A)^+\big) \\
&\leq \operatorname{rank}\big(A^+\big) + \operatorname{rank}\big((B - A)^+\big) \\
&= \operatorname{rank} A + \operatorname{rank}(B - A) \\
&= \operatorname{rank} B,
\end{aligned}$$

where the last equality follows using **6.5**. Thus B has the same rank as $A^+ + (B - A)^+$ and the proof is complete.   □

We now present a characterization of the star order in terms of g-inverses.

6.7 *Let A, B be $m \times n$ matrices. Then $A <^* B$ if and only if every minimum norm g-inverse of B is a minimum norm g-inverse of A, and every least squares g-inverse of B is then a least squares g-inverse of A.*

Proof First suppose $A <^* B$. Let B_m^- be an arbitrary minimum norm g-inverse of B. Then (see Exercise 3 in Chap. 4)

$$B_m^- = B^+ + V\big(I - BB^+\big) \tag{6.6}$$

for some matrix V. First note that by **6.5**, B_m^- is a g-inverse of A.

Since $B^+ = A^+ + (B - A)^+$ by **6.6**, $B^+A = A^+A + (B - A)^+A$. However by **6.4**, $\mathscr{C}(A) \perp \mathscr{C}(B - A)$, and by **6.3**, this latter space is the same as the row space of $(B - A)^+$. Thus $(B - A)^+A = 0$ and hence $B^+A = A^+A$.

Also, $A - BB^+A = A - BA^+A = A - AA^+A = 0$, since $BA^+ = AA^+$. These observations, together with (6.6), yield $B_m^- A = A^+A$, which is symmetric. Therefore B_m^- is a minimum norm g-inverse of A. Similarly, we can show that any least squares g-inverse of B is a least squares g-inverse of A.

We now show the "if" part. For any matrix V, $B^+ + V(I - BB^+)$ is a minimum norm g-inverse of B, and hence, by hypothesis, of A. Thus

$$A(B^+ + V(I - BB^+))A = A.$$

Note that B^+ is a minimum norm g-inverse of B and hence it is a g-inverse of A. Thus $AB^+A = A$. Therefore $AV(I - BB^+)A = A$. Since V is arbitrary, we conclude that $(I - BB^+)A = 0$. Similarly, using the fact that any least squares g-inverse of B is a least squares g-inverse of A, we conclude that $A(I - B^+B) = 0$. Thus for arbitrary U, V,

$$B^+ + (I - B^+B)U + V(I - BB^+)$$

is a g-inverse of A. Since any g-inverse of B is of the above form, we conclude that it must be a g-inverse of A, and hence $A <^- B$. Thus by **6.2**, $(B - A)B^- A = 0$ for any g-inverse B^- of B. Therefore for any minimum norm g-inverse B_m^- of B,

$$0 = (B - A)B_m^- A = (B - A)A'(B_m^-)'$$

and hence

$$(B - A)A' = (B - A)A'(B_m^-)'A' = 0.$$

Similarly we can show that $A'(B - A) = 0$ and hence $A <^* B$. That completes the proof. $\square$

6.3 Exercises

1. If A, B are positive semidefinite matrices then show that they are parallel summable.
2. Let $A_1, \ldots, A_k$ be $m \times n$ matrices and let $A = \sum_{i=1}^k A_i$. Show that rank $A = \sum_{i=1}^k \text{rank}(A_i)$ only if for every nonempty, proper subset S of $\{1, \ldots, k\}$,

$$\text{rank } A = \text{rank}\left(\sum_{i \in S} A_i\right) + \text{rank}\left(\sum_{i \notin S} A_i\right).$$

3. Let A be a positive semidefinite matrix. Show that for any choice of the g-inverse, $x'(A + xx')^- x$ equals

$$\frac{x'A^- x}{1 + x'A^- x},$$

   if $x \in \mathscr{C}(A)$ and 1 otherwise.
4. Let A be an $m \times n$ matrix and let b be an $m \times 1$ vector. If G is a least squares g-inverse of A, then show that $\|A^+b\| \le \|Gb\|$. (Thus $x^0 = A^+b$ has minimum norm among all least squares solutions of the system $Ax = b$, which may or may not be consistent.)
5. Let B be an $m \times n$ matrix. Show that the class of minimum norm g-inverses of B is given by $B^+ + V(I - BB^+)$ where V is arbitrary.

6. Let A, B be $m \times n$ matrices. Show that $A <^* B$ if and only if $A^+ <^* B^+$.

7. Let $A_1, \ldots, A_k$ be $m \times n$ matrices and let $A = \sum_{i=1}^{k} A_i$. Give equivalent conditions for rank A to equal $\sum_{i=1}^{k} \mathrm{rank}(A_i)$ imitating **6.2**.

8. If A, B are parallel summable, then show that
   - (i) $P(A, B) = P(B, A)$
   - (ii) A', B' are parallel summable and $P(A', B') = (P(A, B))'$
   - (iii) $\mathscr{C}(P(A, B)) = \mathscr{C}(A) \cap \mathscr{C}(B)$.

9. Let $A_1, \ldots, A_k$ be $m \times n$ matrices and let $A = \sum_{i=1}^{k} A_i$. Consider the statements
   - (a) every A^- is a g-inverse of each A_i
   - (b) every A^- satisfies $A_i A^- A_j = 0$, $i \neq j$
   - (c) for every A^-, $\mathrm{rank}(A_i A^- A_i) = \mathrm{rank}(A_i)$, $i = 1, \ldots, k$
   - (d) rank $A = \sum_{i=1}^{k} \mathrm{rank}(A_i)$.

   Prove that (a) $\Rightarrow$ (b),(c),(d); (b),(c) $\Rightarrow$ (a),(d); (d) $\Rightarrow$ (a),(b),(c).

10. Let N, U, V be matrices of order $m \times n$, $m \times p$, $q \times n$ respectively, let

$$F = \begin{bmatrix} N & U \\ V & 0 \end{bmatrix}$$

and suppose

$$\mathrm{rank}\, F = \mathrm{rank}\begin{bmatrix} N & U \end{bmatrix} + \mathrm{rank}\, V = \begin{bmatrix} N \\ V \end{bmatrix} + \mathrm{rank}\, U.$$

Let

$$\begin{bmatrix} C_1 & C_2 \\ C_3 & -C_4 \end{bmatrix}$$

be a g-inverse of F. Show that

$$U C_3 U = U, \qquad V C_2 V = V$$

and

$$U C_3 N = N C_2 V = U C_4 V.$$

Furthermore, show that the common matrix in the equation above is invariant under the choice of the g-inverse of F. (This matrix is known as the *shorted matrix N* relative to the column space of U and the row space of V.)

11. An $n \times n$ matrix V is said to be *almost definite* if $x'Vx = 0$ implies $Vx = 0$ for any $x \in \mathbb{R}^n$. Prove that any positive semidefinite matrix is almost definite. Let V be an almost definite $n \times n$ matrix and let X be $n \times m$. Then show that

$$\mathrm{rank} = \begin{bmatrix} V & X \\ X' & 0 \end{bmatrix} = \mathrm{rank}\begin{bmatrix} V & X \end{bmatrix} + \mathrm{rank}\, X.$$

12. Let $A_1, \ldots, A_k$ be $m \times m$ matrices and let $A = \sum_{i=1}^{k} A_i$. Consider the statements
   - (1) each A_i is idempotent
   - (2) $A_i A_j = 0$, $i \neq j$ and $\mathrm{rank}(A_i^2) = \mathrm{rank}(A_i)$ for all i

(3) A is idempotent

(4) rank $A = \sum_{i=1}^{k} \text{rank}(A_i)$.

Prove that

(i) (1) and (2) together imply (3) and (4)

(ii) (1) and (3) together imply (2) and (4)

(iii) (2) and (4) together imply (1) and (4).

Chapter 7
Linear Estimation

7.1 Linear Model

Let y be a column vector with components $y_1, \ldots, y_n$. We call y a *random vector* if each y_i is a random variable. The expectation of y, denoted by $E(y)$, is the column vector whose i-th component is $E(y_i)$. Clearly,

$$E(Bx + Cy) = BE(x) + CE(y)$$

where x, y are random vectors and B, C are constant nonrandom matrices.

If x, y are random vectors of order m, n respectively, then the *covariance matrix* between x and y, denoted by $\text{cov}(x, y)$, is an $m \times n$ matrix whose (i, j)-entry is $\text{cov}(x_i, y_j)$.

The *dispersion matrix*, or the *variance-covariance matrix* of y, denoted by $D(y)$, is defined to be $\text{cov}(y, y)$. The dispersion matrix is obviously symmetric.

If b, c are constant vectors then

$$
\begin{aligned}
\text{cov}(b'x, c'y) &= \text{cov}(b_1 x_1 + \cdots + b_m x_m, c_1 y_1 + \cdots + c_n y_n) \\
&= \sum_{i=1}^{m} \sum_{j=1}^{n} b_i c_j \, \text{cov}(x_i, y_j) \\
&= b' \, \text{cov}(x, y) c.
\end{aligned}
$$

It follows that if B, C are constant matrices then

$$\text{cov}(Bx, Cy) = B \, \text{cov}(x, y) C'.$$

Setting $x = y$ and $b = c$ gives

$$\text{var}(b'x) = b' D(x) b.$$

Since variance is nonnegative we conclude that $D(x)$ is positive semidefinite. Note that $D(x)$ is positive definite unless there exists a linear combination $b'x$ which is constant with probability one.

R.B. Bapat, *Linear Algebra and Linear Models*, Universitext,
DOI 10.1007/978-1-4471-2739-0_7, © Springer-Verlag London Limited 2012

We now introduce the concept of a *linear model*. Suppose we conduct an experiment which gives rise to the random variables $y_1, \ldots, y_n$. We make the assumption that the distribution of the random variables is controlled by some (usually a small number of) unknown parameters. In a linear model, the basic assumption is that $E(y_i)$ is a linear function of the parameters $\beta_1, \ldots, \beta_p$ with known coefficients. In matrix notation this can be expressed as

$$E(y) = X\beta$$

where y is the $n \times 1$ vector with components $y_1, \ldots, y_n$; X is a known nonrandom matrix of order $n \times p$ and β is the $p \times 1$ vector of parameters $\beta_1, \ldots, \beta_p$. We also assume that $y_1, \ldots, y_n$ are uncorrelated and that $\text{var}(y_i) = \sigma^2$ for all i; this property is called *homoscedasticity*. Thus

$$D(y) = \sigma^2 I.$$

Another way to write the model is

$$y = X\beta + \varepsilon$$

where the vector ε satisfies $E(\varepsilon) = 0, D(\varepsilon) = \sigma^2 I$.

We do not make any further assumption about the distribution of y at present. Our first objective is to find estimates of $\beta_1, \ldots, \beta_p$ and their linear combinations. We also seek an estimate of σ^2.

7.2 Estimability

Consider the linear model

$$E(y) = X\beta, \qquad D(y) = \sigma^2 I \tag{7.1}$$

where y is $n \times 1$, X is $n \times p$ and β is $p \times 1$.

The linear parametric function $\ell'\beta$ is said to be *estimable* if there exists a linear function $c'y$ of the observations such that $E(c'y) = \ell'\beta$ for all $\beta \in \mathbb{R}^p$.

The condition $E(c'y) = \ell'\beta$ is equivalent to $c'X\beta = \ell'\beta$ and since this must hold for all $\beta \in \mathbb{R}^p$, we must have $c'X = \ell'$. Thus $\ell'\beta$ is estimable if and only if $\ell' \in \mathscr{R}(X)$.

The following facts concerning generalized inverse are used in the sequel.

(i) For any matrix X, $\mathscr{R}(X) = \mathscr{R}(X'X)$. This is seen as follows. Clearly, $\mathscr{R}(X'X) \subset \mathscr{R}(X)$. However $X'X$ and X have the same rank and therefore their row spaces have the same dimension. This implies that the spaces must be equal. As a consequence we can write $X = MX'X$ for some matrix M.

(ii) The matrix $AC^- B$ is invariant under the choice of the g-inverse C^- of C if $\mathscr{C}(B) \subset \mathscr{C}(C)$ and $\mathscr{R}(A) \subset \mathscr{R}(C)$. This is seen as follows. We may write $B = CX$ and $A = YC$ for some X and Y. Then $AC^- B = YCC^- CX = YCX$, which does not depend on the choice of the g-inverse.

(iii) The matrix $X(X'X)^-X'$ is invariant under the choice of the g-inverse. This is immediate from (ii) since $\mathscr{R}(X) = \mathscr{R}(X'X)$.

(iv) $X(X'X)^-X'X = X$, $X'X(X'X)^-X' = X'$. This is easily proved by writing $X = MX'X$.

7.1 *Let $\ell'\beta$ be an estimable function and let G be a least squares g-inverse of X. Then $\ell'Gy$ is an unbiased linear estimate of $\ell'\beta$ with minimum variance among all unbiased linear estimates of $\ell'\beta$. We say that $\ell'Gy$ is the BLUE (best linear unbiased estimate) of $\ell'\beta$. The variance of $\ell'Gy$ is $\sigma^2\ell'(X'X)^-\ell$.*

Proof Since $\ell'\beta$ is estimable, $\ell' = u'X$ for some u. Then

$$E(\ell'Gy) = u'XGX\beta = u'X\beta = \ell'\beta$$

and hence $\ell'Gy$ is unbiased for $\ell'\beta$. Any other linear unbiased estimate is of the form $(\ell'G + w')y$, where $w'X = 0$.

Now

$$\begin{aligned}\text{var}\{(\ell'G + w')y\} &= \sigma^2(\ell'G + w')(G'\ell + w) \\ &= \sigma^2(u'XG + w')(G'X'u + w).\end{aligned}$$

Since G is a least squares g-inverse of X,

$$u'XGw = u'G'X'w = 0$$

and therefore

$$\begin{aligned}\text{var}\{(\ell'G + w')y\} &= \sigma^2(u'(XG)(XG)'u + w'w) \\ &\geq \sigma^2 u'(XG)(XG)'u \\ &= \text{var}(\ell'Gy).\end{aligned}$$

Therefore $\ell'Gy$ is the BLUE of $\ell'\beta$. The variance of $\ell'Gy$ is $\sigma^2\ell'GG'\ell$. It is easily seen that for any choice of g-inverse, $(X'X)^-X'$ is a least squares g-inverse of X. In particular, using the Moore–Penrose inverse,

$$\begin{aligned}\ell'GG'\ell &= \ell'(X'X)^+(X'X)(X'X)^+\ell \\ &= \ell'(X'X)^+\ell \\ &= \ell'(X'X)^-\ell,\end{aligned}$$

since $\ell'(X'X)^-\ell = u'X(X'X)^-X'u$ is invariant with respect to the choice of g-inverse. $\qquad\square$

Example Consider the model

$$E(y_{ij}) = \alpha_i + \beta_j, \quad i = 1, 2; \; j = 1, 2.$$

We can express the model in standard form as

$$
E \begin{bmatrix} y_{11} \\ y_{12} \\ y_{21} \\ y_{22} \end{bmatrix} = \begin{bmatrix} 1 & 0 & 1 & 0 \\ 1 & 0 & 0 & 1 \\ 0 & 1 & 1 & 0 \\ 0 & 1 & 0 & 1 \end{bmatrix} \begin{bmatrix} \alpha_1 \\ \alpha_2 \\ \beta_1 \\ \beta_2 \end{bmatrix}
$$

so that X is the 4×4 matrix on the right-hand side. Let S be the set of all vectors $(\ell_1, \ell_2, m_1, m_2)$ such that $\ell_1 + \ell_2 = m_1 + m_2$. Note that if $x \in \mathscr{R}(X)$ then $x \in S$. Thus $\mathscr{R}(X) \subset S$. Clearly $\dim(S) = 3$ and the rank of X is 3 as well. Therefore $\mathscr{R}(X) = S$ and we conclude that $\ell_1 \alpha_1 + \ell_2 \alpha_2 + m_1 \beta_1 + m_2 \beta_2$ is estimable if and only if $\ell_1 + \ell_2 = m_1 + m_2$.

We compute

$$
X'X = \begin{bmatrix} 2 & 0 & 1 & 1 \\ 0 & 2 & 1 & 1 \\ 1 & 1 & 2 & 0 \\ 1 & 1 & 0 & 2 \end{bmatrix}
$$

and

$$
(X'X)^- = \frac{1}{4} \begin{bmatrix} 0 & 0 & 0 & 0 \\ 0 & 4 & -2 & -2 \\ 0 & -2 & 3 & 1 \\ 0 & -2 & 1 & 3 \end{bmatrix}
$$

is one possible g-inverse. Thus

$$
X(X'X)^- X' = \frac{1}{4} \begin{bmatrix} 3 & 1 & 1 & -1 \\ 1 & 3 & -1 & 1 \\ 1 & -1 & 3 & 1 \\ -1 & 1 & 1 & 3 \end{bmatrix}.
$$

Now we can compute the BLUE of any estimable function $u'X\beta$ as $u'X(X'X)^- \times X'y$. For example, if $u' = (1, 0, 0, 0)'$ then we get the BLUE of $\alpha_1 + \beta_1$ as

$$
\frac{1}{4}(3y_{11} + y_{12} + y_{21} - y_{22}).
$$

The model (7.1) is said to be a *full rank model* (or a *regression model*) if X has full column rank, i.e., rank $X = p$. For such models the following results can easily be verified.

(i) $\mathscr{R}(X) = \mathbb{R}^p$ and therefore every function $\ell'\beta$ is estimable.

(ii) $X'X$ is nonsingular.

(iii) Let $\widehat{\beta}_i$ be the BLUE of β_i and let $\widehat{\beta}$ be the column vector with components $\widehat{\beta}_1, \ldots, \widehat{\beta}_p$. Then $\widehat{\beta} = (X'X)^{-1}X'y$. The dispersion matrix of $\widehat{\beta}$ is $\sigma^2(X'X)^{-1}$.

(iv) The BLUE of $\ell'\beta$ is $\ell'\widehat{\beta}$ with variance $\sigma^2\ell'(X'X)^{-1}\ell$.

Parts (iii), (iv) constitute the *Gauss–Markov Theorem*. The next result is the Hadamard inequality for positive semidefinite matrices.

7.2 *Let A be an $n \times n$ positive semidefinite matrix. Then*

$$|A| \le a_{11} \cdots a_{nn}. \tag{7.2}$$

Furthermore, if A is positive definite, then equality holds in the above inequality if and only if A is a diagonal matrix.

Proof If A is singular, then $|A| = 0$, whereas $a_{ii} \ge 0$ for all i, and the result is trivial. So suppose A is nonsingular. Then each $a_{ii} > 0$. Let $D = \text{diag}(\sqrt{a_{11}}, \dots, \sqrt{a_{nn}})$ and let $B = D^{-1}AD^{-1}$. Then B is positive semidefinite and $b_{ii} = 1$ for each i. Let $\lambda_1, \dots, \lambda_n$ be the eigenvalues of B. By the arithmetic mean-geometric mean inequality,

$$\frac{1}{n} \sum_{i=1}^{n} \lambda_i \ge \prod_{i=1}^{n} \lambda_i^{\frac{1}{n}}.$$

Since

$$\sum_{i=1}^{n} \lambda_i = \text{trace } B = n,$$

and $\prod_{i=1}^{n} \lambda_i = |B|$, we get $|B| \le 1$. Therefore

$$\left| D^{-1}AD^{-1} \right| \le 1$$

and the inequality (7.2) follows. If A is positive definite and if equality holds in (7.2), then it must hold in the arithmetic mean-geometric mean inequality in the proof above. But then $\lambda_1, \dots, \lambda_n$ are all equal, and it follows by the spectral theorem that B is a scalar multiple of the identity matrix. Then A must be diagonal. $\quad\square$

7.3 *Let X be an $n \times n$ matrix and suppose $|x_{ij}| \le 1$ for all i, j. Then*

$$\left| X'X \right| \le n^n.$$

Proof Let $A = X'X$. Then

$$a_{ii} = \sum_{j=1}^{n} x_{ji}^2 \le n$$

and $|A| = |X'X|$. The result follows by **7.2**. $\quad\square$

An application of **7.3** is illustrated by the following example. Suppose four objects are to be weighed using an ordinary chemical balance (without bias) with two pans. We are allowed four weighings. In each weighing we may put some of the objects in the right pan and some in the left pan. Any procedure that specifies this allocation is called a *weighing design*. Let β_1, β_2, β_3, β_4 be the true weights of the objects. Define $x_{ij} = 1$ or -1 depending upon whether we put the j-th object in the right pan or in the left pan in the i-th weighing. Let y_i denote the weight needed to achieve balance in the i-th weighing. If the sign of y_i is positive, then the weight is required in the left pan, otherwise in the right pan. Then we have the model $E(y) = X\beta$, where $X = (x_{ij})$, y is the 4×1 vector with components y_i, and β is the 4×1 vector with components β_i. As usual, we make the assumption that the y_is are uncorrelated with common variance σ^2. The dispersion matrix of $\widehat{\beta}$ is $\sigma^2 (X'X)^{-1}$, assuming $X'X$ to be nonsingular. Thus to get more precision we must make the $X'X$ matrix "large". One measure of largeness of a positive semidefinite matrix is the determinant. (This is the D-optimality criterion, which we will encounter again in Chap. 10 in the context of block designs.) The matrix

$$X = \begin{bmatrix} 1 & 1 & 1 & 1 \\ 1 & 1 & -1 & -1 \\ 1 & -1 & -1 & 1 \\ 1 & -1 & 1 & -1 \end{bmatrix}$$

satisfies $|X'X| = 4^4$, and by **7.3** this is the maximum determinant possible.

A square matrix is called a *Hadamard matrix* if each entry is 1 or -1 and the rows are orthogonal. The matrix X is a Hadamard matrix.

7.3 Residual Sum of Squares

We continue to consider the model (7.1). The equations $X'X\beta = X'y$ are called the *normal equations*. The equations are consistent, since $\mathscr{C}(X') = \mathscr{C}(X'X)$. Let $\widehat{\beta}$ be a solution of the normal equations. Then $\widehat{\beta} = (X'X)^- X'y$ for some choice of the g-inverse. The *residual sum of squares* (RSS) is defined to be

$$(y - X\widehat{\beta})'(y - X\widehat{\beta}).$$

The RSS is invariant under the choice of the g-inverse $(X'X)^-$ although $\widehat{\beta}$ may depend on the choice. Thus $\widehat{\beta}$ is not unique and does not admit any statistical interpretation. By "fitting the model" we generally mean calculating the BLUEs of parametric functions of interest and computing RSS.

7.4 *The minimum of* $(y - X\beta)'(y - X\beta)$ *is attained at* $\widehat{\beta}$.

Proof We have

$$\begin{aligned} &(y - X\beta)'(y - X\beta) \\ &= (y - X\widehat{\beta} + X\widehat{\beta} - X\beta)'(y - X\widehat{\beta} + X\widehat{\beta} - X\beta) \\ &= (y - X\widehat{\beta})'(y - X\widehat{\beta}) + (\widehat{\beta} - \beta)'X'X(\widehat{\beta} - \beta), \end{aligned}$$

since

$$X'(y - X\widehat{\beta}) = X'\left(y - X(X'X)^- X'y\right) = 0.$$

It follows that

$$(y - X\beta)'(y - X\beta) \geq (y - X\widehat{\beta})'(y - X\widehat{\beta}).$$

That completes the proof.   □

7.5 *Let* rank $X = r$. *Then* $E(y - X\widehat{\beta})'(y - X\widehat{\beta}) = (n - r)\sigma^2$.

Proof We have

$$E(y - X\beta)(y - X\beta)' = D(y) = \sigma^2 I.$$

Thus

$$\begin{aligned}
E(yy') &= E(y)\beta'X' + X\beta E(y') - X\beta\beta'X' + \sigma^2 I \\
&= X\beta\beta'X' + \sigma^2 I.
\end{aligned} \tag{7.3}$$

We will use the notation

$$P = I - X(X'X)^- X'.$$

Observe that P is a symmetric, idempotent matrix and $PX = 0$. These properties will be useful. Now

$$\begin{aligned}
E(y - X\widehat{\beta})(y - X\widehat{\beta})' &= E(y - X(X'X)^- X'y)'(y - X(X'X)^- X'y) \\
&= E(y'Py) \\
&= E(\text{trace}(y'Py)) \\
&= E(\text{trace}(Pyy')) \\
&= \text{trace } PE(yy') \\
&= \sigma^2 \text{ trace } P,
\end{aligned}$$

by (7.3) and the fact that $PX = 0$. Finally,

$$\begin{aligned}
\text{trace } P &= n - \text{trace } X(X'X)^- X' \\
&= n - \text{trace}(X'X)^- X'X \\
&= n - \text{rank}((X'X)^- X'X),
\end{aligned}$$

since $(X'X)^- X'X$ is idempotent. However

$$\text{rank}((X'X)^- X'X) = \text{rank}(X'X) = \text{rank } X = r,$$

and the proof is complete.   □

We conclude from **7.5** that RSS$/(n - r)$ is an unbiased estimator of σ^2. For computations it is more convenient to use the expressions

$$\text{RSS} = y'y - \widehat{\beta}'X'X\widehat{\beta} = y'y - y'X\widehat{\beta}.$$

One-Way Classification   Consider the model

$$y_{ij} = \alpha_i + \varepsilon_{ij}, \quad i = 1, \ldots, k; \; j = 1, \ldots, n_i,$$

where ε_{ij} are independent with mean 0 and variance σ^2. The model can be written as

$$
\begin{bmatrix} y_{11} \\ \vdots \\ y_{1n_1} \\ \vdots \\ y_{k1} \\ \vdots \\ y_{kn_k} \end{bmatrix} = \begin{bmatrix} 1 & 0 & \cdots & 0 \\ \vdots & & & \\ 1 & 0 & \cdots & 0 \\ 0 & 1 & & 0 \\ \vdots & \vdots & & \vdots \\ 0 & 1 & & 0 \\ & \cdots & & \\ 0 & 0 & & 1 \\ \vdots & \vdots & & \vdots \\ 0 & 0 & & 1 \end{bmatrix} \begin{bmatrix} \alpha_1 \\ \vdots \\ \alpha_k \end{bmatrix} + \varepsilon.
$$

Thus

$$X'X = \mathrm{diag}(n_1, \ldots, n_k)$$

and

$$
X'y = \begin{bmatrix} y_{1.} \\ \vdots \\ y_{k.} \end{bmatrix}
$$

where

$$y_{i.} = \sum_{j=1}^{n_i} y_{ij}, \quad i = 1, \ldots, k.$$

Thus the model is of full rank and the BLUEs of α_i are given by the components of

$$
\widehat{\alpha} = (X'X)^{-1} X'y = \begin{bmatrix} \overline{y}_{1.} \\ \vdots \\ \overline{y}_{k.} \end{bmatrix}
$$

where $\overline{y}_{i.} = \frac{y_{i.}}{n_i}, i = 1, \ldots, k$. Now

$$\mathrm{RSS} = y'y - \widehat{\alpha}'X'y = \sum_{i=1}^{k}\sum_{j=1}^{n_i} y_{ij}^2 - \sum_{i=1}^{k} \frac{y_{i.}^2}{n_i}.$$

Since the rank of X is k, by **7.5**, $E(\mathrm{RSS}) = (n-k)\sigma^2$, where $n = \sum_{i=1}^{k} n_i$ and $\mathrm{RSS}/(n-k)$ is an unbiased estimator of σ^2.

Consider the usual model $E(y) = X\beta, D(y) = \sigma^2 I$, where y is $n \times 1$, X is $n \times p$. Suppose we have a priori linear restriction $L\beta = z$ on the parameters. We assume that $\mathscr{R}(L) \subset \mathscr{R}(X)$ and that the equation $L\beta = z$ is consistent.

Let $\widehat{\beta} = (X'X)^- X'y$ for a fixed g-inverse $(X'X)^-$ and let

$$\tilde{\beta} = \widehat{\beta} - (X'X)^- L'\left(L(X'X)^- L'\right)^-(L\widehat{\beta} - z).$$

7.6 *The minimum of $(y - X\beta)'(y - X\beta)$ subject to $L\beta = z$ is attained at $\beta = \tilde{\beta}$.*

Proof Since $\mathcal{R}(L) \subset \mathcal{R}(X)$ and since rank $X = \text{rank}(X'X)$, then $L = WX'X$ for some W. Let $T = WX'$. Now

$$
\begin{aligned}
L(X'X)^- L' &= WX'X(X'X)^- X'XW' \\
&= WX'XW' \\
&= TT'.
\end{aligned}
$$

Since $L\beta = z$ is consistent, $Lv = z$ for some v. Thus

$$
\begin{aligned}
L(X'X)^- L'(L(X'X)^- L')^- z &= L(X'X)^- L'(L(X'X)^- L)^- Lv \\
&= TT'(TT')^- TXv \\
&= TXv \\
&= Lv \\
&= z.
\end{aligned}
\tag{7.4}
$$

Similarly,

$$
\begin{aligned}
L(X'X)^- L'(L(X'X)^- L')^- L\widehat{\beta} &= TT'(TT')^- WX'X(X'X)^- X'y \\
&= TT'(TT')^- WX'y \\
&= TT'(TT')^- Ty \\
&= Ty,
\end{aligned}
\tag{7.5}
$$

and

$$
\begin{aligned}
L\widehat{\beta} &= L(X'X)^- X'y \\
&= WX'X(X'X)^- X'y \\
&= WX'y \\
&= Ty.
\end{aligned}
\tag{7.6}
$$

Using (7.4), (7.5), (7.6) we see that $L\tilde{\beta} = z$ and therefore $\tilde{\beta}$ satisfies the restriction $L\beta = z$.

Now for any β satisfying $L\beta = z$,

$$
\begin{aligned}
(y - X\beta)'(y - X\beta) \\
= (y - X\tilde{\beta} + X(\tilde{\beta} - \beta))'(y - X\tilde{\beta} + X(\tilde{\beta} - \beta)) \\
= (y - X\tilde{\beta})'(y - X\tilde{\beta}) + (\tilde{\beta} - \beta)'X'X(\tilde{\beta} - \beta)
\end{aligned}
\tag{7.7}
$$

since we can show that $(\tilde{\beta} - \beta)'X'(y - X\tilde{\beta}) = 0$ as follows. We have

$$
\begin{aligned}
X'X\tilde{\beta} &= X'X\widehat{\beta} - X'X(X'X)^- L'(L(X'X)^- L')^- (L\widehat{\beta} - z) \\
&= X'y - L'(L(X'X)^- L')^- (L\widehat{\beta} - z),
\end{aligned}
$$

since $L' = X'XW'$. Hence

$$X'(y - X\tilde{\beta}) = L'(L(X'X)^- L')^-(L\widehat{\beta} - z)$$

and since $L\tilde{\beta} = L\beta = z$, it follows that

$$(\tilde{\beta} - \beta)'X'(y - X\tilde{\beta}) = (\tilde{\beta} - \beta)'L'(L(X'X)^- L')^-(L\tilde{\beta} - z)$$
$$= 0.$$

From (7.7) it is clear that

$$(y - X\beta)'(y - X\beta) \geq (y - X\tilde{\beta})'(y - X\tilde{\beta})$$

if $L\beta = z$ and the proof is complete.   □

7.7 rank $L = \text{rank}\, T = \text{rank}(L(X'X)^- L')$.

Proof Since $L(X'X)^- L' = TT'$, then $\text{rank}(L(X'X)^- L') = \text{rank}(TT') = \text{rank}\, T$.
Clearly, rank $L = \text{rank}(TX) \leq \text{rank}\, T$. Since rank $X = \text{rank}(X'X)$, then $X = MX'X$ for some M. Thus $T = WX' = WX'XM' = LM'$. Therefore rank $T \leq$ rank L and hence rank $T = \text{rank}\, L$.   □

We note some simplifications that occur if additional assumptions are made. Thus suppose that rank $X = p$ so that we have a full-rank model. We also assume that L is $m \times p$ of rank m. Then by **7.7**,

$$\text{rank}(L(X'X)^{-1} L') = \text{rank}\, L = m$$

and hence $L(X'X)^{-1} L'$ is nonsingular. It reduces to a scalar if $m = 1$.

Example Consider the model $E(y_i) = \theta_i$, $i = 1, 2, 3, 4$; where y_i are uncorrelated with variance σ^2. Suppose we have the restriction $\theta_1 + \theta_2 + \theta_3 + \theta_4 = 0$ on the parameters. We find the RSS. The model in standard form has $X = I_4$. The restriction on the parameters can be written as $L\theta = 0$, where $L = (1, 1, 1, 1)$. Thus

$$\widehat{\theta} = (X'X)^- X'y$$

and

$$\tilde{\theta} = \widehat{\theta} - (X'X)^- L'(L(X'X)^- L')^- L\widehat{\theta}$$

$$= y - \begin{bmatrix} \overline{y} \\ \overline{y} \\ \overline{y} \\ \overline{y} \end{bmatrix}.$$

Thus RSS $= (y - X\tilde{\theta})'(y - X\tilde{\theta}) = 4\overline{y}^2$.

Example Consider an alternative formulation of the one-way classification model considered earlier:

$$y_{ij} = \mu + \alpha_i + \varepsilon_{ij}, \quad i = 1, \ldots, k; \ j = 1, \ldots, n_i;$$

where ε_{ij} are independent with mean 0 and variance σ^2. This model arises when we want to compare k treatments. We have n_i observations on the i-th treatment. The parameter μ is interpreted as the "general effect," and α_i is the "effect due to the i-th treatment". We wish to find the RSS. Instead of writing the model in standard form we follow a different approach. The RSS is the minimum value of

$$\sum_{i=1}^{k}\sum_{j=1}^{n_i}(y_{ij} - \mu - \alpha_i)^2. \tag{7.8}$$

We use the fact that if $u_1, \ldots, u_m$ are real numbers then

$$\sum_{i=1}^{m}(u_i - \theta)^2$$

is minimized when $\theta = \bar{u}$, the mean of $u_1, \ldots, u_n$. This is easily proved using calculus. The sum (7.8) is minimized when $\mu + \alpha_i = \bar{y}_{i.}$, $i = 1, \ldots, k$; and therefore

$$\text{RSS} = \sum_{i=1}^{k}\sum_{j=1}^{n_i}(y_{ij} - \bar{y}_{i.})^2.$$

Now suppose we wish to find the RSS subject to the constraints $\alpha_i - \alpha_j = 0$ for all i, j. Since $\alpha_i - \alpha_j$ is estimable, we may proceed to apply **7.6**. Thus we must calculate $\tilde{\alpha}$ using the formula immediately preceding **7.6**. However, again there is a more elementary way. Let α denote the common value of $\alpha_1, \ldots, \alpha_k$. Then we must minimize

$$\sum_{i=1}^{k}\sum_{j=1}^{n_i}(y_{ij} - \mu - \alpha)^2$$

and this is achieved by setting

$$\mu + \alpha = \bar{y}_{..} = \frac{1}{n}\sum_{i=1}^{k}\sum_{j=1}^{n_i}y_{ij},$$

where $n = \sum_{i=1}^{k}n_i$. Thus the RSS now is

$$\sum_{i=1}^{k}\sum_{j=1}^{n_i}(y_{ij} - \bar{y}_{..})^2.$$

The computation of RSS subject to linear restrictions will be useful in deriving a test of the hypothesis that the restrictions are indeed valid. This will be achieved in the next chapter.

7.4 General Linear Model

7.8 *Let X be an $n \times m$ matrix and let V be a positive semidefinite $n \times n$ matrix. Then*

$$\text{rank}\begin{bmatrix} V & X \\ X' & 0 \end{bmatrix} = \text{rank}\begin{bmatrix} V & 0 \\ X' & 0 \end{bmatrix} + \text{rank}\begin{bmatrix} 0 & X \\ 0 & 0 \end{bmatrix}$$
$$= \text{rank}\,[V, X] + \text{rank}\,X.$$

Proof By **6.2**, the result will be proved if we show that the column spaces of

$$\begin{bmatrix} V \\ X' \end{bmatrix} \quad \text{and} \quad \begin{bmatrix} X \\ 0 \end{bmatrix}$$

are virtually disjoint. Suppose there exists a nonzero vector in the intersection of the two column spaces. Then there exist vectors a, b such that

$$Va = Xb \neq 0 \tag{7.9}$$

and $X'a = 0$. Then $a'V = b'X'$ and hence $a'Va = b'X'a = 0$. Since V is positive semidefinite, it follows that $Va = 0$ and this contradicts (7.9).   □

In the remainder of this chapter we assume that X, V are as in **7.8** and that

$$\begin{bmatrix} V & X \\ X' & 0 \end{bmatrix}^{-} = \begin{bmatrix} C_1 & C_2 \\ C_3 & -C_4 \end{bmatrix} \tag{7.10}$$

is one possible g-inverse.

7.9 *The following assertions are true*:

  (i) $X'C_2X = X$, $XC_3X = X$
 (ii) $XC_4X' = XC_4'X' = VC_3'X' = XC_3V = VC_2X' = XC_2'V$
(iii) $X'C_1X$, $X'C_1V$ and VC_1X are all zero matrices
 (iv) $VC_1VC_1V = VC_1V = VC_1'VC_1V = VC_1'V$
  (v) trace $VC_1 = \text{rank}\,[V, X] = \text{rank}\,X = \text{trace}\,VC_1'$.

Proof We have

$$\begin{bmatrix} V & X \\ X' & 0 \end{bmatrix}\begin{bmatrix} C_1 & C_2 \\ C_3 & -C_4 \end{bmatrix}\begin{bmatrix} V & X \\ X' & 0 \end{bmatrix} = \begin{bmatrix} V & X \\ X' & 0 \end{bmatrix}. \tag{7.11}$$

This gives, after simplification,

$$VC_1V + XC_3V + VC_2X' - XC_4X' = V, \tag{7.12}$$

$$VC_1X + XC_3X = X, \qquad X'C_1V + X'C_2X' = X', \tag{7.13}$$

$$X'C_1X = 0. \tag{7.14}$$

By **7.8** and **7.9** we see that the matrix on the right-hand side of (7.10) is a g-inverse of

$$\begin{bmatrix} V & 0 \\ X' & 0 \end{bmatrix}, \qquad \begin{bmatrix} 0 & X \\ 0 & 0 \end{bmatrix}$$

as well. Thus we can write two more equations similar to (7.11), which give, after simplification

$$VC_1 V + VC_2 X' = V, \qquad X'C_1 V + X'C_2 X' = X', \qquad (7.15)$$

and

$$XC_3 X = X. \qquad (7.16)$$

Since $\begin{bmatrix} V & X \\ X' & 0 \end{bmatrix}$ is symmetric, $\begin{bmatrix} C_1' & C_2' \\ C_3' & -C_4' \end{bmatrix}$ is also a possible g-inverse. Therefore, we can replace C_1 by C_1', C_2 by C_3', C_3 by C_2' and C_4 by C_4' in (7.12)–(7.16).

Assertions (i), (ii), (iii) follow from these equations by trivial manipulations. We will prove (iv), (v). We have

$$VC_1 V + VC_2 X' = V, \qquad X'C_1 V = 0. \qquad (7.17)$$

Thus

$$VC_1 VC_1 V + VC_1 VC_2 X' = VC_1 V$$

and since $VC_2 X' = XC_2' V$ and $VC_1 X = 0$ we get $VC_1 VC_1 V = VC_1 V$. Equations (7.17) also imply

$$VC_1' VC_1 V + VC_1' VC_2 X' = VC_1' V$$

and again $VC_2 X' = XC_2' V$, $VC_1' X = 0$ give

$$VC_1' VC_1 V = VC_1' V. \qquad (7.18)$$

Taking the transpose on both sides of (7.18) we get $VC_1' VC_1 V = VC_1 V$ and (iv) is proved. Now

$$\text{rank} \begin{bmatrix} V & X \\ X' & 0 \end{bmatrix} = \text{rank} \begin{bmatrix} V & X \\ X' & 0 \end{bmatrix} \begin{bmatrix} C_1 & C_2 \\ C_3 & -C_4 \end{bmatrix}$$

$$= \text{trace} \begin{bmatrix} VC_1 + XC_3 & VC_2 - XC_4 \\ X'C_1 & X'C_2 \end{bmatrix}$$

$$= \text{trace}(VC_1 + XC_3) + \text{trace } X'C_2$$

$$= \text{trace } VC_1 + \text{rank } X + \text{rank } X' \qquad (7.19)$$

where we have made use of (i). Also by **6.2**,

$$\text{rank} \begin{bmatrix} V & X \\ X' & 0 \end{bmatrix} = \text{rank}[V, X] - \text{rank } X. \qquad (7.20)$$

It follows from (7.19), (7.20) that

$$\text{trace } VC_1 = \text{rank}[V, X] - \text{rank } X.$$

Similarly

$$\text{trace } VC_1' = \text{rank}[V, X] - \text{rank } X,$$

and (v) is proved.   □

Consider the *general linear model* $E(y) = X\beta$, $D(y) = \sigma^2 V$, where y is $n \times 1$, X is $n \times p$ and V is a (known) positive semidefinite $p \times p$ matrix. (The setup that we have considered so far is a special case with $V = I$.) We do not make any assumption about the rank of X.

We first remark that if V is positive definite, then making the transformation $z = V^{-1/2}y$, we get the model $E(z) = V^{-1/2}X\beta$, $D(z) = \sigma^2 I$, which can be treated by methods developed earlier. When V is singular such a simple transformation is not available.

7.10 *The BLUE of an estimable function $\ell'\beta$ is $\ell'\widehat{\beta}$ where $\widehat{\beta} = C_3 y$ or $\widehat{\beta} = C_2' y$.*

Proof Since $\ell'\beta$ is estimable, there exists a linear function $u'y$ such that $E(u'y) = \ell'\beta$. Thus $u'X = \ell'$. If $\widehat{\beta} = C_3 y$, then

$$\begin{aligned} E(\ell'\widehat{\beta}) = E(\ell'C_3 y) &= \ell'C_3 X\beta \\ &= u'XC_3 X\beta = u'X\beta = \ell'\beta, \end{aligned}$$

since $XC_3 X = X$ by **7.9**. Thus $\ell'\widehat{\beta}$ is unbiased for $\ell'\beta$.

Let $w'y$ be any other unbiased estimate of $\ell'\beta$. Then $w'X = \ell'$. We have

$$\begin{aligned} \frac{1}{\sigma^2} \text{var}(w'y) \\ = w'Vw \\ = (w - C_3'\ell + C_3'\ell)'V(w - C_3'\ell + C_3'\ell) \\ = (w - C_3'\ell)'V(w - C_3'\ell) + \ell'C_3 VC_3'\ell + 2\ell'C_3 V(w - C_3'\ell). \end{aligned} \quad (7.21)$$

Observe that

$$\begin{aligned} \ell'C_3 V(w - C_3'\ell) &= 2w'XC_3 V(w - C_3'X'w) \\ &= 2w'XC_3 V(I - C_3'X')w \\ &= 0, \end{aligned}$$

since by **7.9**,

$$XC_3 VC_3'X' = XC_3 XC_3 V = XC_3 V.$$

Substituting in (7.21) we get

$$\frac{1}{\sigma^2} \text{var}(w'y) \geq \ell'C_3 VC_3'\ell$$

$$= \frac{1}{\sigma^2} \text{var}(\ell'C_3 y).$$

The case $\widehat{\beta} = C_2' y$ can be handled similarly.   □

7.11 *Let $\widehat{\beta} = C_3 y$ or $\widehat{\beta} = C_2' y$. If $\ell'\beta$, $m'\beta$ are estimable functions, then*

$$\operatorname{cov}(\ell'\widehat{\beta}, m'\widehat{\beta}) = \sigma^2 \ell' C_4 m = \sigma^2 m' C_4 \ell.$$

In particular, $\operatorname{var}(\ell'\widehat{\beta}) = \sigma^2 \ell' C_4 \ell$.

Proof Since $\ell'\beta$, $m'\beta$ are estimable, $\ell' = u'X$, $m' = w'X$ for some u, w. If $\widehat{\beta} = C_3 y$, then

$$\begin{aligned}
\operatorname{cov}(\ell'\widehat{\beta}, m'\widehat{\beta}) &= \operatorname{cov}(u'XC_3 y, w'XC_3 y) \\
&= \sigma^2 u' X C_3 V C_3' X' w \\
&= \sigma^2 u' X C_3 V w \\
&= \sigma^2 u' X C_4 X' w \\
&= \sigma^2 \ell' C_4 m
\end{aligned}$$

by **7.9**. Since the transpose of the matrix on the right hand side of (7.20) is also a possible g-inverse, we have

$$\operatorname{cov}(\ell'\widehat{\beta}, m'\widehat{\beta}) = \sigma^2 m' C_4 \ell.$$

The case $\widehat{\beta} = C_2' y$ also follows by the same observation. $\qquad\square$

7.12 *An unbiased estimate of σ^2 is $\alpha^{-1} y' C_1 y$ where $\alpha = \operatorname{rank}[V, X] - \operatorname{rank} X$.*

Proof Suppose $u'V = 0$ for some u. Then

$$\begin{aligned}
\operatorname{var}(u'(y - X\beta)) &= u'[E(y - X\beta)(y - X\beta)']u \\
&= u'Vu \\
&= 0,
\end{aligned}$$

and hence $u'(y - X\beta) = 0$ (with probability one). Thus $y - X\beta \in \mathscr{C}(V)$ and therefore $y - X\beta = Vw$ for some w. We have

$$\begin{aligned}
(y - X\beta)'C_1(y - X\beta) &= y'C_1(y - X\beta) - \beta'X'C_1 Vw \\
&= y'C_1(y - X\beta),
\end{aligned}$$

since, by **7.9**, $X'C_1 V = 0$. Thus

$$\begin{aligned}
E(y - X\beta)'C_1(y - X\beta) &= E(y'C_1 y) - \beta'X'C_1 X\beta \\
&= E(y'C_1 y), \tag{7.22}
\end{aligned}$$

since, by **7.9**, $X'C_1 X = 0$. However,

$$\begin{aligned}
E(y - X\beta)'C_1(y - X\beta) &= E\{\operatorname{trace}(y - X\beta)'C_1(y - X\beta)\} \\
&= E\{\operatorname{trace} C_1(y - X\beta)(y - X\beta)'\} \\
&= \operatorname{trace} C_1 E(y - X\beta)(y - X\beta)' \\
&= \sigma^2 \operatorname{trace} C_1 V \\
&= \sigma^2\{\operatorname{rank}[V, X] - \operatorname{rank} X\},
\end{aligned}$$

where again we have used **7.9**. Substituting in (7.22) the result is proved. $\qquad\square$

7.5 Exercises

1. Answer the following questions with reference to the linear model $E(y_1) = \beta_1 + \beta_2$, $E(y_2) = 2\beta_1 - \beta_2$, $E(y_3) = \beta_1 - \beta_2$, where y_1, y_2, y_3 are uncorrelated with a common variance σ^2.
   (i) Find two different linear functions of y_1, y_2, y_3 which are unbiased for β_1. Determine their variances and the covariance between the two.
   (ii) Find two linear functions of y_1, y_2, y_3 which are both unbiased for β_2 and are uncorrelated.
   (iii) Write the model in terms of the new parameters $\theta_1 = \beta_1 + 2\beta_2$, $\theta_2 = \beta_1 - 2\beta_2$.

2. Consider the model $E(y_1) = 2\beta_1 - \beta_2 - \beta_3$, $E(y_2) = \beta_2 - \beta_4$, $E(y_3) = \beta_2 + \beta_3 - 2\beta_4$ with the usual assumptions. Determine the estimable functions.

3. Consider the model $E(y_1) = \beta_1 + \beta_2$, $E(y_2) = \beta_1 - \beta_2$, $E(y_3) = \beta_1 + 2\beta_2$ with the usual assumptions. Obtain the BLUE of $2\beta_1 + \beta_2$ and find its variance.

4. Consider the model $E(y_1) = 2\beta_1 + \beta_2$, $E(y_2) = \beta_1 - \beta_2$, $E(y_3) = \beta_1 + \alpha\beta_2$ with the usual assumptions. Determine α so that the BLUEs of β_1, β_2 are uncorrelated.

5. Suppose the matrix

$$A = \begin{bmatrix} 1 & a & b \\ a & 1 & c \\ b & c & 1 \end{bmatrix}$$

is positive definite, where a, b, c are real numbers, not all zero. Show that

$$a^2 + b^2 + c^2 - 2abc > 0.$$

6. Let

$$A = \begin{bmatrix} 2 & a & 1 \\ -1 & 1 & a \\ 1 & -1 & a \end{bmatrix}.$$

Show that $|A| \leq (a^2 + 2)\sqrt{a^2 + 5}$.

7. Let A be a positive semidefinite matrix which is partitioned as

$$\begin{bmatrix} A_{11} & A_{12} \\ A_{21} & A_{22} \end{bmatrix},$$

where A_{11} is a square matrix. Show that

$$|A| \leq |A_{11}||A_{22}|.$$

8. Let A be a $n \times n$ positive definite matrix partitioned as

$$A = \begin{bmatrix} a_{11} & x' \\ x & B \end{bmatrix}.$$

Show that

$$a_{11}|B| - |A| \geq \frac{x'x}{\lambda_1(B)}|B|.$$

Hence conclude that $|A| \leq a_{11}|B|$.

9. Show that there exists a Hadamard matrix of order 2^k for any positive integer k.
10. Consider the model $E(y_1) = \beta_1 + \beta_2$, $E(y_2) = 2\beta_1$, $E(y_3) = \beta_1 - \beta_2$ with the usual assumptions. Find the RSS.
11. Suppose the one-way classification model is written as

$$y_{ij} = \mu + \alpha_i + \varepsilon_{ij}, \quad i = 1, \ldots, k; \; j = 1, \ldots, n_i,$$

where ε_{ij} are independent with mean zero and variance σ^2. The parameter μ is normally referred to as the "general effect". What are the estimable functions? Is it correct to say that the grand mean $\overline{y}_{..}$ is an unbiased estimator of μ?
12. Consider the model $E(y_1) = \beta_1 + 2\beta_2$, $E(y_2) = 2\beta_1$, $E(y_3) = \beta_1 + \beta_2$ with the usual assumptions. Find the RSS subject to the restriction $\beta_1 = \beta_2$.
13. Consider the one-way classification model (with $k \geq 2$)

$$y_{ij} = \alpha_i + \varepsilon_{ij}, \quad i = 1, \ldots, k; \; j = 1, \ldots, n_i;$$

where ε_{ij} are independent with mean 0 and variance σ^2. Find the RSS subject to the restriction $\alpha_1 = \alpha_2$.

Chapter 8
Tests of Linear Hypotheses

8.1 Multivariate Normal Distribution

Let u be a random vector of order n whose components $u_1, \ldots, u_n$ are independent standard normal variables. Let X be an $r \times n$ matrix and let μ be a constant $r \times 1$ vector. The vector $y = Xu + \mu$ is said to have (an r-dimensional) *multivariate normal distribution*.

Clearly, $E(y) = XE(u) + \mu = \mu$ and $D(y) = XD(u)X' = XX'$. Let $\Sigma = XX'$. We now obtain the characteristic function $\phi_y(t)$ of y, defined as

$$\phi_y(t) = E\big(\exp(it'y)\big).$$

First we have

$$\phi_u(t) = E\big(\exp(it'u)\big)$$
$$= \prod_{j=1}^{n} E\big(\exp(it_j u_j)\big)$$
$$= \prod_{j=1}^{n} \exp\left(-\frac{t_j^2}{2}\right)$$
$$= \exp\left(-\frac{t't}{2}\right).$$

Now

$$\phi_y(t) = E\big(\exp(it'y)\big)$$
$$= E\big(\exp(it'(Xu + \mu))\big)$$
$$= \exp(it'\mu) E\big(\exp(it'Xu)\big)$$
$$= \exp(it'\mu)\phi_u(t'X)$$
$$= \exp(it'\mu)\exp\left(-\frac{1}{2}t'XX't\right)$$
$$= \exp\left(it'\mu - \frac{1}{2}t'\Sigma t\right). \tag{8.1}$$

R.B. Bapat, *Linear Algebra and Linear Models*, Universitext,
DOI 10.1007/978-1-4471-2739-0_8, © Springer-Verlag London Limited 2012

Thus the distribution of y depends only on μ and Σ. Therefore we will use the notation $y \sim N(\mu, \Sigma)$. We now show that when Σ is nonsingular, y has the density function given by

$$f(y) = \frac{1}{(2\pi)^{\frac{n}{2}} |\Sigma|^{\frac{1}{2}}} \exp\left(-\frac{1}{2}(y - \mu)' \Sigma^{-1}(y - \mu)\right). \qquad (8.2)$$

We will show that if a random vector y has the density function given by (8.2), then the characteristic function of y is (8.1). Then by the uniqueness of the distribution corresponding to a characteristic function it will follow that if y is $N(\mu, \Sigma)$, where Σ is nonsingular, then the density function of y is (8.2).

We first verify that the function (8.2) integrates to 1 and hence is a density function. Make the transformation $z = \Sigma^{-1/2}(y - \mu)$. The Jacobian of the transformation is the absolute values of $|(\frac{\partial z_i}{\partial y_j})|$ and is easily seen to be $|\Sigma^{-\frac{1}{2}}|$. Thus

$$\int_{-\infty}^{\infty} \cdots \int_{-\infty}^{\infty} f(y) \, dy_1 \cdots dy_n$$

$$= \int_{-\infty}^{\infty} \cdots \int_{-\infty}^{\infty} \frac{1}{(2\pi)^{\frac{n}{2}} |\Sigma|^{\frac{1}{2}}}$$

$$\times \exp\left(-\frac{1}{2} z'z\right) |\Sigma|^{\frac{1}{2}} \, dz_1 \cdots dz_n$$

$$= \frac{1}{(2\pi)^{\frac{n}{2}}} \int_{-\infty}^{\infty} \cdots \int_{-\infty}^{\infty} \exp\left(-\frac{1}{2} \sum_{j=1}^{n} z_j^2\right) dz_1 \cdots dz_n$$

$$= \prod_{j=1}^{n} \int_{-\infty}^{\infty} \frac{1}{\sqrt{2\pi}} \exp\left(-\frac{1}{2} \sum_{j=1}^{n} z_j^2\right) dz_j$$

$$= 1,$$

since each term in the product is the total integral of a standard normal density.

The characteristic function of y is given by

$$\int_{-\infty}^{\infty} \cdots \int_{-\infty}^{\infty} \frac{1}{(2\pi)^{\frac{n}{2}} |\Sigma|^{\frac{1}{2}}} \exp\left(-\frac{1}{2}(y - \mu)' \Sigma^{-1}(y - \mu)\right) \exp(it'y) \, dy_1 \cdots dy_n.$$

$$(8.3)$$

Make the transformation $z = y - \mu$ in (8.3). The Jacobian is clearly 1. Thus the integral in (8.3) equals

$$\int_{-\infty}^{\infty} \cdots \int_{-\infty}^{\infty} \frac{1}{(2\pi)^{\frac{n}{2}} |\Sigma|^{\frac{1}{2}}} \exp\left(-\frac{1}{2} z' \Sigma^{-1} z\right) \exp(it'(z + \mu)) \, dz_1 \cdots dz_n, \quad (8.4)$$

which is the same as

$$\exp\left(it'\mu - \frac{1}{2} t' \Sigma t\right) \times \Delta,$$

where

$$\Delta = \frac{1}{(2\pi)^{\frac{n}{2}}|\Sigma|^{\frac{1}{2}}} \int_{-\infty}^{\infty} \cdots \int_{-\infty}^{\infty} \exp\left(-\frac{1}{2}(z - \Sigma t)'\Sigma^{-1}(z - \Sigma t)\right) dz_1 \cdots dz_n.$$

Make the transformation $u = z - \Sigma t$ in Δ. Then it reduces to the integral of a standard normal density and therefore equals 1. We conclude that the characteristic function of y is given by

$$\exp\left(it'\mu - \frac{1}{2}t'\Sigma t\right).$$

If $y \sim N(\mu, \Sigma)$, then for any matrix B, it can be seen using the characteristic function, that $By \sim N(B\mu, B\Sigma B')$. We leave the proof as an exercise.

Let $y \sim N(\mu, \Sigma)$ and suppose y, μ and Σ are conformally partitioned as

$$y = \begin{pmatrix} y_1 \\ y_2 \end{pmatrix}, \qquad \mu = \begin{pmatrix} \mu_1 \\ \mu_2 \end{pmatrix}, \qquad \Sigma = \begin{bmatrix} \Sigma_{11} & \Sigma_{12} \\ \Sigma_{21} & \Sigma_{22} \end{bmatrix}. \tag{8.5}$$

The characteristic function of y_1 is obtained by setting $t_2 = 0$ where

$$t = \begin{pmatrix} t_1 \\ t_2 \end{pmatrix},$$

is the corresponding partitioning of t. Thus

$$\phi_{y_1}(t_1) = \exp\left(it_1'\mu_1 - \frac{1}{2}t_1'\Sigma_{11}t_1\right)$$

and therefore $y_1 \sim N(\mu_1, \Sigma_{11})$. Similarly, $y_2 \sim N(\mu_2, \Sigma_{22})$.

8.1 *Let $y \sim N(\mu, \Sigma)$ and suppose that y, μ and Σ are conformally partitioned as in (8.5). Then y_1, y_2 are independent if and only if $\Sigma_{12} = 0$.*

Proof If y_1, y_2 are independent then $\text{cov}(y_1, y_2) = \Sigma_{12} = 0$. We now show that the converse is also true. Thus suppose that $\Sigma_{12} = 0$. Then

$$t'\Sigma t = t_1'\Sigma_{11}t_1 + t_2'\Sigma_{22}t_2.$$

Therefore

$$\phi_y(t) = \phi_{y_1}(t_1)\phi_{y_2}(t_2)$$

and hence y_1, y_2 are independent by a well-known property of the characteristic polynomial. □

8.2 *Let $y \sim N(\mu, \sigma^2 I)$ and let A, B be matrices such that $AB' = 0$. Then Ay, By are independent.*

Proof Observe that as remarked earlier,

$$\begin{bmatrix} A \\ B \end{bmatrix} y = \begin{bmatrix} Ay \\ By \end{bmatrix}$$

has multivariate normal distribution. So by **8.2**, Ay, By are independent if $\operatorname{cov}(Ay, By) = AB' = 0$.   □

Now suppose Σ is nonsingular and we will obtain the conditional distribution of y_2 given y_1. Consider the identity (3.6) obtained earlier:

$$\begin{bmatrix} I & 0 \\ X & I \end{bmatrix}\begin{bmatrix} B & C \\ C' & D \end{bmatrix}\begin{bmatrix} I & X' \\ 0 & I \end{bmatrix} = \begin{bmatrix} B & 0 \\ 0 & D - C'B^{-1}C \end{bmatrix}$$

and apply it to Σ, partitioned as in (8.5). Then $X = -\Sigma_{12}\Sigma_{11}^{-1}$. Let

$$S = \begin{bmatrix} I & 0 \\ X & I \end{bmatrix}.$$

Then

$$S^{-1} = \begin{bmatrix} I & 0 \\ -X & I \end{bmatrix},$$

and we conclude that

$$\Sigma = \begin{bmatrix} I & 0 \\ -X & I \end{bmatrix}\begin{bmatrix} \Sigma_{11} & 0 \\ 0 & \Sigma_{22} - \Sigma_{21}\Sigma_{11}^{-1}\Sigma_{12} \end{bmatrix}\begin{bmatrix} I & -X' \\ 0 & I \end{bmatrix}.$$

Therefore

$$\Sigma^{-1} = S'\begin{bmatrix} \Sigma_{11}^{-1} & 0 \\ 0 & \tilde{\Sigma}_{22}^{-1} \end{bmatrix}S, \tag{8.6}$$

where

$$\tilde{\Sigma}_{22} = \Sigma_{22} - \Sigma_{21}\Sigma_{11}^{-1}\Sigma_{12},$$

the Schur complement of Σ_{11} in Σ.

Now

$$(y - \mu)'\Sigma^{-1}(y - \mu)$$
$$= [(y_1 - \mu_1)', (y_2 - \mu_2)']\Sigma^{-1}\begin{bmatrix} y_1 - \mu_1 \\ y_2 - \mu_2 \end{bmatrix}$$
$$= (y_1 - \mu_1)'\Sigma_{11}^{-1}(y_1 - \mu_1)$$
$$+ \left((y_2 - \mu_2)' + (y_1 - \mu_1)'X'\right)\tilde{\Sigma}_{22}^{-1}\left((y_2 - \mu_2) + X(y_1 - \mu_1)\right)$$

using (8.6). Also,

$$|\Sigma| = |\Sigma_{11}||\tilde{\Sigma}_{22}|.$$

Substitute these expressions in the density function of y given in (8.2) and then divide by the marginal density of y_1, that is, a $N(\mu_1, \Sigma_{11})$ density to get the conditional density of y_2 given y_1. It turns out that the conditional distribution of y_2 given y_1 is multivariate normal with mean vector

$$\mu_2 - X(y_1 - \mu_1) = \mu_2 + \Sigma_{21}\Sigma_{11}^{-1}(y_1 - \mu_1)$$

and the dispersion matrix $\tilde{\Sigma}_{22}$.

8.2 Quadratic Forms and Cochran's Theorem

8.3 *Let $y \sim N(0, I_n)$ and let A be a symmetric $n \times n$ matrix. Then $y'Ay$ has a chi-square distribution with r degrees of freedom (χ_r^2) if and only if A is idempotent and* rank $A = r$.

Proof If A is idempotent with rank r, then there exists an orthogonal matrix P such that

$$A = P' \begin{bmatrix} I_r & 0 \\ 0 & 0 \end{bmatrix} P.$$

Let $z = Py$. Then $z \sim N(0, I_n)$. We have

$$
\begin{aligned}
y'Ay &= y'P' \begin{bmatrix} I_r & 0 \\ 0 & 0 \end{bmatrix} Py \\
&= z' \begin{bmatrix} I_r & 0 \\ 0 & 0 \end{bmatrix} z \\
&= z_1^2 + \cdots + z_r^2 \\
&\sim \chi_r^2.
\end{aligned}
$$

Conversely, suppose $y'Ay \sim \chi_r^2$. Since $A = A'$, there exists an orthogonal matrix P such that

$$A = P' \operatorname{diag}(\lambda_1, \ldots, \lambda_n) P,$$

where $\lambda_1, \ldots, \lambda_n$ are the eigenvalues of A. Again, let $z = Py$ so that $z \sim N(0, I_n)$. The characteristic function of $y'Ay$ is given by

$$
\begin{aligned}
\phi(t) &= E\big(\exp(ity'Ay)\big) \\
&= E\left(\exp\left(it \sum_{j=1}^{n} \lambda_j z_j^2\right)\right) \\
&= \prod_{j=1}^{n} E\big(\exp(it\lambda_j z_j^2)\big) \\
&= \prod_{j=1}^{n} (1 - 2it\lambda_j)^{-\frac{1}{2}},
\end{aligned}
\tag{8.7}
$$

since $z_j^2 \sim \chi_1^2$. However, since $y'Ay \sim \chi_r^2$, its characteristic function is

$$\phi(t) = (1 - 2it)^{-r/2}. \tag{8.8}$$

Equating (8.7), (8.8) we get

$$(1 - 2it)^r = \prod_{j=1}^{n} (1 - 2it\lambda_j) \tag{8.9}$$

for all t. The left-hand side of (8.9) is a polynomial in t with r roots, all equal to $1/2i$. Therefore the right-hand side also must have the same roots. This is possible precisely when r of the λ_is are equal to 1, the rest being zero. Therefore A is idempotent with rank r.   □

8.4 *Let $y \sim N(0, I_n)$ and let A_1, A_2 be symmetric, idempotent matrices. Then $y'A_1 y$, $y'A_2 y$ are independent if and only if $A_1 A_2 = 0$.*

Proof Suppose $A_1 A_2 = 0$. Then by **8.2**, $A_1 y$, $A_2 y$ are independent. Hence

$$y'A_1 y = (A_1 y)'(A_1 y), \qquad y'A_2 y = (A_2 y)'(A_2 y)$$

are independent since they are (measurable) functions of independent random variables.

Conversely, let $y'A_1 y$, $y'A_2 y$ be independent. By **8.3**, $y'A_1 y$, $y'A_2 y$ are chi-square and therefore

$$y'A_1 y + y'A_2 y = y'(A_1 + A_2)y$$

must be chi-square. Again, by **8.3**, $A_1 + A_2$ is idempotent. Therefore

$$
\begin{aligned}
A_1 + A_2 &= (A_1 + A_2)^2 \\
&= A_1^2 + A_2^2 + A_1 A_2 + A_2 A_1 \\
&= A_1 + A_2 + A_1 A_2 + A_2 A_1.
\end{aligned}
$$

Hence

$$A_1 A_2 + A_2 A_1 = 0.$$

This gives, upon post-multiplication by A_2,

$$A_1 A_2 + A_2 A_1 A_2 = 0. \tag{8.10}$$

Pre-multiply (8.10) by A_2 to get

$$A_2 A_1 A_2 + A_2^2 A_1 A_2 = 2A_2 A_1 A_2 = 0.$$

Hence $A_2 A_1 A_2 = 0$. Substituting in (8.10) we get $A_1 A_2 = 0$.   □

8.5 *Let $y \sim N(0, I_n)$, let A be a symmetric, idempotent matrix and let $\ell \in R^n$ be a nonzero vector. Then $y'Ay$ and $\ell'y$ are independent if and only if $A\ell = 0$.*

Proof We assume, without loss of generality, that $\|\ell\| = 1$. Then $B = \ell\ell'$ is a symmetric idempotent matrix.

First suppose that $y'Ay$ and $\ell'y$ are independent. Then using, as before, the fact that measurable functions of independent random variables are independent, we see that $y'Ay$ and $y'By$ are independent. It follows from **8.4** that $AB = 0$, and then it is an easy exercise to show that $A\ell = 0$.

Conversely, if $A\ell = 0$, then by **8.2**, Ay and $\ell'y$ are independent. Hence $y'Ay = (Ay)'(Ay)$ and $\ell'y$ are independent. That completes the proof.   □

We now prove a matrix theoretic formulation of one version of Cochran's Theorem.

8.6 *Let $A_1, \ldots, A_k$ be $n \times n$ matrices with $\sum_{i=1}^{k} A_i = I$. Then the following conditions are equivalent:*

(i) $\sum_{i=1}^{k} \text{rank}(A_i) = n$

(ii) $A_i^2 = A_i$, $i = 1, \ldots, k$

(iii) $A_i A_j = 0$, $i \neq j$.

Proof (i) $\Rightarrow$ (iii). Let $A_i = B_i C_i$ be a rank factorization, $i = 1, \ldots, k$. Then

$$B_1 C_1 + \cdots + B_k C_k = I$$

and hence

$$\begin{bmatrix} B_1 & \cdots & B_k \end{bmatrix} \begin{bmatrix} C_1 \\ \vdots \\ C_k \end{bmatrix} = I.$$

Since $\sum_{i=1}^{k} \text{rank}(A_i) = n$, $[B_1 \cdots B_k]$ is a square matrix and therefore

$$\begin{bmatrix} C_1 \\ \vdots \\ C_k \end{bmatrix} \begin{bmatrix} B_1 & \cdots & B_k \end{bmatrix} = I.$$

Thus $C_i B_j = 0$, $i \neq j$. It follows that for $i \neq j$,

$$A_i A_j = B_i C_i B_j C_j = 0.$$

(iii) $\Rightarrow$ (ii). Since $\sum_{i=1}^{k} A_i = I$,

$$A_j \left(\sum_{i=1}^{k} A_i \right) = A_j, \quad j = 1, \ldots, k.$$

It follows that $A_j^2 = A_j$.

(ii) $\Rightarrow$ (i). Since A_i is idempotent, $\text{rank}(A_i) = \text{trace}(A_i)$. Now

$$\sum_{i=1}^{k} \text{rank}(A_i) = \sum_{i=1}^{k} \text{trace}(A_i)$$

$$= \text{trace} \left(\sum_{i=1}^{k} A_i \right)$$

$$= n.$$

That completes the proof. $\qquad \qquad \square$

8.3 One-Way and Two-Way Classifications

Suppose we have the vector of observations $y \sim N(0, I_n)$. The quantity $y'y = \sum_{i=1}^{n} y_i^2$ is called the *crude (or raw) sum of squares*. If we are able to decompose

$$y'y = y'A_1 y + \cdots + y'A_k y$$

where A_i are symmetric and if we can verify one of the equivalent conditions in Cochran's Theorem, we may conclude that $y'A_i y$ are independent chi-square random variables. The degrees of freedom are then given by the ranks of A_i.

We first illustrate an application to the one-way classification model discussed earlier. The model is

$$y_{ij} = \mu + \alpha_i + \varepsilon_{ij}, \quad i = 1, \ldots, k; \; j = 1, \ldots, n_i;$$

where we now assume that ε_{ij} are independent $N(0, \sigma^2)$. Suppose we wish to test the hypothesis

$$H_0 : \alpha_1 = \cdots = \alpha_k.$$

Let

$$z_{ij} = \frac{y_{ij} - \mu - \alpha}{\sigma},$$

which is standard normal if H_0 is true and where α denotes the common value of $\alpha_1, \ldots, \alpha_k$. Let z be the vector

$$(z_{11}, \ldots, z_{1n_1}; z_{21}, \ldots, z_{2n_2}; \ldots; z_{k1}, \ldots, z_{kn_k}),$$

and let $n = \sum_{i=1}^{k} n_i$. We use the *dot notation*. Thus

$$z_{i.} = \sum_{j=1}^{n_i} z_{ij}, \qquad \bar{z}_{i.} = \frac{z_{i.}}{n_i},$$

and a similar notation is used when there are more than two subscripts.

We have the identity

$$\sum_{i=1}^{k} \sum_{j=1}^{n_i} z_{ij}^2 \tag{8.11}$$

$$= \sum_{i=1}^{k} \sum_{j=1}^{n_i} (z_{ij} - \bar{z}_{i.} + \bar{z}_{i.} - \bar{z}_{..} + \bar{z}_{..})^2$$

$$= \sum_{i=1}^{k} \sum_{j=1}^{n_i} (z_{ij} - \bar{z}_{i.})^2 + \sum_{i=1}^{k} n_i (\bar{z}_{i.} - \bar{z}_{..})^2 + n\bar{z}_{..}^2, \tag{8.12}$$

since the cross-product terms equal zero. For example

$$\sum_{i=1}^{k}\sum_{j=1}^{n_i}(z_{ij}-\overline{z}_{i.})(\overline{z}_{i.}-\overline{z}_{..})=\sum_{i=1}^{k}(\overline{z}_{i.}-\overline{z}_{..})\sum_{j=1}^{n_i}(z_{ij}-\overline{z}_{i.})$$

$$=0. \tag{8.13}$$

Let A_1, A_2, A_3 be symmetric matrices such that the quadratic forms

$$z'A_1z, \quad z'A_2z, \quad z'A_3z$$

are the three forms in (8.12) respectively. Since each form is a sum of squares, A_i are in fact, positive semidefinite.

Note that $\mathcal{N}(A_3)$ is the orthogonal complement of $\mathbf{1}_n$, the vector of all ones, and hence $\dim(\mathcal{N}(A_3))=n-1$. Furthermore, $\mathcal{N}(A_1)$ is spanned by

$$\begin{bmatrix}\mathbf{1}_{n_1}\\0\\\vdots\\0\end{bmatrix},\begin{bmatrix}0\\\mathbf{1}_{n_2}\\\vdots\\0\end{bmatrix},\ldots,\begin{bmatrix}0\\0\\\vdots\\\mathbf{1}_{n_k}\end{bmatrix}$$

and so $\dim\mathcal{N}(A_1)=k$.

Now, since $A_1+A_2+A_3=I$, then $\sum_{i=1}^{3}\operatorname{rank}A_i\geq n$, and hence

$$\operatorname{rank}(A_2)\geq n-\operatorname{rank}(A_1)-\operatorname{rank}(A_3)$$
$$=n-(n-k)-1$$
$$=k-1. \tag{8.14}$$

We next observe that if $x_1\perp\mathbf{1}_{n_1},\ldots,x_k\in\mathbf{1}_{n_k}$, then

$$\begin{bmatrix}x_1\\0\\\vdots\\0\end{bmatrix},\ldots,\begin{bmatrix}0\\0\\\vdots\\x_k\end{bmatrix}$$

are linearly independent vectors in $\mathcal{N}(A_2)$. Thus we can generate $(n_1-1)+\cdots+(n_k-1)=n-k$ linearly independent vectors in $\mathcal{N}(A_2)$. These $n-k$ vectors, along with $\mathbf{1}_n$, give $n-k+1$ linearly independent vectors in $\mathcal{N}(A_2)$, and thus $\dim\mathcal{N}(A_2)\geq n-k+1$. Therefore $\operatorname{rank}(A_2)\leq k-1$. Combining this observation and (8.14) we see that $\operatorname{rank}(A_2)=k-1$. Hence $\sum_{i=1}^{3}\operatorname{rank}A_i=n$. We conclude by Cochran's Theorem that $z'A_1z$, $z'A_2z$ are independent chi-square variables. It remains to find the degrees of freedom. These are $\operatorname{rank}(A_1)$, $\operatorname{rank}(A_2)$ respectively, which we have already seen to be $n-k$ and $k-1$, respectively.

Therefore, under H_0,

$$\frac{\sum_{i=1}^{k}n_i(\overline{z}_{i.}-\overline{z}_{..})^2/(k-1)}{\sum_{i=1}^{k}\sum_{j=1}^{n_i}(z_{ij}-\overline{z}_{i.})^2/(n-k)}\sim F(k-1,n-k).$$

In terms of y_{ij} we can write this as

$$\frac{\sum_{i=1}^{k}n_i(\overline{y}_{i.}-\overline{y}_{..})^2/(k-1)}{\sum_{i=1}^{k}\sum_{j=1}^{n_i}(y_{ij}-\overline{y}_{i.})^2/(n-k)}\sim F(k-1,n-k),$$

Table 8.1 ANOVA table

Source	d.f.	Sum of squares	Mean sum of squares	F-statistic
Treatments	$k-1$	$SSA = \sum_{i=1}^{k} n_i (\bar{y}_{i.} - \bar{y}_{..})^2$	$MSA = SSA/(k-1)$	
Error	$n-k$	$SSE = \sum_{i=1}^{k} \sum_{j=1}^{n_i} (y_{ij} - \bar{y}_{i.})^2$	$MSE/(n-k)$	MSA/MSE
Total	$n-1$	$SST = \sum_{i=1}^{k} \sum_{j=1}^{n_i} (y_{ij} - \bar{y}_{..})^2$		

and it can be used to test H_0. This test statistic can be justified on intuitive grounds. If the difference *between* populations is more, in comparison to the difference *within* each population, then the statistic will be large and that is when we reject H_0. The statistic can also be shown to have some optimality properties.

In the context of one-way classification, we have the following notation: the *error sum of squares (SSE)* and the *treatment sum of squares (SSA)* are given by

$$SSE = \sum_{i=1}^{k} \sum_{j=1}^{n_i} (y_{ij} - \bar{y}_{i.})^2, \qquad SSA = \sum_{i=1}^{k} n_i (\bar{y}_{i.} - \bar{y}_{..})^2.$$

(SSA stands for the sum of squares due to "factor A", though in one-way classification there is only one factor.)

The *total sum of squares (SST)* is given by $\sum_{i=1}^{k} \sum_{j=1}^{n_i} (y_{ij} - \bar{y}_{..})^2$.
We also have

$$MSE = SSE/(n-k), \qquad MSA = SSA/(k-1).$$

The computations for the test statistic to test the equality of treatment effects are laid out in the *ANOVA (Analysis of Variance) Table* (Table 8.1).

We now describe two-way classification without interaction. Suppose there are two factors, one at a levels and the other at b levels. We have one observation for every combination of a level of the first factor and a level of the second factor. The model is

$$y_{ij} = \mu + \alpha_i + \beta_j + \varepsilon_{ij}, \quad i = 1, \ldots, a; \ j = 1, \ldots, b$$

where ε_{ij} are i.i.d. $N(0, \sigma^2)$. Here α_i denotes the effect of the i-th level of the first factor and β_j the effect of the j-th level of the second factor. Suppose we want to test the hypothesis $H_0 : \alpha_1 = \cdots = \alpha_a$. The subsequent discussion is under the assumption that H_0 is true. Let α be the common value of $\alpha_1, \ldots, \alpha_a$. Let

$$z_{ij} = \frac{y_{ij} - \mu - \alpha - \beta_j}{\sigma}, \quad i = 1, \ldots, a; \ j = 1, \ldots, b.$$

Then z_{ij} are i.i.d. $N(0, 1)$. Let z be the vector

$$(z_{11}, \ldots, z_{1b}; z_{21}, \ldots, z_{2b}; \ldots; z_{a1}, \ldots, z_{ab}).$$

We have

$$z_{ij} = (z_{ij} - \bar{z}_{i.} - \bar{z}_{.j} + \bar{z}_{..})$$
$$+ (\bar{z}_{i.} - \bar{z}_{..}) + (\bar{z}_{.j} - \bar{z}_{..}) + \bar{z}_{..}$$

and as before

$$\sum_{i=1}^{a}\sum_{j=1}^{b} z_{ij}^2 = \sum_{i=1}^{a}\sum_{j=1}^{b}(z_{ij} - \bar{z}_{i.} - \bar{z}_{.j} + \bar{z}_{..})^2$$

$$+ b\sum_{i=1}^{a}(\bar{z}_{i.} - \bar{z}_{..})^2 + a\sum_{j=1}^{b}(\bar{z}_{.j} - \bar{z}_{..})^2 + ab\bar{z}_{..}^2,$$

since the cross-product terms equal zero. Thus we can write

$$z'z = z'A_1z + z'A_2z + z'A_3z + z'A_4z$$

where A_1, A_2, A_3, A_4 are symmetric (in fact positive semidefinite) matrices. We can argue, as in the case of one-way classification, that Cochran's Theorem is applicable, and conclude that $z'A_iz$ are independent chi-square random variables. We leave the verification as an exercise. It can also be seen that

$$\mathrm{rank}(A_1) = (a-1)(b-1), \qquad \mathrm{rank}(A_2) = a - 1.$$

Note that

$$\sum_{i=1}^{a}\sum_{j=1}^{b}(z_{ij} - \bar{z}_{i.} - \bar{z}_{.j} + \bar{z}_{..})^2 = \frac{1}{\sigma^2}\sum_{i=1}^{a}\sum_{j=1}^{b}(y_{ij} - \bar{y}_{i.} - \bar{y}_{.j} + \bar{y}_{..})^2$$

and

$$\sum_{i=1}^{a}(\bar{z}_{i.} - \bar{z}_{..})^2 = \frac{1}{\sigma^2}\sum_{i=1}^{a}(\bar{y}_{i.} - \bar{y}_{..})^2.$$

Thus

$$\frac{b\sum_{i=1}^{a}(\bar{y}_{i.} - \bar{y}_{..})^2/(a-1)}{\sum_{i=1}^{a}\sum_{j=1}^{b}(y_{ij} - \bar{y}_{i.} - \bar{y}_{.j} + \bar{y}_{..})^2/(a-1)(b-1)}$$

is distributed as F with $(a-1, (a-1)(b-1))$ degrees of freedom and can be used to test H_0. A test for $H_0 : \beta_1 = \cdots = \beta_b$ is constructed similarly.

If we take more than one, but equal number of, observations per every level combination, then the model is

$$y_{ijk} = \mu + \alpha_i + \beta_j + \varepsilon_{ijk};$$

$i = 1, \ldots, a; \; j = 1, \ldots, b; \; k = 1, \ldots, n;$ where n denotes the number of observations per each level combination. The analysis in this case is similar and one can show that under $H_0 : \alpha_1 = \cdots = \alpha_a,$

$$\frac{bn\sum_{i=1}^{a}(\bar{y}_{i..} - \bar{y}_{...})^2/(a-1)}{n\sum_{i=1}^{a}\sum_{j=1}^{b}(\bar{y}_{ij.} - \bar{y}_{i..} - \bar{y}_{.j.} + \bar{y}_{...})^2/(abn - a - b + 1)}$$

is distributed as F with $(a-1, abn - a - b + 1)$ degrees of freedom.

If $k = 1, \ldots, n_{ij}$, then the statistic, in general, is not expressible in a compact form. However if n_{ij} satisfy the relation

$$n_{ij} = \frac{n_{i.} n_{.j}}{n_{..}},$$

then the F-statistic can be derived in a similar way as for the case of equal n_{ij}.

Two-Way Classification with Interaction   Consider the model

$$y_{ijk} = \mu + \alpha_i + \beta_j + \gamma_{ij} + \varepsilon_{ijk};$$

$i = 1, \ldots, a;\ j = 1, \ldots, b;\ k = 1, \ldots, n;$ where $n > 1$, and ε_{ijk} are i.i.d. $N(0, \sigma^2)$. Then under the hypothesis that the γ_{ij}s are all equal, it can be shown that the statistic

$$\frac{n \sum_{i=1}^a \sum_{j=1}^b (\overline{y}_{ij.} - \overline{y}_{i..} - \overline{y}_{.j.} + \overline{y}_{...})^2}{\sum_{i=1}^a \sum_{j=1}^b \sum_{k=1}^n (y_{ijk} - \overline{y}_{ij.})^2} \times \frac{ab(n-1)}{(a-1)(b-1)}$$

is distributed as F with $((a-1)(b-1), ab(n-1))$ degrees of freedom. We omit the proof.

The calculations of the F-statistic are often displayed in the ANOVA (Analysis of Variance) table.

8.4 Linear Hypotheses

We now bring in a normality assumption in our linear model and assume

$$y \sim N(X\beta, \sigma^2 I_n),$$

where y is $n \times 1$, X is $n \times p$ and β is $p \times 1$. Let rank $X = r$.

We have seen that

$$\text{RSS} = \min_{\beta} (y - X\beta)'(y - X\beta)$$

and the minimum is attained at

$$\widehat{\beta} = (X'X)^- X'y.$$

8.7 $\frac{\text{RSS}}{\sigma^2} \sim \chi^2_{n-r}$.

Proof As before, let $P = I - X(X'X)^- X'$. From the proof of **7.5** in Chap. 7,

$$\text{RSS} = y'Py = (y - X\beta)'P(y - X\beta),$$

since $PX = 0$. It follows by **8.3** that RSS/σ^2 is distributed as χ^2. The degrees of freedom equal rank P and this was seen to be $n - r$.   □

Now consider the hypothesis $H : L\beta = z$. We make the assumption, as before, that $\mathcal{R}(L) \subset \mathcal{R}(X)$ and that the equation $L\beta = z$ is consistent. Following Sect. 7.3, let $L = WX'X$, $WX' = T$. Then

$$\text{RSS}_H = \min_{\beta:L\beta=z} (y - X\beta)'(y - X\beta),$$

is attained at $\tilde{\beta}$, where

$$\tilde{\beta} = \widehat{\beta} - (X'X)^- L'(TT')^- (L\widehat{\beta} - z).$$

Therefore,

$$X\tilde{\beta} = (I - P)y - T'(TT')^- (Ty - z)$$
$$= (I - P)y - T'(TT')^- (Ty - TX\beta + TX\beta - z). \tag{8.15}$$

If H is true, then $TX\beta = L\beta = z$, and therefore by (8.15),

$$y - X\tilde{\beta} = Py + U(y - X\beta),$$

where $U = T'(TT')^- T$. Thus

$$\text{RSS}_H = (y - X\tilde{\beta})'(y - X\tilde{\beta})$$
$$= y'Py + (y - X\beta)'U(y - X\beta),$$

as $PU = 0$. Since U is idempotent, we conclude that

$$\frac{\text{RSS}_H - \text{RSS}}{\sigma^2} \sim \chi^2_{\text{rank } U}. \tag{8.16}$$

Also, since $PU = 0$, RSS and $\text{RSS}_H - \text{RSS}$ are independently distributed. We have

$$\text{rank } U = \text{rank}(T'(TT')^- T)$$
$$= \text{trace}(T'(TT')^- T)$$
$$= \text{trace}((TT')^- TT')$$
$$= \text{rank}((TT')^- TT')$$
$$= \text{rank}(TT')$$
$$= \text{rank } T.$$

It follows from **7.7** in Chap. 7 that $\text{rank } U = \text{rank } L$. We conclude that

$$\frac{(\text{RSS}_H - \text{RSS})/\text{rank } L}{\text{RSS}/(n - r)} \sim F(\text{rank } L, n - r)$$

and can be used to test H.

Maximum Likelihood Estimates of β and σ^2   Let $y \sim N(X\beta, \sigma^2 I_n)$, where y is $n \times 1$, X is $n \times p$ and β is $p \times 1$. Let rank $X = r$. Before proceeding further we make a small digression and show that the maximum likelihood estimates of β and σ^2 are given by $\hat{\beta} = (X'X)^- X'y$ and $\hat{\sigma}^2 = \text{RSS}/n = \frac{1}{n}(y - X\hat{\beta})'(y - X\hat{\beta})$.

The likelihood function of y is given by

$$L(\beta, \sigma^2; y) = \frac{1}{(2\pi\sigma^2)^{\frac{n}{2}}} \exp\left\{-\frac{1}{2\sigma^2}(y - X\beta)'(y - X\beta)\right\}.$$

Therefore the log-likelihood function is

$$\log L(\beta, \sigma^2; y) = -\frac{n}{2}\log(2\pi) - \frac{n}{2}\log\sigma^2 - \frac{1}{2\sigma^2}(y - X\beta)'(y - X\beta).$$

Differentiate $\log L(\beta, \sigma^2; y)$ with respect to the components of β and σ^2 and observe that setting the derivatives equal to zero, we get the equations

$$X'X\hat{\beta} = X'y, \qquad \hat{\sigma}^2 = \frac{1}{n}(y - X\hat{\beta})'(y - X\hat{\beta}).$$

Hence the maximum likelihood estimates are as claimed. (The solutions of the equations obtained by equating the derivative of the log likelihood to zero indeed maximize the likelihood provided the matrix of second derivatives (or the Hessian) evaluated at the solutions is negative definite. There is a tradition in Statistics textbooks to gloss over, or to ignore this point, which we follow, and do not go into further technicalities.)

8.5 Multiple Correlation

Suppose the random vector $(y, x_1, \ldots, x_p)'$ of order $p + 1$ has the dispersion matrix

$$V = \begin{bmatrix} \sigma^2 & u' \\ u & \Sigma \end{bmatrix}, \tag{8.17}$$

where Σ is positive definite of order p.

We wish to find the linear combination

$$\alpha'x = \alpha_1 x_1 + \cdots + \alpha_p x_p, \quad \alpha \neq 0$$

which has the maximum correlation with y. The maximum value is called the *multiple correlation coefficient* between y and $x_1, \ldots, x_p$, denoted by $r_{y(x_1,\ldots,x_p)}$.

Thus

$$
\begin{aligned}
r^2_{y(x_1,\ldots,x_p)} &= \max_{\alpha \neq 0}\left\{\text{correlation}(y, \alpha'x)\right\}^2 \\
&= \max_{\alpha \neq 0} \frac{(\text{cov}(y, \alpha'x))^2}{\text{var}(y)\,\text{var}(\alpha'x)} \\
&= \max_{\alpha \neq 0} \frac{(\alpha'u)^2}{\sigma^2 \alpha' \Sigma \alpha} \\
&= \frac{u'\Sigma^{-1}u}{\sigma^2},
\end{aligned}
$$

by **5.3** of Chap. 5. The maximum is attained at $\alpha = \Sigma^{-1}u$.

We get another expression for $r^2_{y(x_1,\ldots,x_p)}$ as follows. Let $Z = V^{-1}$. Then, by the Schur complement formula for the determinant,

$$\frac{1}{z_{11}} = \frac{|V|}{|\Sigma|} = \sigma^2 - u'\Sigma^{-1}u.$$

Hence

$$r^2_{y(x_1,\ldots,x_p)} = 1 - \frac{1}{\sigma^2 z_{11}}.$$

Suppose the vector $(y, x_1, \ldots, x_p)'$ has the multivariate normal distribution with mean vector $(\tau, \mu')'$ and dispersion matrix V partitioned as in (8.17). The conditional distribution of y given $x_1, \ldots, x_p$ is

$$N\left(\tau + u'\Sigma^{-1}(X - \mu), \sigma^2 - u'\Sigma^{-1}u\right).$$

Thus the conditional variance of y given $x = (x_1, \ldots, x_p)'$ is

$$\sigma^2\left(1 - r^2_{y(x_1,\ldots,x_p)}\right).$$

The conditional expectation of y given x (also known as the line of regression of y on x) is

$$u'\Sigma^{-1}x + \tau - u'\Sigma^{-1}\mu$$

and recall that $u'\Sigma^{-1}x$ is precisely the linear combination of $x_1, \ldots, x_p$ which has maximum correlation with y. Thus the multiple correlation coefficient admits special interpretation if the distribution of the variables is multivariate normal.

Suppose there are random variables $y, x_1, \ldots, x_p$ in a given situation and we want to study the relationship between y and the x_is. In particular we may want to predict the value of y given the values of x_is. We first observe $x_1, \ldots, x_p$. Then treating these as fixed, we take an observation on y, after conducting any experiment in the process that may be necessary. If we now stipulate the model

$$E(y) = \beta_0 + \beta_1 x_1 + \cdots + \beta_p x_p$$

with the usual assumptions on var(y), then we have a linear model. The $E(y)$ term in the model is to be really interpreted as the conditional expectation $E(y|x_1, \ldots, x_p)$. Thus the model is valid even if $y, x_1, \ldots, x_p$ are observed simultaneously. If we have n data points on the variables, then the model can be written as

$$E(y_i) = \beta_0 + \beta_1 x_{i1} + \cdots + \beta_p x_{ip}, \quad i = 1, \ldots, n \tag{8.18}$$

and can be analyzed by the methods developed for a linear model. Such a model is called a *regression model*. Since the x'_{ij}s are observations on a random variable we can assume the model to be of full rank. In fact, under mild assumptions on the distribution of $x_1, \ldots, x_p$, it can be proved that the coefficient matrix of the model will have full column rank with probability 1. Thus the terms "full-rank model" and "regression model" are used interchangeably.

Consider the model (8.18) where $y_1, \ldots, y_n$ are independent $N(0, \sigma^2)$. The model can be expressed as

$$E(y) = \begin{bmatrix} 1 & X \end{bmatrix} \begin{bmatrix} \beta_0 \\ \beta_1 \\ \vdots \\ \beta_p \end{bmatrix},$$

where 1 is the column vector of all one's. We assume the model to be full-rank and therefore the BLUEs of $\beta_0, \ldots, \beta_p$ are given by

$$\begin{bmatrix} \widehat{\beta_0} \\ \widehat{\beta_1} \\ \vdots \\ \widehat{\beta_p} \end{bmatrix} = \left(\begin{bmatrix} 1' \\ X' \end{bmatrix} \begin{bmatrix} 1 & X \end{bmatrix} \right)^{-1} \begin{bmatrix} 1' \\ X' \end{bmatrix} y$$

$$= \begin{bmatrix} n & 1'X \\ X'1 & X'X \end{bmatrix}^{-1} \begin{bmatrix} 1'y \\ X'y \end{bmatrix}.$$

It can be verified that

$$\begin{bmatrix} n & 1'X \\ X'1 & X'X \end{bmatrix}^{-1} = \begin{bmatrix} \frac{1}{n-1'M1} & z' \\ z & (X'QX)^{-1} \end{bmatrix},$$

where $M = X(X'X)^{-1}X'$, $Q = I - \frac{1}{n}11'$ and

$$z = -\frac{1}{n}(X'QX)^{-1}X'1.$$

Thus the BLUEs of $\beta_1, \ldots, \beta_p$ are given by

$$\begin{bmatrix} \widehat{\beta_1} \\ \vdots \\ \widehat{\beta_p} \end{bmatrix} = (X'QX)^{-1}X'Qy. \tag{8.19}$$

The sample dispersion matrix of the variables $y, x_1, \ldots, x_p$ is computed as follows. Let

$$S = \begin{bmatrix} y_1 \\ \vdots & X \\ y_n \end{bmatrix}.$$

Then the dispersion matrix is

$$S'S - \frac{1}{n}S'11'S = S'QS = \begin{bmatrix} y'Qy & y'QX \\ X'Qy & X'QX \end{bmatrix}.$$

Thus the linear function of $x_1, \ldots, x_p$ which has maximum correlation with y is obtained by taking

$$\alpha = (X'QX)^{-1}X'Qy$$

and this coincides with (8.19). To summarize, the linear function $\beta_1 x_1 + \cdots + \beta_p x_p$ having maximum correlation with y is obtained by taking $\beta_i = \widehat{\beta}_i$, the least squares estimate of β_i.

Let

$$\widehat{y}_i = \widehat{\beta}_0 + \widehat{\beta}_1 x_{i1} + \cdots + \widehat{\beta}_p x_{pi}, \quad i = 1, \ldots, n$$

be the predicted value of y_i. Let

$$\widehat{y} = (\widehat{y}_1, \ldots, \widehat{y}_n)'$$

and let $\overline{\widehat{y}} = \frac{1}{n} 1' \widehat{y}$. Then

$$r^2_{y(x_1,\ldots,x_p)} = \{\text{correlation}(y, \widehat{\beta}_1 x_1 + \cdots + \widehat{\beta}_p x_p)\}^2$$

$$= \{\text{correlation}(y, \widehat{y})\}^2$$

$$= \frac{\{\sum_{i=1}^{n} (y_i - \overline{y})(\widehat{y}_i - \overline{\widehat{y}})\}^2}{\sum_{i=1}^{n} (y_i - \overline{y})^2 \sum_{i=1}^{n} (\widehat{y}_i - \overline{\widehat{y}})^2}.$$

The square root of the expression above is the multiple correlation coefficient calculated from a sample and it is known as the *coefficient of determination*.

We now derive the F-statistic for the hypothesis $H : \beta_1 = \cdots = \beta_p = 0$. We have

$$\text{RSS} = \sum_{i=1}^{n} (y_i - \widehat{y}_i)^2$$

and the corresponding degrees of freedom are $n - p - 1$.

To find RSS_H we must minimize

$$\sum_{i=1}^{n} (y_i - \beta_0)^2$$

and this is achieved when $\beta_0 = \overline{y}$. The degrees of freedom now are p. Thus the statistic

$$\frac{(\text{RSS}_H - \text{RSS})/p}{\text{RSS}/(n - p - 1)} = \frac{\sum_{i=1}^{n} (y_i - \overline{y})^2 - \sum_{i=1}^{n} (y_i - \widehat{y}_i)^2}{\sum_{i=1}^{n} (y_i - \widehat{y}_i)^2} \times \frac{n - p - 1}{p} \quad (8.20)$$

is $F(p, n - p - 1)$ if H is true.

8.6 Exercises

1. Let $X = (X_1, X_2)$ follow a bivariate normal distribution with mean vector $(1, 2)$ and dispersion matrix $\begin{bmatrix} 2 & 1 \\ 1 & 2 \end{bmatrix}$. (i) Find the joint distribution of $X_1 + X_2$ and $X_1 - X_2$. (ii) Find the conditional distribution of X_1 given $X_2 = -2$.

2. Let X_1, X_2 be a random sample from a standard normal distribution. Determine Y_1, Y_2, both linear functions of X_1, X_2, such that $Y = (Y_1, Y_2)$ has a bivariate normal distribution with mean vector $(-2, 3)$ and dispersion matrix $\begin{bmatrix} 5 & -3 \\ -3 & 2 \end{bmatrix}$.

3. Let X_1, X_2 be a random sample from a standard normal distribution. Determine the linear functions of X_1, X_2 which are distributed independently of $(X_1 - X_2)^2$.

4. Let A be an $n \times n$ matrix. Using Cochran's Theorem show that A is idempotent if and only if rank $A + \text{rank}(I - A) = n$.

5. Let $X_1, \ldots, X_n$ be a random sample from a standard normal distribution. Show, using Cochran's Theorem, that

$$\overline{X} = \sum_{i=1}^{n} X_i \quad \text{and} \quad \sum_{i=1}^{n}(X_i - \overline{X})^2$$

are independently distributed.

6. Three teaching methods, A, B, C, are to be compared. Each method was administered to a group of 4 students and the scores obtained by the students on a test are given below. Carry out an F-test at level of significance .01 to decide if the mean scores under the three methods are significantly different.

$$\text{Method A:} \quad 75, 79, 71, 69$$

$$\text{Method B:} \quad 82, 93, 86, 88$$

$$\text{Method C:} \quad 78, 81, 76, 81$$

7. The defective items produced on three machines M1, M2, M3 by four operators O1, O2, O3, O4 are given in the following table.

	O1	O2	O3	O4
M1	29	25	36	22
M2	28	19	40	28
M3	35	28	34	30

Carry out a test for significant differences between the machines as well as significant differences between the operators.

8. Consider the model $y_1 = \theta_1 + \theta_2 + \varepsilon_1$, $y_2 = 2\theta_1 + \varepsilon_2$, $y_3 = \theta_1 - \theta_2 + \varepsilon_3$ where ε_i, $i = 1, 2, 3$ are i.i.d. $N(0, \sigma^2)$. Derive the F-statistics to test $\theta_1 = \theta_2$.

9. Consider the model $Y = \beta_1 + \beta_2 x_1 + \beta_3 x_2 + \varepsilon$ with the usual assumptions. Derive the test for the hypothesis $\beta_2 = 0$ and also for the hypothesis $\beta_3 = 0$ using the data given below:

Y	10	12	6	14	20	5	8	15	13	21	14	11	18	17	27
x_1	21	32	46	91	20	65	26	74	48	81	93	88	46	24	11
x_2	2.67	3.12	2.11	4.21	6.43	1.76	2.88	6.15	7.20	9.12	3.21	4.87	5.38	8.71	8.11

10. Let (X_1, X_2, X_3) follow a trivariate normal distribution with mean 0 and dispersion matrix $\begin{bmatrix} 3 & -1 & -1 \\ -1 & 3 & -1 \\ -1 & -1 & 3 \end{bmatrix}$. Find the multiple correlation coefficient between X_1 and X_2, X_3.

11. The following table gives y, the score obtained in the final examination by 12 students, x_1, their IQ score, x_2, the score in the periodical examination and x_3, the score in the homework. Fit the model $E(y) = \beta_0 + \beta_1 x_1 + \beta_2 x_2 + \beta_3 x_3$. Find

the multiple correlation coefficient (actually the coefficient of determination) between y and x_1, x_2, x_3. Test the hypothesis that $\beta_1 = \beta_2 = \beta_3 = 0$.

y	89	67	56	94	43	32	77	87	86	90	42	56
x_1	115	110	104	123	102	103	116	112	110	121	107	108
x_2	82	65	62	83	48	41	71	84	81	88	49	43
x_3	97	88	90	92	78	76	89	94	95	99	85	79

12. Consider the partitioned matrix

$$X = \begin{bmatrix} A & B \\ C & D \end{bmatrix}$$

and suppose $\mathscr{C}(B) \subset \mathscr{C}(A)$, $\mathscr{R}(C) \subset \mathscr{R}(A)$. Let $\tilde{D} = D - CA^- B$ be the "generalized Schur complement" of D in X. Show that D is well-defined and

$$\operatorname{rank} X = \operatorname{rank} A + \operatorname{rank} \tilde{D}.$$

Similarly, if $\mathscr{C}(C) \subset \mathscr{C}(D)$, $\mathscr{R}(B) \subset \mathscr{R}(D)$ then $\tilde{A} = A - BD^- C$ is well-defined and rank $X = \operatorname{rank} D + \operatorname{rank} \tilde{A}$. We will refer to this result as the generalized Schur complement formula for rank and it is a useful tool to obtain rank identities.

13. Let $y \sim N(\mu, \Sigma)$ and suppose y, μ and Σ are conformally partitioned as in (8.5). Obtain the conditional distribution of y_2 given y_1 when Σ is possibly singular.

14. Let $y \sim N(0, \Sigma)$ where Σ is a positive semidefinite $n \times n$ matrix of rank r. Show that there exists an $n \times r$ matrix B such that $y = Bx$ where $x \sim N(0, I_r)$ and $\Sigma = BB'$.

15. Let $y \sim N(0, \Sigma)$ where Σ is a positive semidefinite $n \times n$ matrix. Let A be a symmetric $n \times n$ matrix. Prove that $y'Ay$ has chi-square distribution if and only if $\Sigma A \Sigma A \Sigma = \Sigma A \Sigma$, in which case the degrees of freedom equal rank($A\Sigma$).

16. Let A, B be symmetric idempotent matrices such that $A \geq B$. Prove that $A - B$ is idempotent. State the analogous result for distribution of quadratic forms.

17. Let A be a symmetric matrix. Show that A is idempotent if and only if $A^4 = A$.

18. Let y be an $n \times 1$ vector with multivariate normal distribution. Show that $y_1, \ldots, y_n$ are pairwise independent if and only if they are mutually independent.

19. Let $y \sim N(0, I_n)$. Find the conditional distribution of y given $y_1 + \cdots + y_n = 0$.

20. Consider the model

$$y_{ij} = \alpha_i + \beta_j + \varepsilon_{ij}, \quad i = 1, \ldots, a; \ j = 1, \ldots, b$$

where ε_{ij} are i.i.d. $N(0, \sigma^2)$. Derive a necessary and sufficient condition for

$$\sum_{i=1}^{a} c_i \alpha_i + \sum_{j=1}^{b} d_j \beta_j$$

to be estimable.

21. In an agricultural experiment, three fertilizers are to be compared using 36 plots. Let α_i be the effect of the i-th fertilizer, $i = 1, 2, 3$. Write the appropriate linear model. How many plots should be allocated to each fertilizer if we want to estimate $\alpha_1 + 2\alpha_2 + \alpha_3$ with maximum precision?

22. Some varieties of guayule, a Mexican rubber plant, were compared with respect to yield of rubber. These were planted in five blocks of seven plots each. The yield, measured in suitable units, is given in the following table, where each row represents a variety and each column represents a block.

4.46	9.14	6.22	4.42	6.64
1.43	4.04	6.29	6.78	7.32
2.43	1.74	5.29	5.48	6.32
2.08	5.02	2.29	6.46	7.26
6.43	4.01	7.69	6.73	8.12
2.96	4.35	2.11	5.43	1.21
6.45	5.84	3.87	6.71	5.32

(i) Test whether there is a significant difference between the varieties.

(ii) Test whether the average yield of varieties 1, 5, 7 is different from that of varieties 3, 4, 6.

(iii) Construct a 95 percent confidence interval for the yield of variety 2.

23. The angles $\theta_1, \theta_2, \theta_3$ of a triangular field were measured in an aerial survey and the observations y_1, y_2, y_3 were obtained. Set up a linear model and making the necessary assumptions derive a test for the hypothesis that $\theta_1 = \theta_2 = \theta_3$.

24. We follow the notation of Sect. 8.5 here. Show that the following assertions hold:

(i) $\mathbf{1}'y = \mathbf{1}'\widehat{y}$ and hence $\overline{y} = \overline{\widehat{y}}$.

(ii) $(y - \widehat{y})'\widehat{y} = 0$.

(iii) $\sum_{i=1}^{n}(y_i - \overline{y})^2 = \sum_{i=1}^{n}(y_i - \widehat{y}_i)^2 + \sum_{i=1}^{n}(\widehat{y}_i - \overline{y})^2$.

(iv) The statistic in (8.20) is $\frac{r^2}{1-r^2} \times \frac{n-p-1}{p}$, where $r^2 = r_{y(x_1,...,x_p)}$.

Part (iv) can be interpreted as follows. If y bears a relationship with $x_1, \ldots, x_p$ which is close to linear, then r^2 is close to 1, and $\frac{r^2}{1-r^2}$ is large. This also indicates that $\beta_1, \ldots, \beta_p$ are significantly different from zero and therefore we must reject the hypothesis that β_i are zero. Therefore the fact that the F-statistic is $\frac{r^2}{1-r^2}$ (up to a constant) is intuitively justified.

Chapter 9
Linear Mixed Models

9.1 Fixed Effects and Random Effects

In the previous two chapters we have considered the linear model $E(y) = X\beta$, $D(y) = \sigma^2 I$. In this model, $\beta_1, \beta_2, \ldots,$ are assumed to be parameters which are unknown but fixed. We are interested in estimating certain linear combinations of the parameters, and in testing hypotheses about them. In several circumstances it makes sense to treat all or some of the parameters as not fixed, but unobserved random variables. To distinguish between the two types of parameters, we refer to the parameters, treated as unknown constants, as *fixed effects*, and the parameters which are taken to be random, as *random effects*. If a model contains only fixed effects then it is called a *fixed effects model*. Thus the linear models considered in the earlier chapters are fixed effects models. If a model contains only random effects, apart from an overall mean, which is a fixed effect, then it is called a *random effects model*. A model with both fixed effects and random effects is called a *mixed effects model* (or a *mixed model*).

We give some examples. Let us suppose that we wish to compare the level of service in three five-star hotels, A, B, C. We may choose a sample of guests from each hotel and arrive at some measure of satisfaction, y_{ij}, indicating the response of the j-th guest from the i-th hotel. If the sample sizes from the three hotels are n_1, n_2, n_3, then we have the fixed effects one-way classification model $y_{ij} = \mu + a_i + \varepsilon_{ij}$; $j = 1, \ldots, n_i$; $i = 1, 2, 3$. Now imagine that we want to test the hypothesis that the level of service is not significantly different across all five-star hotels in the state. Then the three hotels may be considered as selected at random from all the five-star hotels in the state. In this situation it is more meaningful to consider the effect a_i due to the i-th hotel as random. We assume the a_i to be i.i.d. with mean 0 and variance σ_1^2. As usual, ε_{ij} are assumed i.i.d. with mean 0 and variance σ^2. We also assume a_i and ε_{ij} to be uncorrelated. The overall mean μ is considered fixed. We thus have a one-way random effects model.

We now give an example of a two-way mixed model. Let us suppose that the fuel efficiency of four brands of automobiles is to be compared. We run the experiment with a car of each brand and test it with tyres of three different companies. The model will be $y_{ij} = \mu + \alpha_i + \beta_j + \varepsilon_{ij}$, where α_i is the effect of the i-th car, and β_j is the effect of the j-th set of tyres. Since the cars and tyres that we actually use in the experiment are chosen from the entire lot of the particular brands at random, it is reasonable to assume both α_i and β_j to be random effects. In the same example imagine that we have four cars already with us and we want to know which one is more fuel efficient (we may want to decide which of these should be used for a long trip we plan to undertake). In that case α_i should be treated as fixed effects while β_j would still be random. We then have an example of a mixed model.

In this chapter we will denote the dispersion matrix of a random vector y by $\text{cov}(y)$, rather than $D(y)$. The $n \times n$ matrix of all ones is denoted by J_n. We will use the following models for illustration in this chapter.

9.1 *One-way random effects model (unbalanced case): The model is*

$$y_{ij} = \mu + a_i + \varepsilon_{ij}, \quad i = 1, \ldots, k; \ j = 1, \ldots, n_i; \ n = \sum_{i=1}^{i} n_i,$$

with the following assumptions: $a_i \sim N(0, \sigma_1^2)$, $\varepsilon_{ij} \sim N(0, \sigma^2)$, $\text{cov}(a_i, a_j) = 0$, $i \neq j$; $\text{cov}(\varepsilon_{ij}, \varepsilon_{rs}) = 0$, $(i, j) \neq (r, s)$; $\text{cov}(a_i, \varepsilon_{rs}) = 0$. *Let* Σ_i *be the* $n_i \times n_i$ *matrix given by*

$$\Sigma_i = \sigma_1^2 \mathbf{1}_{n_i} \mathbf{1}'_{n_i} + \sigma^2 I_{n_i} = \sigma_1^2 J_{n_i} + \sigma^2 I_{n_i},$$

$i = 1, \ldots, k$, *and let* V *be the block diagonal matrix with its blocks being* $\Sigma_1, \ldots, \Sigma_k$. *Note that if* y *is the* $n \times 1$ *vector of observations, then* $\text{cov}(y) = V$.

9.2 *One-way random effects model (balanced case): This is the same as* **9.1**, *except that* $n_i = m; i = 1, \ldots, k$.

9.3 *Linear mixed model: The model is*

$$y = X\beta + Z_1 a_1 + \cdots + Z_k a_k + \varepsilon$$

with the following assumptions: y *is an* $n \times 1$ *vector of observations,* X *is an* $n \times p$ *known matrix, not necessarily of full column rank,* β *is a vector of fixed effects,* Z_i *is a known* $n \times r_i$ *matrix of rank* r_i, $i = 1, \ldots, k$, a_i *are random effects with* $E(a_i) = 0$, $\text{cov}(a_i) = \sigma_i^2 I_{r_i}$, $i = 1, \ldots, k$, $\text{cov}(a_i, a_j) = 0$, $i \neq j$, $\text{cov}(a_i, \varepsilon) = 0$, $i = 1, \ldots, k$, ε *is an* $n \times 1$ *vector of errors with* $E(\varepsilon) = 0$, $\text{cov}(\varepsilon) = \sigma^2 I_n$. *It can be seen (see* **9.4**) *that* $E(y) = X\beta$ *and* $\text{cov}(y) := V = \sigma^2 I_n + \sum_{j=1}^{k} \sigma_j^2 Z_j Z_j'$. *We set* $\sigma_0^2 = \sigma^2$ *and* $Z_0 = I_n$. *Then* $V = \sum_{j=0}^{k} \sigma_j^2 Z_j Z_j'$,

It can be seen that model **9.1** is a special instance of model **9.3**. Before proceeding further we prove the following easy result.

9.4 *Consider the model* $y = X\beta + Z_1 a_1 + \cdots + Z_k a_k + \varepsilon$ *as in* **9.3**. *Then* $E(y) = X\beta$ *and* $\text{cov}(y) = \sigma^2 I_n + \sum_{i=1}^{k} \sigma_i^2 Z_i Z_i'$.

Proof We have

$$E(y) = E\left(X\beta + \sum_{i=1}^{k} Z_i a_i + \varepsilon\right)$$

$$= X\beta + E\left(\sum_{i=1}^{k} Z_i a_i + \varepsilon\right)$$

$$= X\beta.$$

Also,

$$\text{cov}(y) = \text{cov}\left(X\beta + \sum_{i=1}^{k} Z_i a_i + \varepsilon\right)$$

$$= \text{var}\left(\sum_{i=1}^{k} Z_i a_i\right) + \text{var}(\varepsilon)$$

$$= \sum_{i=1}^{k} \text{var}(Z_i a_i) + \sigma^2 I_n$$

$$= \sum_{i=1}^{k} Z_i \text{var}(a_i) Z_i' + \sigma^2 I_n$$

$$= \sum_{i=1}^{k} \sigma_i^2 Z_i Z_i' + \sigma^2 I_n.$$

That completes the proof. $\square$

Linear mixed models are appropriate when we are interested not just in inference concerning linear functions of the parameters but want to make a more careful investigation of the variances and covariances of the observations. We model the variances and covariances as arising due to the random effects, apart from the usual variance of the error. Therefore the variances of the random effects are called *variance components*.

In a linear mixed model, as far as estimation of the fixed effects is concerned, we can use the theory developed earlier for fixed effects models. We first review models in which the variance-covariance matrix of the observations is not necessarily a scalar matrix. Consider the linear model $y = X\beta + \varepsilon$, $\text{cov}(y) = \sigma^2 V$, where y is $n \times 1$, X is $n \times k$ and V is a known $n \times n$ positive definite matrix. Note that this is a special case of the general linear model considered in Sect. 7.4, where V was assumed only to be positive semidefinite. As remarked in Sect. 7.4, we may make a transformation $z = V^{-\frac{1}{2}} y$ and derive results for the present model from those obtained in the case of models with variance-covariance matrix $\sigma^2 I_n$. The estimators thus obtained are called *generalized least squares estimators*. The main results can be summarized as follows.

The normal equations in this case are $X'V^{-1}X\beta = X'V^{-1}y$, which are consistent. Let $\hat{\beta} = (X'V^{-1}X)^-X'V^{-1}y$ be a solution. If $\ell'\beta$ is estimable, then $\ell'\hat{\beta}$ is its unique best linear unbiased estimate (BLUE). If X has full column rank, then the BLUE of β is given by $\hat{\beta} = (X'V^{-1}X)^{-1}X'V^{-1}y$. The variance-covariance matrix of $\hat{\beta}$ is then given by $\sigma^2(X'V^{-1}X)^{-1}$.

Now consider the mixed model $y = X\beta + Z_1a_1 + \cdots + Z_ka_k + \varepsilon$ as in **9.3**. The dispersion matrix of Y is given by $V = \sigma^2 I_n + \sum_{j=1}^{k} \sigma_j^2 Z_j Z_j'$, which is clearly positive definite. Since $\sigma^2, \sigma_j^2, j = 1, \ldots, k$, are unknown, this model is not a general linear model in the sense discussed earlier. However for estimating linear functions of β, we treat this as a general linear model, after replacing σ^2, σ_j^2 by their estimates. Thus, setting $\hat{\beta} = (X'\hat{V}^{-1}X)^-X'\hat{V}^{-1}y$, we estimate an estimable function $\ell'\beta$ by $\ell'\hat{\beta}$. The estimator $\hat{\beta}$ is called the *estimated generalized least squares estimator (EGLS)*.

In the subsequent sections we take up the problem of inference concerning the variances of the random effects, or the variance components.

9.2 ML and REML Estimators

We first illustrate the maximum likelihood estimation of the variance components in a one-way random effects model.

The model is

$$y_{ij} = \mu + a_i + \varepsilon_{ij}, \quad i = 1, \ldots, k; \; j = 1, \ldots, n_i;$$

with the usual assumptions as in **9.1**. We set $n = \sum_{i=1}^{k} n_i$. Let Σ_i be the $n_i \times n_i$ matrix given by

$$\Sigma_i = \sigma_1^2 \mathbf{1}_{n_i} \mathbf{1}_{n_i}' + \sigma^2 I_{n_i} = \sigma_1^2 J_{n_i} + \sigma^2 I_{n_i},$$

$i = 1, \ldots, k$, and let V be the block diagonal matrix with its blocks being $\Sigma_1, \ldots, \Sigma_k$.

The eigenvalues of Σ_i are given by $\sigma^2 + n_i \sigma_1^2$ with multiplicity 1 and σ^2 with multiplicity $n_i - 1$. Hence

$$|\Sigma_i| = \left(\sigma^2 + n_i\sigma_1^2\right)\left(\sigma^2\right)^{n_i - 1}.$$

Therefore

$$|V| = \prod_{i=1}^{k}\left(\sigma^2 + n_i\sigma_1^2\right)(\sigma)^{2(n_i - 1)}.$$

We also note that

$$\Sigma_i^{-1} = \frac{1}{\sigma^2}\left(I_{n_i} - \frac{\sigma_1^2}{\sigma^2 + n_i\sigma_1^2} J_{n_i}\right).$$

The likelihood function is given by

$$L(\mu, \sigma^2, \sigma_1^2; y)$$

$$= (2\pi)^{-n/2} |V|^{-1/2} \exp\left\{-\frac{1}{2}(y - \mu\mathbf{1_n})'V^{-1}(y - \mu\mathbf{1_n})\right\}$$

$$= (2\pi)^{-n/2} \sigma^{-(n-k)} \prod_{i=1}^{k} (\sigma^2 + n_i\sigma_1^2)^{-1/2}$$

$$\times \exp\left\{-\frac{1}{2\sigma^2}\left\{\sum_{i=1}^{k}\sum_{j=1}^{n_i}(y_{ij} - \mu)^2 - \sum_{i=1}^{k}\frac{\sigma_1^2}{\sigma^2 + n_i\sigma_1^2}(y_{i.} - n_i\mu)^2\right\}\right\}.$$

Thus

$$\log L(\mu, \sigma^2, \sigma_1^2; y) = -\frac{n}{2}\log(2\pi) - \frac{1}{2}(n-k)\log\sigma^2$$

$$- \frac{1}{2}\sum_{i=1}^{k}\log(\sigma^2 + n_i\sigma_1^2) - \frac{1}{2\sigma^2}\sum_{i=1}^{k}\sum_{j=1}^{n_i}(y_{ij} - \mu)^2$$

$$+ \frac{1}{2\sigma^2}\sum_{i=1}^{k}\frac{\sigma_1^2}{\sigma^2 + n_i\sigma_1^2}(y_{i.} - n_i\mu)^2$$

$$= -\frac{n}{2}\log(2\pi) - \frac{1}{2}(n-k)\log\sigma^2$$

$$- \frac{1}{2}\sum_{i=1}^{k}\log(\sigma^2 + n_i\sigma_1^2) - \frac{1}{2\sigma^2}\sum_{i=1}^{k}\sum_{j=1}^{n_i}(y_{ij} - \bar{y}_{i.})^2$$

$$- \sum_{i=1}^{k}\frac{n_i(\bar{y}_{i.} - \mu)^2}{2(\sigma^2 + n_i\sigma_1^2)}.$$

Setting the partial derivatives with respect to the parameters equal to zero we get the equations

$$\frac{\partial L}{\partial \mu} = \sum_{i=1}^{k}\frac{n_i(\bar{y}_{i.} - \mu)}{\sigma^2 + n_i\sigma_1^2} = 0,$$

$$\frac{\partial L}{\partial \sigma_1^2} = -\frac{1}{2}\sum_{i=1}^{k}\frac{n_i}{\sigma^2 + n_i\sigma_1^2} + \sum_{i=1}^{k}\frac{n_i^2(\bar{y}_{i.} - \mu)^2}{2(\sigma^2 + n_i\sigma_1^2)^2} = 0,$$

$$\frac{\partial L}{\partial \sigma^2} = -\frac{n-k}{2\sigma^2} - \frac{1}{2}\sum_{i=1}^{k}\frac{1}{\sigma^2 + n_i\sigma_1^2} + \frac{1}{2\sigma^4}\sum_{i=1}^{k}\sum_{j=1}^{n_i}(y_{ij} - \bar{y}_{i.})^2$$

$$+ \sum_{i=1}^{k}\frac{n_i(\bar{y}_{i.} - \mu)^2}{2(\sigma^2 + n_i\sigma_1^2)^2} = 0.$$

From the first equation we get the explicit formula for the ML (*maximum likelihood*) estimate of μ as

$$\hat{\mu} = \left(\sum_{i=1}^{k} \frac{n_i}{\sigma^2 + n_i\sigma_1^2}\right)^{-1} \sum_{i=1}^{k} \frac{n_i\bar{y}_{i.}}{\sigma^2 + n_i\sigma_1^2}. \tag{9.1}$$

Note that this estimate coincides with the generalized least squares estimate of μ. The equations for the ML estimates of σ_1^2 and σ^2 do not yield closed form solutions and must be solved by iterative methods. The resulting solutions are the ML estimates if they are positive. Otherwise the ML estimate should be taken to be zero.

Recall that in the context of one-way classification, we have the following notation: the *error sum of squares (SSE)* and the *treatment sum of squares (SSA)* are given by

$$\text{SSE} = \sum_{i=1}^{k}\sum_{j=1}^{n_i}(y_{ij} - \bar{y}_{i.})^2, \qquad \text{SSA} = \sum_{i=1}^{k} n_i(\bar{y}_{i.} - \bar{y}_{..})^2.$$

We also have

$$\text{MSE} = \text{SSE}/(n - k), \qquad \text{MSA} = \text{SSA}/(k - 1).$$

In the balanced case, that is when each $n_1 = n_2 = \cdots = n_k = m$, the ML estimates admit closed form expressions given by

$$\hat{\mu} = \bar{y}_{..}, \quad \hat{\sigma}^2 = \text{SSE}/(n - k), \quad \text{and} \quad \hat{\sigma}_1^2 = \frac{1}{n}(\text{SSA} - k\hat{\sigma}^2).$$

Now consider the model

$$Y = X\beta + Z_1 a_1 + \cdots + Z_k a_k + \varepsilon$$

with the assumptions as in **9.3**. The dispersion matrix of Y is given by $V = \sigma^2 I_n + \sum_{j=1}^{k}\sigma_j^2 Z_j Z_j'$. We set $\sigma_0^2 = \sigma^2$ and $Z_0 = I_n$. Then $V = \sum_{j=0}^{k}\sigma_j^2 Z_j Z_j'$.

The likelihood function is given by

$$L(\beta, V; y) = (2\pi)^{-n/2}|V|^{-1/2}\exp\{-(y - X\beta)'V^{-1}(y - X\beta)\}.$$

Differentiating the logarithm of the likelihood with respect to the parameters and setting equal to zero we have the equations

$$\frac{\partial \log L}{\partial \beta} = X'V^{-1}y - X'V^{-1}X\beta = 0$$

$$\frac{\partial \log L}{\partial \sigma_j^2} = -\frac{1}{2}\text{trace}(V^{-1}Z_j Z_j') + (y - X\beta)'V^{-1}Z_j Z_j' V^{-1}(y - X\beta) = 0.$$

As before, the equations for the ML estimates do not yield closed form solutions in general and must be solved by iterative methods. The resulting solutions for σ_j^2 are the ML estimates if they are positive. Otherwise the ML estimate should be taken to be zero.

We now describe the *restricted (or residual) maximum likelihood or the REML* method of estimation of variance components. We first prove a preliminary result. Let A be an $n \times n$ matrix such that each element of A is a differentiable function of x. We denote by $\frac{dA}{dx}$, the matrix with (i, j)-element $\frac{da_{ij}}{dx}$. Denote the cofactor of a_{ij} by $\text{cof} \, a_{ij}$. With this notation we have the following.

9.5 *Let A be an $n \times n$ matrix such that each element of A is a differentiable function of x. Then the following assertions hold:*

(i) $\frac{d}{dx}|A| = \text{trace}((\text{adj } A)\frac{dA}{dx})$

(ii) *If* $|A| > 0$, *then* $\frac{d}{dx}\log|A| = \text{trace}(A^{-1}\frac{dA}{dx})$.

Proof (i) We have,

$$\frac{d}{dx}|A| = \sum_{i=1}^{n}\sum_{j=1}^{n}\left(\frac{d}{da_{ij}}|A|\right)\left(\frac{da_{ij}}{dx}\right)$$

$$= \sum_{i=1}^{n}\sum_{j=1}^{n}(\text{cof} \, a_{ji})\frac{da_{ij}}{dx}$$

$$= \text{trace}\left(\text{adj } A \frac{dA}{dx}\right).$$

(ii) We have,

$$\frac{d}{dx}\log|A| = \frac{1}{|A|}\frac{d}{dx}|A|$$

$$= \text{trace}\left(\frac{\text{adj } A}{|A|}\frac{dA}{dx}\right) \quad \text{by (i)}$$

$$= \text{trace}\left(A^{-1}\frac{dA}{dx}\right).$$

That completes the proof. $\qquad\qquad\qquad\qquad\qquad\qquad\qquad\qquad\qquad\qquad\square$

Let $y \sim N_n(X\beta, \Sigma)$, where $\Sigma = \sum_{i=1}^{k}\sigma_i^2 Z_i Z_i' + \sigma^2 I_n$ and X is $n \times p$ of rank $r \leq p$. As before, we set $\sigma_0^2 = \sigma^2$ and $Z_0 = I_n$ so that $\Sigma = \sum_{i=0}^{k}\sigma_i^2 Z_i Z_i'$. In the REML method, we choose a matrix K of full row rank and with maximal number of rows such that $KX = 0$. Since X has rank r, K must be of order $(n-r) \times n$. In fact the rows of $I - X(X'X)^-X'$ form a basis for the left null space of X for any g-inverse, and hence $K = C(I - X(X'X)^-X')$ for some C. Note that $Ky \sim N_{n-r}(0, K\Sigma K')$. In the REML method we use the ML method with Ky, instead of y, to get the estimates of σ_j^2, $j = 0, 1, \ldots, k$.

The log-likelihood of Ky is

$$\log L\left(\sigma_0^2, \sigma_1^2, \ldots, \sigma_k^2; y\right)$$

$$= \frac{n-r}{2}\log(2\pi) - \frac{1}{2}\log\left|K\Sigma K'\right| - \frac{1}{2}y'K'\left(K\Sigma K'\right)^{-1}Ky$$

$$= \frac{n-r}{2} \log(2\pi) - \frac{1}{2} \log \left| K \left(\sum_{i=0}^{k} \sigma_i^2 Z_i Z_i' \right) K' \right|$$

$$- \frac{1}{2} y' K' \left(K \left(\sum_{i=0}^{k} \sigma_i^2 Z_i Z_i' \right) K' \right)^{-1} K y.$$

Differentiating with respect to each σ_i^2 and using **9.5** we get

$$\frac{\partial}{\partial \sigma_i^2} \log L \left(\sigma_0^2, \sigma_1^2, \ldots, \sigma_k^2; y \right)$$

$$= -\frac{1}{2} \text{trace} \left((K \Sigma K')^{-1} \frac{\partial}{\partial \sigma_i^2} K \Sigma K' \right)$$

$$+ \frac{1}{2} y' K' (K \Sigma K')^{-1} \left(\frac{\partial}{\partial \sigma_i^2} K \Sigma K' \right) (K \Sigma K')^{-1} K y$$

$$= -\frac{1}{2} \text{trace} (K \Sigma K')^{-1} K Z_i Z_i' K'$$

$$+ \frac{1}{2} y' K' (K \Sigma K')^{-1} K Z_i Z_i' K' (K \Sigma K')^{-1} K y$$

$$= -\frac{1}{2} \text{trace} \, K' (K \Sigma K')^{-1} K Z_i Z_i'$$

$$+ \frac{1}{2} y' K' (K \Sigma K')^{-1} K Z_i Z_i' K' (K \Sigma K')^{-1} K y.$$

Setting the partial derivatives equal to zero we get

$$\text{trace} \, K' (K \Sigma K')^{-1} K Z_i Z_i' = y' K' (K \Sigma K')^{-1} K Z_i Z_i' K' (K \Sigma K')^{-1} K y, \quad (9.2)$$

$i = 0, 1, \ldots, k.$

Recall that if y has mean vector μ and covariance matrix Σ, then for any symmetric matrix A, $E(y' A y) = \mu' A \mu + \text{trace} \, A \Sigma$. Applying this identity to $K y$ we see that

$$E \left(y' K' (K \Sigma K')^{-1} K Z_i Z_i' K' (K \Sigma K')^{-1} K y \right)$$

$$= \text{trace} (K \Sigma K')^{-1} K Z_i Z_i' K' (K \Sigma K')^{-1} K \Sigma K'$$

$$= \text{trace} \, K (K \Sigma K')^{-1} K Z_i Z_i'.$$

Therefore the expected value of the right-hand side of (9.2) equals the left-hand side.

There is another approach to derive the REML estimates which uses the *marginal* (*or restricted*) *likelihood function*. The marginal likelihood may be described as the part of the likelihood that is location invariant. It is obtained by integrating the likelihood function with respect to the location parameter.

We illustrate the approach with the balanced one-way classification. The model is

$$y_{ij} = \mu + a_i + \varepsilon_{ij}, \quad i = 1, \ldots, k; \ j = 1, \ldots, m;$$

with the usual assumptions as in **9.2**. The total number of observations is $n = mk$. The log-likelihood can be expressed as (see Exercise 7)

$$\log L(\mu, \sigma^2, \sigma_1^2; y) = -\frac{n}{2}\log(2\pi) - \frac{1}{2}k(m-1)\log\sigma^2 - \frac{k}{2}\log(\sigma^2 + m\sigma_1^2)$$
$$-\frac{\text{SSE}}{2\sigma^2} - \frac{\text{SSA}}{2(\sigma^2 + m\sigma_1^2)} - \frac{km(\bar{y}_{..} - \mu)^2}{2(\sigma^2 + m\sigma_1^2)}.$$

The part of the likelihood that involves μ is $\exp\{-\frac{km(\bar{y}_{..} - \mu)^2}{2(\sigma^2 + m\sigma_1^2)}\}$. It may be verified that

$$\int_{-\infty}^{\infty} \exp\left\{-\frac{km(\bar{y}_{..} - \mu)^2}{2(\sigma^2 + m\sigma_1^2)}\right\} d\mu = \frac{\sqrt{2\pi}}{\sqrt{km}}(\sigma^2 + m\sigma_1^2)^{\frac{1}{2}}.$$

Substituting in the expression for log-likelihood we get the log of the marginal likelihood as

$$\log L(\sigma^2, \sigma_1^2; y) = -\frac{1}{2}(n-1)\log(2\pi) - \frac{1}{2}\log(km) - \frac{1}{2}k(m-1)\log\sigma^2$$
$$-\frac{1}{2}(k-1)\log(\sigma^2 + m\sigma_1^2) - \frac{\text{SSE}}{2\sigma^2} - \frac{\text{SSA}}{2(\sigma^2 + m\sigma_1^2)}.$$

Differentiating with respect to σ^2, σ_1^2 we get

$$\frac{\partial \log L}{\partial \sigma^2} = -\frac{k(m-1)}{2\sigma^2} + \frac{\text{SSE}}{2\sigma^4} - \frac{k-1}{2(\sigma^2 + m\sigma_1^2)} + \frac{\text{SSA}}{2(\sigma^2 + m\sigma_1^2)^2}$$

and

$$\frac{\partial \log L}{\partial \sigma_1^2} = -\frac{m(k-1)}{2(\sigma^2 + m\sigma_1^2)} + \frac{m(\text{SSA})}{2(\sigma^2 + m\sigma_1^2)^2}.$$

Setting the derivatives equal to zero and solving for the estimates we obtain the REML estimates as

$$\hat{\sigma}^2 = \text{MSE}, \qquad \hat{\sigma}_1^2 = \frac{\text{MSA} - \text{MSE}}{m}.$$

We omit the proof that the marginal likelihood approach gives the same REML estimates as those obtained by the earlier approach of using the distribution of Ky for a suitable matrix K.

9.3 ANOVA Estimators

In the ANOVA method of estimation of variance components the basic technique is to equate the mean squares to their expected values and to solve for the variance component estimates.

We illustrate the approach with balanced one-way classification. The model is

$$y_{ij} = \mu + a_i + \varepsilon_{ij}, \quad i = 1, \ldots, k; \ j = 1, \ldots, m;$$

with the usual assumptions as in **9.2**. Note that $n = mk$. The sums of squares are given by

$$\text{SSA} = m \sum_{i=1}^{k} (\bar{y}_{i.} - \bar{y}_{..})^2, \qquad \text{SSE} = \sum_{i=1}^{k} \sum_{j=1}^{m} (y_{ij} - \bar{y}_{i.})^2.$$

We proceed to find $E(\text{SSA})$ and $E(\text{SSE})$. We have

$$\bar{y}_{i.} = \frac{1}{m} \sum_{j=1}^{m} y_{ij}$$

$$= \frac{1}{m} \sum_{j=1}^{m} (\mu + a_i + \varepsilon_{ij})$$

$$= \mu + a_i + \bar{\varepsilon}_{i.}$$

and

$$\bar{y}_{..} = \frac{1}{km} \sum_{i=1}^{k} \sum_{j=1}^{m} y_{ij}$$

$$= \frac{1}{km} \sum_{i=1}^{k} \sum_{j=1}^{m} (\mu + a_i + \varepsilon_{ij})$$

$$= \mu + \bar{a}. + \bar{\varepsilon}_{..}.$$

Thus

$$E(\text{SSA}) = m E \left\{ (a_i - \bar{a}.) + (\bar{\varepsilon}_{i.} - \bar{\varepsilon}_{..}) \right\}^2$$
$$= m E \left(a_i^2 + \bar{\varepsilon}_{i.}^2 + \bar{a}.^2 + \bar{\varepsilon}_{..}^2 - 2a_i \bar{a}. - 2\bar{\varepsilon}_{i.} \bar{\varepsilon}_{..} \right).$$

Using the assumptions in the model the expectation can be computed as

$$E(\text{SSA}) = mk \left(\sigma_1^2 + \frac{\sigma^2}{m} + \frac{\sigma_1^2}{k} + \frac{\sigma^2}{km} - \frac{2\sigma_1^2}{k} - \frac{2m\sigma^2}{km^2} \right)$$

$$= mk \left(\sigma_1^2 \left(1 - \frac{1}{k} \right) + \frac{\sigma^2}{m} \left(1 - \frac{1}{k} \right) \right)$$

$$= (k-1)(\sigma^2 + m\sigma_1^2).$$

Therefore

$$E(\text{MSA}) = E \left(\text{SSA}/(k-1) \right) = \sigma^2 + m\sigma_1^2.$$

Similarly it can be shown that

$$E(\text{SSE}) = k(m-1)\sigma^2.$$

Solving the two equations we get the estimates

$$\hat{\sigma}^2 = \text{MSE} = \frac{\text{SSE}}{k(m-1)}, \qquad \hat{\sigma}_1^2 = \frac{\text{MSA} - \text{MSE}}{m}.$$

The estimate $\hat{\sigma}^2$ is necessarily nonnegative. However, $\hat{\sigma}_1^2$ may be negative, in which case we take $\hat{\sigma}_1^2$ to be zero. It is easy to see that $\hat{\sigma}^2$ and $\hat{\sigma}_1^2$ are unbiased.

We may compute $E(\text{SSA})$ and $E(\text{SSE})$ using the expression for the expectation of a quadratic form. We compute $E(\text{SSE})$ using this approach. Let y be the $n \times 1$ vector of observations $y_{11}, \ldots, y_{1m}, \ldots, y_{k1}, \ldots, y_{km}$. Let

$$
W = \begin{bmatrix} \mathbf{1_m} & 0 & \cdots & 0 \\ 0 & \mathbf{1_m} & & \vdots \\ \vdots & \cdots & \cdots & \vdots \\ 0 & \cdots & \cdots & \mathbf{1_m} \end{bmatrix}
\tag{9.3}
$$

be of order $n \times k$. Note that

$$
\text{SSE} = y' \left(I_n - \frac{1}{m} W W' \right) y.
\tag{9.4}
$$

We have $E(y) = \mu \mathbf{1_n}$ and $\text{cov}(y) = \Sigma$, where Σ is a block matrix with each block equal to $\sigma_1^2 J_m + \sigma^2 I_m$. We use the fact that if y has mean vector μ and covariance matrix Σ, then for any symmetric matrix A, $E(y'Ay) = \mu'A\mu + \text{trace } A\Sigma$. With $A = I_n - \frac{1}{m} W W'$ we see that $\mathbf{1_n'} A \mathbf{1_n} = 0$ and hence

$$
E(\text{SSE}) = k \text{ trace} \left(I_m - \frac{1}{m} J_m \right) (\sigma_1^2 J_m + \sigma^2 I_m)
$$

$$
= k \text{ trace} \left(\sigma_1^2 J_m + \sigma^2 I_m - \frac{\sigma_1^2}{m} J_m^2 - \frac{\sigma^2}{m} J_m \right)
$$

$$
= k \left(\sigma_1^2 m + \sigma^2 m - \frac{\sigma_1^2}{m} m^2 - \frac{\sigma^2}{m} m \right)
$$

$$
= k(m - 1)\sigma^2.
$$

In one-way classification with random effects, the equality of treatment effects is represented by the null hypothesis $H_0 : \sigma_1^2 = 0$. We derive an F-statistic to test H_0. We do have the normality assumption in the model that $y \sim N_n(\mu \mathbf{1_n}, \Sigma)$, where as before, Σ is a block matrix with each block equal to $\sigma_1^2 J_m + \sigma^2 I_m$.

Let $A = I_n - \frac{1}{m} W W'$. Then as observed in (9.4), $\text{SSE} = y'Ay$. Since $A \mathbf{1_n} = 0$, $\text{SSE} = (y - \mu \mathbf{1_n})' A (y - \mu \mathbf{1_n})$. Note that $y - \mu \mathbf{1_n} \sim N_n(0, \Sigma)$ and $\Sigma^{-\frac{1}{2}} (y - \mu \mathbf{1_n}) \sim N_n(0, I_n)$. It is easily verified that $\sigma^{-2} A \Sigma$ is idempotent and (refer to the computation of $E(\text{SSE})$)

$$
\text{rank } \frac{A\Sigma}{\sigma^2} = \text{trace } \frac{A\Sigma}{\sigma^2} = k(m - 1).
$$

It follows from these observations and **8.3** that $\text{SSE}/\sigma^2 = y'By/\sigma^2$ is distributed as chi-square with $k(m - 1)$ degrees of freedom. (We must apply **8.3** to the vector $\Sigma^{-\frac{1}{2}} (y - \mu \mathbf{1_n})$, or use a generalized version of it as given in Exercise 15, Chap. 8).

We turn to the distribution of SSA. Let B be the $n \times n$ block matrix defined as

$$B = \frac{1}{m} \begin{bmatrix} J_k & 0 & \cdots & 0 \\ 0 & J_k & \cdots & 0 \\ \vdots & \vdots & \ddots & \vdots \\ 0 & 0 & \cdots & J_k \end{bmatrix}.$$

It may be verified that

$$\text{SSA} = y'\left(B - \frac{1}{n}J_n\right)y = (y - \mu\mathbf{1_n})'\left(B - \frac{1}{n}J_n\right)(y - \mu\mathbf{1_n}).$$

Also, $(\sigma^2 + m\sigma_1^2)^{-1}(B - \frac{1}{n}J_n)$ is idempotent and

$$\text{rank } \frac{1}{\sigma^2 + m\sigma_1^2}\left(B - \frac{1}{n}J_n\right) = \text{trace } \frac{1}{\sigma^2 + m\sigma_1^2}\left(B - \frac{1}{n}J_n\right) = k - 1.$$

It follows that under H_0, $(\sigma^2 + m\sigma_1^2)^{-1}\text{SSA} = (\sigma^2 + m\sigma_1^2)^{-1}y'(B - \frac{1}{n}J_n)y$ follows chi-square distribution with $k - 1$ degrees of freedom.

Finally, it can be seen that $A\Sigma(B - \frac{1}{n}J_n) = 0$ and (by **8.4**) SSE and SSA are independently distributed.

We conclude that under H_0,

$$\frac{\text{MSA}}{\text{MSE}} = \frac{\text{SSA}/(\sigma^2(k-1))}{\text{SSE}/(\sigma^2 k(m-1))} = \frac{\text{SSA}/(k-1)}{\text{SSE}/(k(m-1))}$$

is distributed as F with $k - 1$, $k(m - 1)$ degrees of freedom. We may reject $H_0 : \sigma_1^2 = 0$ in favor of $H_1 : \sigma_1^2 > 0$ for sufficiently large values of this statistic.

We now consider the two-way random effects model without interaction. Suppose there are two factors, factor A at a levels and factor B at b levels. We have one observation for every combination of a level of the first factor and a level of the second factor. The model is

$$y_{ij} = \mu + a_i + b_j + \varepsilon_{ij}, \quad i = 1,\ldots,a; \; j = 1,\ldots,b,$$

where a_i are i.i.d. $N(0, \sigma_a^2)$, b_j are i.i.d. $N(0, \sigma_b^2)$, ε_{ij} are i.i.d. $N(0, \sigma^2)$ and any two of $a_i, b_j, \varepsilon_{ij}$ are uncorrelated. The sums of squares are given by

$$\text{SSA} = b \sum_{i=1}^{a}(\overline{y}_{i.} - \overline{y}_{..})^2, \qquad \text{SSB} = a \sum_{j=1}^{b}(\overline{y}_{.j} - \overline{y}_{..})^2,$$

$$\text{SSE} = \sum_{i=1}^{a}\sum_{j=1}^{b}(y_{ij} - \overline{y}_{i.} - \overline{y}_{.j} + \overline{y}_{..})^2.$$

The mean squares are given by

$$\text{MSA} = \text{SSA}/(a - 1), \qquad \text{MSB} = \text{SSB}/(b - 1),$$
$$\text{MSE} = \text{SSE}/\{(a - 1)(b - 1)\}.$$

It can be shown that

$$E(\text{MSA}) = \sigma^2 + b\sigma_a^2, \qquad E(\text{MSB}) = \sigma^2 + a\sigma_b^2, \qquad E(\text{MSE}) = \sigma^2.$$

Thus the ANOVA estimates of the variance components are given by

$$\hat{\sigma}^2 = \text{MSE}, \qquad \hat{\sigma}_a^2 = \frac{\text{MSA} - \text{MSE}}{b}, \qquad \hat{\sigma}_b^2 = \frac{\text{MSB} - \text{MSE}}{a}.$$

Now consider the two-way random effects model with interaction,

$$y_{ijk} = \mu + a_i + b_j + c_{ij} + \varepsilon_{ijk};$$

$i = 1, \ldots, a;\ j = 1, \ldots, b;\ k = 1, \ldots, n;\ n > 1$, where a_i are i.i.d. $N(0, \sigma_a^2)$, b_j are i.i.d. $N(0, \sigma_b^2)$, c_{ij} are i.i.d. $N(0, \sigma_{ab}^2)$, ε_{ijk} are i.i.d. $N(0, \sigma^2)$ and any two of a_i, b_j, c_{ij}, ε_{ijk} are uncorrelated. Here c_{ij} represents the effect due to interaction between the i-th level of the first factor and the j-th level of the second factor.

The sums of squares are given by

$$\text{SSA} = bn \sum_{i=1}^{a} (\bar{y}_{i..} - \bar{y}_{...})^2, \qquad \text{SSB} = an \sum_{j=1}^{b} (\bar{y}_{.j.} - \bar{y}_{...})^2,$$

$$\text{SSAB} = n \sum_{i=1}^{a} \sum_{j=1}^{b} (\bar{y}_{ij.} - \bar{y}_{i..} - \bar{y}_{.j.} + \bar{y}_{...})^2, \qquad \text{SSE} = \sum_{i=1}^{a} \sum_{j=1}^{b} \sum_{k=1}^{n} (y_{ijk} - \bar{y}_{ij.})^2.$$

The mean squares are given by

$$\text{MSA} = \text{SSA}/(a-1), \qquad \text{MSB} = \text{SSB}/(b-1),$$
$$\text{MSAB} = \text{SSAB}/(a-1)(b-1), \qquad \text{MSE} = \text{SSE}/ab(n-1).$$

It can be shown that

$$E(\text{MSA}) = \sigma^2 + nb\sigma_a^2 + n\sigma_{ab}^2, \qquad E(\text{MSB}) = \sigma^2 + na\sigma_b^2 + n\sigma_{ab}^2,$$
$$E(\text{MSAB}) = \sigma^2 + n\sigma_{ab}^2, \qquad E(\text{MSE}) = \sigma^2.$$

Thus the ANOVA estimates of the variance components are given by

$$\hat{\sigma}_a^2 = \frac{\text{MSA} - \text{MSAB}}{nb}, \qquad \hat{\sigma}_b^2 = \frac{\text{MSB} - \text{MSAB}}{na},$$

$$\hat{\sigma}_{ab}^2 = \frac{\text{MSAB} - \text{MSE}}{n}, \qquad \hat{\sigma}^2 = \text{MSE}.$$

Finally, consider the two-way mixed effects model with interaction,

$$y_{ijk} = \mu + \alpha_i + b_j + c_{ij} + \varepsilon_{ijk};$$

$i = 1, \ldots, a;\ j = 1, \ldots, b;\ k = 1, \ldots, n;\ n > 1$, where α_i are fixed effects, b_j are i.i.d. $N(0, \sigma_b^2)$, c_{ij} are i.i.d. $N(0, \sigma_{ab}^2)$, ε_{ijk} are i.i.d. $N(0, \sigma^2)$ and any two of b_j, c_{ij}, ε_{ijk} are uncorrelated.

It can be shown that the expected values of MSB, MSAB, MSE and the ANOVA estimates of σ_b^2 and σ_{ab}^2 are the same as in the case of the two-way random effects model with interaction:

$$\hat{\sigma}_b^2 = \frac{\text{MSB} - \text{MSAB}}{na}, \qquad \hat{\sigma}_{ab}^2 = \frac{\text{MSAB} - \text{MSE}}{n}.$$

9.4 Prediction of Random Effects

Consider the mixed model

$$Y = X\beta + Z_1a_1 + \cdots + Z_ka_k + \varepsilon$$

with the assumptions as in **9.3**. We consider the problem of estimating the realized values of the random components $a_1, \ldots, a_k$, given the data. Let us rewrite the model as

$$Y = X\beta + Za + \varepsilon,$$

where $Z = [Z_1, \ldots, Z_k]$ and $a = [a_1', \ldots, a_k']'$. Note that $\varepsilon \sim N_n(0, \sigma^2 I_n)$ and $a_i \sim N_{r_i}(0, \sigma_i^2 I_{r_i})$, $i = 1, \ldots, k$. Let T be the block diagonal matrix with blocks $\sigma_1^2 I_{r_1}, \ldots, \sigma_k^2 I_{r_k}$. Observe that a and y are jointly multivariate normal with covariance matrix

$$\begin{aligned}
\mathrm{cov}(a, y) &= \mathrm{cov}(a, X\beta + Za + \varepsilon) \\
&= \mathrm{cov}(a, Za + \varepsilon) \\
&= \mathrm{cov}(a, Za) \\
&= TZ'.
\end{aligned}$$

Assume first that β and V are known. Then we may use the techniques of Sect. 8.5 on multiple correlation and take the conditional expectation $E(a|y)$ as the *best linear predictor* (BLP) of a, given y. Using the expression for conditional expectation derived in Sect. 8.5, we have

$$\begin{aligned}
E(a|y) &= E(a) + \mathrm{cov}(a, y)\big(\mathrm{cov}(y)\big)^{-1}\big(y - E(y)\big) \\
&= TZ'V^{-1}(y - X\beta).
\end{aligned}$$

We estimate T, V by $\hat{T}$, $\hat{V}$, respectively, which are obtained by replacing $\sigma^2, \sigma_1^2, \ldots, \sigma_k^2$ by their REML estimates. We estimate β by the estimated generalized least squares estimator

$$\hat{\beta} = \big(X'\hat{V}^{-1}X\big)^{-1}X'\hat{V}^{-1}y.$$

With these substitutions in $E(a|y)$, we get the *estimated best linear unbiased predictor* (EBLUP)

$$\hat{E}(a|y) = \hat{T}Z'\hat{V}^{-1}(y - X\hat{\beta}). \tag{9.5}$$

We obtain an explicit formula for $\hat{E}(a|y)$ in the case of balanced one-way random effects model. Consider the model

$$y_{ij} = \mu + a_i + \varepsilon_{ij}, \quad i = 1, \ldots, k; \; j = 1, \ldots, m;$$

with the usual assumptions as in **9.2**. Note that $n = mk$. With reference to (9.5), we see that in this special case, $\hat{V}$ is the block diagonal matrix with its blocks given by $\hat{\Sigma}_1^{-1}, \ldots, \hat{\Sigma}_k^{-1}$, where

$$\hat{\Sigma}_i^{-1} = \frac{1}{\hat{\sigma}^2}\left(I_m - \frac{\hat{\sigma}_1^2}{\hat{\sigma}^2 + m\hat{\sigma}_1^2}J_m\right), \quad i = 1, \ldots, k.$$

Also, $Z = W$, given in (9.3), $\hat{T} = \hat{\sigma}_1^2 I_k$, and $\hat{\beta} = \hat{\mu}\mathbf{1_n} = \overline{y}_{..}\mathbf{1_n}$.
Substituting in (9.5) we get, after simplification,

$$\text{EBLUP}(a_i) = \frac{m\hat{\sigma}_1^2}{\hat{\sigma}^2 + m\hat{\sigma}_1^2}(\overline{y}_{i.} - \overline{y}_{..}), \quad i = 1, \ldots, k.$$

The EBLUP of a linear function $\sum_{i=1}^{k}\alpha_i a_i$ is given by $\sum_{i=1}^{k}\alpha_i\text{EBLUP}(a_i)$. If we consider the one-way fixed effects model, then the BLUE of a contrast $\sum_{i=1}^{k}\alpha_i a_i$ is given by

$$\sum_{i=1}^{k}\alpha_i(\overline{y}_{i.} - \overline{y}_{..}), \quad i = 1, \ldots, k.$$

Comparing with the EBLUP of $\sum_{i=1}^{k}\alpha_i a_i$, we find that it differs only in terms of multiplication of $\alpha_i(\overline{y}_{i.} - \overline{y}_{..})$ by the factor $\frac{m\hat{\sigma}_1^2}{\hat{\sigma}^2 + m\hat{\sigma}_1^2} < 1$. For this reason the EBLUP is called the "shrinkage estimator".

9.5 Exercises

1. Consider the linear model $y = X\beta + \varepsilon$, $\text{cov}(y) = \sigma^2 V$, where y is $n \times 1$, X is $n \times k$ of rank k and V is a known $n \times n$ positive definite matrix. Show that the *OLSE (ordinary least squares estimator)* $X(X'X)^{-1}X'y$ of $X\beta$ and the BLUE $X(X'V^{-1}X)^{-1}X'V^{-1}y$ of $X\beta$ coincide if and only if $VX = XQ$ for some matrix Q.

2. Consider the one-way random effects model $y_{ij} = \mu + a_i + \varepsilon_{ij}$, $i = 1, \ldots, k$; $j = 1, \ldots, m$; with the usual assumptions as in **9.2**. Show that the OLSE and the BLUE of μ coincide.

3. Consider the mixed model

$$y_{ijk\ell} = \mu + \alpha_i + \beta_j + \tau_{ij} + a_k + b_{ik} + c_{ijk} + \varepsilon_{ijk\ell},$$

   $i = 1, \ldots, 4$; $j = 1, 2$; $k = 1, \ldots, 20$; $\ell = 1, \ldots, 6$, where α_i, β_j, τ_{ij} are fixed effects and a_i, b_{ik}, c_{ijk} are random effects. State the usual assumptions and write the model as a special case of **9.3** by identifying matrices $X, Z_1, Z_2, \ldots$.

4. Consider the mixed model $y_{ijk} = \mu + \tau_i + a_{ij} + \varepsilon_{ijk}$, $i = 1, 2$; $j = 1, \ldots, 5$; $k = 1, 2$, where a_{ij} are i.i.d. $N(0, \sigma_1^2)$, ε_{ijk} are i.i.d. $N(0, \sigma^2)$ and a_{ij} and ε_{ijk} are uncorrelated. Convince yourself that this is a special case of **9.3**. If y is the vector of observations, show that $\text{cov}(y)$ is a block diagonal matrix with each block equal to $\Sigma_1 = \sigma_1^2 J_2 + \sigma^2 I_2$.

5. Consider the one-way random effects model $y_{ij} = \mu + a_i + \varepsilon_{ij}$, $i = 1, \ldots, k$; $j = 1, \ldots, n_i$; $n = \sum_{i=1}^{k} n_i$, with the usual assumptions as in **9.1**. Show that the generalized least squares estimator of μ is given by (9.1).

6. Consider the one-way random effects model, $y_{ij} = \mu + a_i + \varepsilon_{ij}$, $i = 1, \ldots, k$; $j = 1, \ldots, n_i$; $n = \sum_{i=1}^{k} n_i$, with the usual assumptions as in **9.1**. Find the ANOVA estimates of the variance components.

7. Consider the one-way random effects model $y_{ij} = \mu + a_i + \varepsilon_{ij}$, $i = 1, \ldots, k$; $j = 1, \ldots, m$, with the usual assumptions as in **9.2**. Show that the log likelihood function equals

$$\log L\left(\mu, \sigma^2, \sigma_1^2; y\right) = -\frac{n}{2}\log(2\pi) - \frac{1}{2}(n - k)\log\sigma^2 - \frac{k}{2}\log\left(\sigma^2 + m\sigma_1^2\right)$$

$$- \frac{\text{SSE}}{2\sigma^2} - \frac{\text{SSA}}{2(\sigma^2 + m\sigma_1^2)} - \frac{n(\bar{y}_{..} - \mu)^2}{2(\sigma^2 + m\sigma_1^2)}.$$

8. Consider the one-way random effects model $y_{ij} = \mu + a_i + \varepsilon_{ij}$, $i = 1, \ldots, k$; $j = 1, \ldots, m$; with the usual assumptions as in **9.2**. Show that if $\sigma_1^2 = 0$, then the ML estimate of σ^2 is given by $\tilde{\sigma}^2 = (\text{SSE} + \text{SSA})/n$. Find the maximum of the likelihood function without any restriction, and then with the restriction $\sigma_1^2 = 0$. Construct the likelihood ratio for testing the hypothesis $H : \sigma_1^2 = 0$ and show that it is an increasing function of the F-statistic MSA/MSE.

9. Let $y_1, \ldots, y_n$ be i.i.d. $N(\mu, \sigma^2)$ variables. Show that the REML estimate of σ^2 is $\hat{\sigma}^2 = \frac{1}{n-1}\sum_{i=1}^{n}(y_i - \bar{y})^2$.

10. Consider the one-way random effects model $y_{ij} = \mu + a_i + \varepsilon_{ij}$, $i = 1, \ldots, k$; $j = 1, \ldots, m$, with the usual assumptions as in **9.2**. Show that the correlation between y_{ij} and $y_{i\ell}$ (the *intraclass correlation*) is given by $\frac{\sigma_1^2}{\sigma^2 + \sigma_1^2}$ and find a $100(1 - \alpha)$ percent confidence interval for the same.

Chapter 10
Miscellaneous Topics

10.1 Principal Components

Suppose in a statistical survey we collect observations on a large number of random variables $x_1, \ldots, x_n$, and we want to study the variability in the data. It is desirable to reduce the number of variables to a few variables which "explain" the total variation. Suppose the new variables are $y_1, \ldots, y_p$, $p \leq n$; where each y_i is a function of $x_1, \ldots, x_n$. For mathematical simplicity it is convenient to let $y_1, \ldots, y_p$ be linear functions of $x_1, \ldots, x_n$.

The first *principal component* is defined to be the linear combination

$$\alpha_1 x_1 + \cdots + \alpha_n x_n; \quad \|\alpha\| = 1$$

with maximum variance. Let Σ be the dispersion matrix of $x = (x_1, \ldots, x_n)'$ which we assume to be positive definite. Then

$$\text{var}(\alpha' x) = \alpha' \Sigma \alpha.$$

Thus in order to find the first principal component we must maximize $\alpha' \Sigma \alpha$ subject to $\|\alpha\| = 1$. By **5.1**, this maximum is $\lambda_1(\Sigma)$ and is attained at a unit eigenvector corresponding to $\lambda_1(\Sigma)$.

Let $v_1, \ldots, v_n$ be an orthonormal set of eigenvectors corresponding to the eigenvalues $\lambda_1, \ldots, \lambda_n$ of Σ, respectively. The second principal component is a linear combination

$$\beta_1 x_1 + \cdots + \beta_n x_n; \quad \|\beta\| = 1$$

which is uncorrelated with the first principal component and has maximum variance. In order to find the second principal component we must maximize $\beta' \Sigma \beta$ subject to $\|\beta\| = 1$ and $\beta' \Sigma \alpha = 0$, i.e., $\beta' v_1 = 0$. By **5.7**, this maximum is $\lambda_2(\Sigma)$, attained at $\beta = v_2$.

In general, we may define the k-th principal component as a linear combination

$$\gamma_1 x_1 + \cdots + \gamma_n x_n; \quad \|\gamma\| = 1$$

R.B. Bapat, *Linear Algebra and Linear Models*, Universitext,
DOI 10.1007/978-1-4471-2739-0_10, © Springer-Verlag London Limited 2012

which is uncorrelated with the first $k - 1$ principal components and which has maximum variance. By a similar analysis as before, the k-th principal component is obtained when $\gamma = v_k$ and its variance is λ_k.

The sum of the variances of the principal components is $\sum_{i=1}^{n} \lambda_i$ which is the same as $\sum_{i=1}^{n} \text{var}(x_i)$. The proportion of the total variability explained by the first k principal components can be defined to be

$$\frac{\sum_{i=1}^{k} \lambda_i}{\sum_{i=1}^{n} \lambda_i}.$$

10.2 Canonical Correlations

Consider a situation where we have two sets of variables, $x_1, \ldots, x_p$ and $y_1, \ldots, y_q$ and we want to study the correlation structure between the two sets. As an example, we might have observations on a group of students. The first set of variables may correspond to "physical" variables such as height, weight, etc., whereas the second set may correspond to "mental" characteristics such as scores on various tests.

Let Σ be the dispersion matrix of

$$(x_1, \ldots, x_p, y_1, \ldots, y_q)'.$$

We assume Σ to be positive definite and suppose it is partitioned as

$$\Sigma = \begin{bmatrix} \Sigma_{11} & \Sigma_{12} \\ \Sigma_{21} & \Sigma_{22} \end{bmatrix}$$

where Σ_{11} is $p \times p$.

The first pair of *canonical variates* is a pair of linear combinations $\alpha' x$, $\beta' y$ with unit variance such that the correlation between them is maximum. The correlation is called the first *canonical correlation*. We have

$$\text{cov}(\alpha' x, \beta' y) = \alpha' \Sigma_{12} \beta$$

and this is to be maximized subject to the conditions $\alpha' \Sigma_{11} \alpha = \beta' \Sigma_{22} \beta = 1$.

Let

$$u = \Sigma_{11}^{1/2} \alpha, \qquad v = \Sigma_{22}^{1/2} \beta.$$

Then the problem is to find

$$\max_{\|u\|=1, \, \|v\|=1} u'\left(\Sigma_{11}^{-1/2} \Sigma_{12} \Sigma_{22}^{-1/2}\right) v$$

and by **5.5**, this is $\sigma_1(\Sigma_{11}^{-1/2} \Sigma_{12} \Sigma_{22}^{-1/2})$. The maximum is attained when α, β are the respective eigenvectors of

$$\Sigma_{22}^{-1/2} \Sigma_{21} \Sigma_{11}^{-1} \Sigma_{12} \Sigma_{22}^{-1/2} \quad \text{and} \quad \Sigma_{11}^{-1/2} \Sigma_{12} \Sigma_{22}^{-1} \Sigma_{21} \Sigma_{11}^{-1/2}$$

corresponding to $\sigma_1^2(\Sigma_{11}^{-1/2} \Sigma_{12} \Sigma_{22}^{-1/2})$.

Let $v_1' x$, $w_1' y$ denote the first pair of canonical variates. The second pair of canonical variates is defined to be a pair of linear combinations $\gamma' x$, $\delta' y$ such that they have unit variance, $\gamma' x$ is uncorrelated with $v_1' x$, $\delta' y$ is uncorrelated with $w_1' y$, and the two have a maximum correlation; this correlation is called the second canonical correlation. Further canonical variates and canonical correlations are defined similarly. By **5.6**, it can be seen that the canonical correlations correspond to the singular values of $\Sigma_{11}^{-1/2} \Sigma_{12} \Sigma_{22}^{-1/2}$.

10.3 Reduced Normal Equations

Suppose we want to compare v treatments, $1, \ldots, v$. The treatments could be different fertilizers in an agricultural experiment, drugs in medicine, machines in an industrial setting, teaching methods in education and so on. The experimental material is available in the form of units generally referred to as plots. The plots are grouped into blocks such that within each block the plots are as similar as possible. Suppose there are b blocks of sizes $k_1, \ldots, k_b$. Let n denote the total number of plots so that $n = k_1 + \cdots + k_b$.

A *design* (or a *block design*) is an allocation of the v treatments to the n plots. Suppose we get one observation from each plot. The parameters of the model are, μ (general effect), $\tau_1, \ldots, \tau_v$ (effects due to treatments) and $\alpha_1, \ldots, \alpha_b$ (effects due to blocks). The linear model arising out of the design is as follows. The expected value of the observation from any plot is equal to μ, plus the effect due to the corresponding block, plus the effect due to the treatment which is applied to the plot. We assume that the observations are independent normal with variance σ^2.

Let y denote the $n \times 1$ vector of observations and let X be the coefficient matrix in the linear model. Instead of writing X explicitly, it is more convenient to write $X'X$ and $X'y$; these are the only matrices needed to construct the normal equations.

Let $N = (n_{ij})$ denote the $v \times b$ *incidence matrix* of treatments versus blocks. Thus n_{ij} is the number of times the i-th treatment occurs in the j-th block. It can be seen that

$$X'X = \begin{bmatrix} n & k_1 & \cdots & \cdots & k_b & r_1 & \cdots & \cdots & r_v \\ k_1 & k_1 & 0 & \cdots & 0 & & & & \\ \vdots & 0 & k_2 & & 0 & & N' & & \\ \vdots & \vdots & & \ddots & & & & & \\ k_b & 0 & 0 & & k_b & & & & \\ r_1 & & & & & r_1 & 0 & \cdots & 0 \\ \vdots & & & N & & 0 & r_2 & & 0 \\ \vdots & & & & & \vdots & & \ddots & \\ r_v & & & & & 0 & 0 & & r_v \end{bmatrix},$$

where r_i is the number of times treatment i occurs in the entire design, $i = 1, \ldots, v$. Also,

$$X'y = (G, B_1, \ldots, B_b, T_1, \ldots, T_v)'$$

where G is the total of all the observations, B_i is the total of the observations in the i-th block and T_j is the total of the observations corresponding to the j-th treatment. The normal equations are

$$X'X \begin{bmatrix} \mu \\ \alpha_1 \\ \vdots \\ \alpha_b \\ \tau_1 \\ \vdots \\ \tau_v \end{bmatrix} = X'y. \tag{10.1}$$

Our interest is in comparing the treatments and therefore we are not interested in μ or the block effects. We first obtain a general result on reducing the normal equations, eliminating some of the parameters.

10.1 *Consider the linear model* $E(y) = A\beta$, $D(y) = \sigma^2 I$ *and suppose* β, A *and* $z = A'y$ *are conformally partitioned as*

$$\beta = \begin{bmatrix} \beta_1 \\ \beta_2 \end{bmatrix}, \qquad A = \begin{bmatrix} A_1 & A_2 \end{bmatrix}, \qquad z = \begin{bmatrix} z_1 \\ z_2 \end{bmatrix}.$$

Then the equations

$$\left(A_2'A_2 - A_2'A_1(A_1'A_1)^- A_1'A_2\right)\beta_2 = z_2 - A_2'A_1(A_1'A_1)^- z_1 \tag{10.2}$$

are the reduced normal equations for β_2 *in the following sense: A function* $\ell'\beta_2$ *is estimable if and only if*

$$\ell' \in \mathcal{R}\left(A_2'A_2 - A_2'A_1(A_1'A_1)^- A_1'A_2\right) \tag{10.3}$$

and in that case its BLUE is $\ell'\widehat{\beta}_2$ *where* $\widehat{\beta}_2$ *is any solution of* (10.2).

Proof First observe that since $\mathcal{R}(A_1) = \mathcal{R}(A_1'A_1)$, the matrix

$$A_2'A_1(A_1'A_1)^- A_1'A_2$$

is invariant under the choice of the g-inverse.

Suppose that $\ell'\beta_2$ is estimable. Then there exists c such that

$$E(c'y) = \ell'\beta_2.$$

Let

$$y = \begin{bmatrix} y_1 \\ y_2 \end{bmatrix} \quad \text{and} \quad c = \begin{bmatrix} c_1 \\ c_2 \end{bmatrix}$$

be the partitioning of y, c, conformal with $\beta = (\beta_1', \beta_2')'$. Then

$$E(c_1' y_1) + E(c_2' y_2) = \ell' \beta_2 \tag{10.4}$$

and hence

$$c_1' A_1' A_1 \beta_1 + c_1' A_1' A_2 \beta_2 + c_2' A_2' A_1 \beta_1 + c_2' A_2' A_2 \beta_2 = \ell' \beta_2.$$

Therefore

$$c_1' A_1' A_1 + c_2' A_2' A_1 = 0, \tag{10.5}$$

$$c_1' A_1' A_2 + c_2' A_2' A_2 = \ell'. \tag{10.6}$$

By (10.5),

$$c_1' A_1' A_1 (A_1' A_1)^- A_1' A_2 + c_2' A_2' A_1 (A_1' A_1)^- A_1' A_2 = 0$$

and hence

$$c_1' A_1' A_2 + c_2' A_2' A_1 (A_1' A_1)^- A_1' A_2 = 0.$$

Now from (10.6),

$$\ell' = c_2' (A_2' A_2 - A_2' A_1 (A_1' A_1)^- A_1' A_2)$$

and (10.3) is proved.

Conversely, if (10.3) holds, then for some matrix M,

$$\ell' \beta_2 = M (A_2' A_2 - A_2' A_1 (A_1' A_1)^- A_1' A_2) \beta_2.$$

Set

$$c_1' = -M A_2' A_1 (A_1' A_1)^-, \qquad c_2' = M.$$

Then c_1, c_2 satisfy (10.5), (10.6), and hence (10.4) holds. Thus $\ell' \beta_2$ is estimable. Thus we have shown that $\ell' \beta_2$ is estimable if and only if (10.3) holds. The second part is left as an exercise. □

10.4 The *C*-Matrix

We continue to use the notation of the previous section and consider the linear model arising out of a design. The reduced normal equations for the treatment parameters are

$$C\tau = Q$$

where $\tau = (\tau_1, \ldots, \tau_v)'$, Q is a function of y, and the matrix C, known as the *C-matrix* of the design, is give by

$$C = \text{diag}(r_1, \ldots, r_v) - N \text{diag}\left(\frac{1}{k_1}, \ldots, \frac{1}{k_b}\right) N'.$$

Clearly, C is symmetric and it is positive semidefinite since it is the (generalized) Schur complement of a principal submatrix in a positive semidefinite matrix.

The row sums (and hence the column sums) of C are zero. This is seen as follows. Denoting as usual the vector of ones by $\mathbf{1}$,

$$
C\mathbf{1} = \begin{bmatrix} r_1 \\ \vdots \\ r_v \end{bmatrix} - N \begin{bmatrix} \frac{1}{k_1} & & \\ & \ddots & \\ & & \frac{1}{k_b} \end{bmatrix} \begin{bmatrix} k_1 \\ \vdots \\ k_b \end{bmatrix}
$$

$$
= \begin{bmatrix} r_1 \\ \vdots \\ r_v \end{bmatrix} - N\mathbf{1}
$$

$$
= 0.
$$

It follows that C is singular and rank $C \le v - 1$.

We will now consider designs with equal block sizes, $k_1 = \cdots = k_b = k$. We will denote the C-matrix of the design d by C_d.

A function $\ell_1 \tau_1 + \cdots + \ell_v \tau_v$ is estimable if and only if $\ell' = (\ell_1, \ldots, \ell_v)$ is in the row-space of C. Since $C\mathbf{1} = 0$, a necessary condition for estimability is that

$$
\ell_1 + \cdots + \ell_v = 0. \tag{10.7}
$$

The function $\ell_1 \tau_1 + \cdots + \ell_v \tau_v$ is called a *contrast* if (10.7) is satisfied. A contrast of the form $\tau_i - \tau_j, i \ne j$, is called an *elementary contrast*. A design is said to be *connected* if all contrasts are estimable.

10.2 *A design d is connected if and only if the rank of C_d is $v - 1$.*

Proof If d is connected then all contrasts are estimable. In particular, the contrasts $\tau_1 - \tau_2, \tau_1 - \tau_3, \ldots, \tau_1 - \tau_v$ are estimable. Thus the vectors

$$
(1, -1, 0, \ldots, 0)
$$

$$
(1, 0, -1, \ldots, 0)
$$

$$
\vdots
$$

$$
(1, 0, 0, \ldots, -1)
$$

are in $\mathcal{R}(C_d)$. These vectors are linearly independent and therefore rank$(C_d) \ge v - 1$. But it is always true that rank$(C_d) \le v - 1$ (since the null space of C_d contains $\mathbf{1}$) and therefore rank$(C_d) = v - 1$. The converse is proved similarly. $\square$

10.5   E-, A- and D-Optimality

Let $\mathcal{D}(v, b, k)$ denote the class of all connected designs with v treatments arranged in b blocks of size k. It is possible that for some values of v, b, k, this class is empty.

We now consider the problem of choosing a design in $\mathscr{D}(v, b, k)$ which has some desirable properties. Let d be a design. The BLUE of an estimable function $\ell'\tau$ is $\ell'\hat{\tau}$, where $\hat{\tau}$ is a solution of the reduced normal equations and the variance of the BLUE is

$$\sigma^2 \ell' C_d^- \ell$$

for any choice of the g-inverse. The design d is preferable if this variance is "small" for all contrasts. There are many different ways of making this precise thus leading to different optimality criteria.

The design d is said to be *E-optimal* if is connected and it minimizes

$$\max_{\ell'1=0, \|\ell\|=1} \ell' C_d^- \ell. \tag{10.8}$$

We will denote the eigenvalues of C_d by

$$0 = \mu_{0,d} \leq \mu_{1,d} \leq \cdots \leq \mu_{v-1,d}.$$

10.3 *Suppose $\mathscr{D}(v, b, k)$ is nonempty. Then $d^* \in \mathscr{D}(v, b, k)$ is E-optimal if*

$$\mu_{1,d^*} = \max_{d \in \mathscr{D}(v,b,k)} \mu_{1,d}.$$

Proof Let

$$x_0 = \frac{1}{\sqrt{v}} \mathbf{1}, x_1, \ldots, x_{v-1}$$

be an orthonormal set of eigenvectors corresponding to $\mu_{0,d}, \mu_{1,d}, \ldots, \mu_{v-1,d}$ respectively. Thus

$$C_d = \mu_{0,d} x_0 x_0' + \mu_{1,d} x_1 x_1' + \cdots + \mu_{v-1,d} x_{v-1} x_{v-1}'.$$

If d is connected, then

$$C_d^+ = \frac{1}{\mu_{1,d}} x_1 x_1' + \cdots + \frac{1}{\mu_{v-1,d}} x_{v-1} x_{v-1}'.$$

A vector ℓ with $\ell'1 = 0$, $\|\ell\| = 1$ can be expressed as

$$\ell = \beta_1 x_1 + \cdots + \beta_{v-1} x_{v-1}$$

where $\beta_1^2 + \cdots + \beta_{v-1}^2 = 1$. Thus

$$\ell' C_d^+ \ell = \left(\beta_1 x_1' + \cdots + \beta_{v-1} x_{v-1}'\right) C_d^+ (\beta_1 x_1 + \cdots + \beta_{v-1} x_{v-1})$$

$$= \frac{\beta_1^2}{\mu_{1,d}} x_1' x_1 + \cdots + \frac{\beta_{v-1}^2}{\mu_{v-1,d}} x_{v-1}' x_{v-1}$$

$$\leq \frac{1}{\mu_{1,d}}.$$

Equality holds in the above inequality when $\ell = x_1$. The result now follows in view of the definition of E-optimality. $\square$

A design is said to be *binary* if a treatment occurs in any block at most once. We will denote the treatment versus block incidence matrix of the design d by N_d. Then for a binary design d, N_d consists of only zeros and ones.

10.4 *For any* $d \in \mathcal{D}(v, b, k)$, trace $C_d \leq b(k - 1)$. *Equality holds if and only if the design is binary.*

Proof By the definition of C_d it follows that

$$\text{trace}\, C_d = \sum_{i=1}^{v} r_i - \frac{1}{k} \sum_{i=1}^{v} \sum_{j=1}^{b} n_{ij}^2 \tag{10.9}$$

where $N_d = (n_{ij})$. It is an easy exercise to show that if $k < v$, then

$$\sum_{i=1}^{v} \sum_{j=1}^{b} n_{ij}^2$$

is minimized subject to the conditions that each n_{ij} is a nonnegative integer and

$$\sum_{i=1}^{v} \sum_{j=1}^{b} n_{ij} = bk,$$

when each n_{ij} is 0 or 1, in which case,

$$\sum_{i=1}^{v} \sum_{j=1}^{b} n_{ij}^2 = \sum_{i=1}^{v} \sum_{j=1}^{b} n_{ij} = bk.$$

Thus we get from (10.9),

$$\text{trace}\, C_d \leq \sum_{i=1}^{v} r_i - \frac{1}{k} bk = b(k - 1).$$

Equality holds if and only if each n_{ij} is 0 or 1, that is, the design is binary.   □

A design $d^* \in \mathcal{D}(v, b, k)$ is said to be A-optimal if

$$\sum_{i=1}^{v-1} \frac{1}{\mu_{i,d^*}} \leq \sum_{i=1}^{v-1} \frac{1}{\mu_{i,d}} \tag{10.10}$$

for any $d \in \mathcal{D}(v, b, k)$.) The statistical interpretation of A-optimality is given in the following.

10.5 *A design* $d^* \in \mathcal{D}(v, b, k)$ *is A-optimal if it minimizes the average variance of the BLUE of an elementary contrast.*

Proof Consider the elementary contrast $\tau_i - \tau_j$. We can write $\tau_i - \tau_j = z'\tau$ where z is a vector of order v with 1 at position i, -1 at position j, and zeros elsewhere. Let $T = C_d^+$. It can be seen that $T\mathbf{1} = 0$, using for example, the representation of C_d^+ in terms of the spectral decomposition. Then the variance of the BLUE of $\tau_i - \tau_j$ is

$$\sigma^2 z' C_d^+ z = \sigma^2 z' T z = \sigma^2 (t_{ii} + t_{jj} - 2t_{ij}).$$

Hence the average variance of the BLUE of an elementary contrast is $\frac{2\sigma^2}{v(v-1)}$ times

$$\sum_{i<j}(t_{ii} + t_{jj} - 2t_{ij}) = \frac{1}{2}\sum_{i=1}^{v}\sum_{j=1}^{v}(t_{ii} + t_{jj} - 2t_{ij})$$

$$= \frac{1}{2}(2\,\text{trace}\,T - 2\mathbf{1}'T\mathbf{1})$$

$$= \text{trace}\,T, \quad \text{since } T\mathbf{1} = 0$$

$$= \sum_{i=1}^{v-1}\frac{1}{\mu_{i,d}},$$

and the result is proved. $\square$

A design $d^* \in \mathcal{D}(v, b, k)$ is said to be D-optimal if it maximizes $\prod_{i=1}^{v-1}\mu_{i,d}$. To obtain a statistical interpretation of D-optimality, we first establish the following.

10.6 *Let $d \in \mathcal{D}(v, b, k)$. Let P be a $v \times (v-1)$ matrix whose columns form an orthonormal basis for the row-space of C_d. Then the eigenvalues of $P'C_d^- P$ are* $\frac{1}{\mu_{1,d}}, \ldots, \frac{1}{\mu_{v-1,d}}$.

Proof First observe that $P'C_d^- P$ is invariant under the choice of the g-inverse. So we will consider $P'C_d^+ P$. Let

$$z = \left(\frac{1}{\sqrt{v}}, \ldots, \frac{1}{\sqrt{v}}\right)'.$$

Then $Q = (P, z)$ is an orthogonal matrix. We have

$$\begin{bmatrix} P' \\ z' \end{bmatrix} C_d^+ \begin{bmatrix} P & z \end{bmatrix} = \begin{bmatrix} P'C_d^+ P & 0 \\ 0 & 0 \end{bmatrix},$$

since $C_d^+ z = 0$. Thus the eigenvalues of $P'C_d^+ P$ are the same as the nonzero eigenvalues of

$$\begin{bmatrix} P' \\ z' \end{bmatrix} C_d^+ \begin{bmatrix} P & z \end{bmatrix},$$

which, in turn, are the same as the nonzero eigenvalues of C_d^+. $\square$

As an immediate consequence of **10.6** we have

$$|P'C_d^- P| = \prod_{i=1}^{v-1} \frac{1}{\mu_{i,d}}.$$

Let $\beta = P'z$. Then the BLUE of β is $\widehat{\beta} = P'\tau$ and has the dispersion matrix $\sigma^2 P'C_d^- P$. Thus

$$\widehat{\beta} \sim N(\beta, \sigma^2 P'C_d^- P).$$

Therefore a confidence ellipsoid for β is of the form

$$\{\beta' \in \mathbb{R}^{v-1} : (\widehat{\beta} - \beta)'(P'C_d^- P)^{-1}(\widehat{\beta} - \beta) \le c\sigma^2\}. \tag{10.11}$$

The volume of this ellipsoid is proportional to $|P'C_d^- P|$. (See Exercise 13.) Thus a design is D-optimal if it minimizes the volume of the ellipsoid (10.11) over $\mathcal{D}(v, b, k)$ for any c, σ^2.

A design is called a *balanced incomplete block design* (*BIBD*) if it is a binary design such that

(i) $r_1 = \cdots = r_v = r$, say, and
(ii) any two treatments occur together in the same number, say λ, of blocks.

There does not necessarily exist a BIBD in $\mathcal{D}(v, b, k)$ for every given choice of v, b, k. Some necessary conditions for existence can be derived as follows.

If $d \in \mathcal{D}(v, b, k)$ is a BIBD, then

$$N_d 1 = r1$$

and hence $1'N_d 1 = vr$. Similarly, $(1'N_d)1 = k1'1 = bk$. Thus

$$bk = vr. \tag{10.12}$$

We have

$$N_d N_d' = \begin{bmatrix} r & \lambda & \cdots & \lambda \\ \lambda & r & \cdots & \lambda \\ \vdots & & \ddots & \\ \lambda & \lambda & \cdots & r \end{bmatrix}$$

and hence $N_d N_d' 1 = (r + \lambda(v - 1))1$. Also,

$$N_d N_d' 1 = N_d(N_d' 1) = kr1.$$

Thus

$$\lambda(v - 1) = r(k - 1). \tag{10.13}$$

We will use (10.12), (10.13) in subsequent discussion.

A simple way to construct a BIBD is to take v treatments, and let every pair of distinct treatments be a block. Then $k = 2$, $r = v - 1$, $\lambda = 1$ and $b = \frac{1}{2}v(v - 1)$.

Another example of a BIBD is the following design. Here the columns denote blocks.

$$
\begin{array}{ccccccc}
1 & 3 & 1 & 2 & 1 & 2 & 5 \\
2 & 4 & 3 & 4 & 4 & 3 & 6 \\
5 & 5 & 6 & 6 & 7 & 7 & 7
\end{array}
$$

10.7 *Let d^* be a BIBD with parameters v, b, k, r, λ. Then the eigenvalues of C_{d^*} are: 0 with multiplicity 1, and $\frac{v\lambda}{k}$ with multiplicity $v-1$.*

Proof Since d^* is a BIBD,

$$
C_{d^*} = \frac{v\lambda}{k}\left(I - \frac{1}{v}\mathbf{1}\mathbf{1}'\right).
$$

The result follows by (10.12), (10.13).   □

We now prove an optimality property of a BIBD when it exists.

10.8 *Let d^* be a BIBD with parameters v, b, k, r, λ. Then d^* is E-, A-, and D-optimal.*

Proof Let $d \in \mathscr{D}(v, b, k)$. Then

$$
\begin{aligned}
\mu_{1,d} &\le \frac{1}{v-1}\sum_{i=1}^{v-1}\mu_{i,d} \\
&= \frac{\operatorname{trace} C_d}{v-1} \\
&\le \frac{b(k-1)}{v-1} \quad \text{by } \mathbf{10.4} \\
&= \frac{v\lambda}{k} \quad \text{by (10.12), (10.13)} \\
&= \mu_{1,d^*} \quad \text{by } \mathbf{10.7},
\end{aligned}
$$

and hence d^* is E-optimal.

Let $d \in \mathscr{D}(v, b, k)$. By the arithmetic mean–harmonic mean inequality we have,

$$
\begin{aligned}
\sum_{i=1}^{v-1}\frac{1}{\mu_{i,d}} &\ge \frac{(v-1)^2}{\sum_{i=1}^{v-1}\mu_{i,d}} \\
&= \frac{(v-1)^2}{\operatorname{trace} C_d} \\
&\ge \frac{(v-1)^2}{b(k-1)} \quad \text{by } \mathbf{10.4} \\
&= \sum_{i=1}^{v-1}\frac{1}{\mu_{i,d^*}},
\end{aligned}
$$

since $\mu_{i,d^*} = \frac{v\lambda}{k}$, $i = 1, \ldots, v - 1$, and since (10.12), (10.13) hold. Thus (10.10) is satisfied and d^* is A-optimal.

In order to establish the D-optimality of d^*, we must show that for any $d \in \mathscr{D}(v, b, k)$,

$$\prod_{i=1}^{v-1} \mu_{i,d^*} \geq \prod_{i=1}^{v-1} \mu_{i,d}.$$

The proof is similar to that of the A-optimality of d^*, except that we now use the arithmetic mean–geometric mean inequality. That completes the proof.   □

10.6 Exercises

1. Suppose the variance-covariance matrix of a sample from a bivariate distribution is

$$\begin{bmatrix} 60 & 20 \\ 20 & 60 \end{bmatrix}.$$

Find the two principal components and their associated variances.

2. The following variance-covariance matrix was computed from a sample of 50 observations, each consisting of measurements on four characteristics. What percentage of the total variability is accounted for by the last principal component?

$$\begin{bmatrix} 10 & -3 & 2 & 1 \\ -3 & 8 & -1 & 4 \\ 2 & -1 & 10 & -2 \\ 1 & 4 & -2 & 12 \end{bmatrix}$$

3. The following variance-covariance matrix was computed from a sample of 50 observations, each consisting of measurements on four characteristics. Find the canonical correlations and canonical variates between the first two variables and the last two variables.

$$\begin{bmatrix} 6 & 2 & 2 & 7 \\ 2 & 30 & -3 & 20 \\ 2 & -3 & 12 & -2 \\ 7 & 20 & -2 & 22 \end{bmatrix}$$

4. We follow the notation of Sect. 9.2 here. Suppose $\sigma_1, \ldots, \sigma_p$ are the canonical correlations. Show that $\sigma_1, \ldots, \sigma_p$ are the nonzero roots of the equation

$$\begin{vmatrix} -\lambda \Sigma_{11} & \Sigma_{12} \\ \Sigma_{21} & -\lambda \Sigma_{22} \end{vmatrix} = 0.$$

5. Consider the linear model $E(y) = A\beta$, $D(y) = \sigma^2 I$, where

$$A = \begin{bmatrix} 1 & 0 & 1 & 1 & 0 \\ 1 & 1 & 1 & 0 & 1 \\ 0 & 1 & 1 & 0 & 1 \\ 1 & 0 & 1 & 1 & 1 \\ 1 & 0 & 0 & 0 & 1 \end{bmatrix}.$$

Obtain the coefficient matrix in the reduced normal equations for $\beta_3, \beta_4, \beta_5$. Hence determine the estimable functions of $\beta_3, \beta_4, \beta_5$.

6. A *randomized block design* is a design in which every treatment appears once in each block. Consider a randomized block design with b blocks and v treatment. Obtain the variance of the BLUE of $\sum_{i=1}^{v} \ell_i \tau_i$, where $\tau_1, \ldots, \tau_v$ are the treatment effects, $\sum_{i=1}^{v} \ell_i = 0$ and $\sum_{i=1}^{v} \ell_i^2 = 1$.

7. Consider the following design, where each column represents a block. Write down the C-matrix of the design and find its rank. Is the design connected?

$$\begin{array}{cccccc} 1 & 2 & 1 & 2 & 3 & 1 \\ 2 & 4 & 4 & 7 & 7 & 4 \\ 3 & 5 & 6 & 8 & 9 & 10 \end{array}$$

8. Consider a design with v treatments, block size k and replication numbers $r_1, \ldots, r_v$. Show that $\lambda_1(C)$, the largest eigenvalue of the C-matrix, satisfies $\lambda_1(C) \geq \frac{k-1}{k} \max_i r_i$.

9. Let d be a binary design in $\mathcal{D}(v, b, k)$. Suppose the treatment set can be partitioned into p groups, where p divides v, and $\frac{v}{p} = m$, say, such that the following conditions are satisfied: (i) Each group has m treatments. (ii) Two treatments from the same group occur together in α blocks, whereas two treatments from different groups occur together in β blocks. Find the C-matrix of the design and determine its eigenvalues.

10. Let A be an $n \times n$ matrix with every row sum and column sum equal to zero. Show that the cofactors of A are all equal.

11. For any design d, show that the cofactors of C_d are all equal and their common value is $\frac{1}{n} \prod_{i=1}^{v-1} \mu_{i,d}$.

12. Let d be a binary design with v treatments $1, \ldots, v$, and with block size k. For $1 \leq i < j \leq v$, let e^{ij} denote the $v \times 1$ column vector with $1, -1$ at the i, j coordinates respectively, and zeros elsewhere. Suppose treatments i, j occur together in α_{ij} blocks in d. Let Q be the matrix in which e^{ij} appears as a column α_{ij} times, $1 \leq i < j \leq v$. Show that $kC_d = QQ'$. Deduce the fact that C_d is positive semidefinite.

13. Let V be an $m \times m$ positive definite matrix. Prove that the volume of the ellipsoid

$$\{y \in \mathbb{R}^m : y'Vy \leq 1\}$$

in $\mathbb{R}^m$ is

$$\frac{1}{|V|} \times \frac{\pi^{\frac{n}{2}}}{\Gamma(\frac{n+2}{2})}.$$

14. Consider the following designs d_1, d_2 in $\mathscr{D}(5,5,3)$. Which of the two designs would you prefer according to the criteria of E-, A- and D-optimality?

$$
\begin{array}{cccccc}
 & 1 & 2 & 3 & 4 & 5 \\
d_1 : & 5 & 1 & 2 & 3 & 4 \\
 & 4 & 5 & 1 & 2 & 3
\end{array}
\qquad
\begin{array}{cccccc}
 & 1 & 2 & 3 & 4 & 5 \\
d_2 : & 2 & 1 & 1 & 3 & 3 \\
 & 4 & 5 & 2 & 5 & 1
\end{array}
$$

15. Let d be a design and let d' be obtained by deleting some blocks of d. Show that d is better than d' according to the E-, A- and D-optimality criteria.

16. Let ϕ denote a real-valued function defined on the set of vectors in $\mathbb{R}^{v-1}$ with nonnegative coordinates such that
    (i) $\phi(x_1, \ldots, x_{v-1}) = \phi(x_{\sigma(1)}, \ldots, x_{\sigma(v-1)})$ for any permutation σ
    (ii) $\phi(x_1, \ldots, x_{v-1}) \le \phi(\bar{x}, \ldots, \bar{x})$
    (iii) $\phi(x \ldots, x) \le \phi(y, \ldots, y)$ if $x \le y$.
    Call a design $d \in \mathscr{D}(v, b, k)$ "ϕ-optimal" if it minimizes

$$\phi(\mu_{1,d}, \ldots, \mu_{v-1,d})$$

    over $\mathscr{D}(v, b, k)$. Prove the following:
    (i) If $d^* \in \mathscr{D}(v, b, k)$ is a BIBD then d^* is ϕ-optimal.
    (ii) The criteria of E-, A-, and D-optimality can be seen as special cases of ϕ-optimality.

17. If d^* is a BIBD with parameters v, b, r, k, λ, then show that $k^r \ge v^\lambda$.

Chapter 11
Additional Exercises on Rank

1. Let A, B be $m \times n$ matrices. Show that rank A = rank B if and only if there exist nonsingular matrices C and D such that $A = CBD$.

2. Let B, C be matrices of order $n \times m$ and $n \times r$ respectively. Show that $\mathscr{C}(B) = \mathscr{C}(C)$ if and only if rank AB = rank AC for all A.

3. If B is an $n \times r$ matrix of full column rank and C is an $r \times n$ matrix of full row rank, then show that rank A = rank(BA) = rank(AC) for any A.

4. Show that rank(XA) = rank A implies rank(XAF) = rank(AF) for every F. Similarly, show that rank(AY) = rank A implies rank(HAY) = rank(HA) for every H.

5. Suppose rank A = rank(XA). Show that $XAG = XAH$ if and only if $AG = AH$. Similarly, if rank A = rank(AY), then show that $LAY = MAY$ if and only if $LA = MA$.

6. Let A, B be $n \times n$ matrices. Show that rank $\left[\begin{smallmatrix} A+B & A \\ A & A \end{smallmatrix}\right]$ = rank A + rank B.

7. Let A be an $m \times n$ matrix and suppose $A = \left[\begin{smallmatrix} B & C \\ 0 & D \end{smallmatrix}\right]$. Show that rank $A \geq$ rank B + rank D, and that the inequality may be strict.

8. Let A, B be $n \times n$ nonsingular matrices. Show that rank$(A - B)$ = rank$(A^{-1} - B^{-1})$.

9. Let A be an $n \times n$ matrix of rank $n - 1$, and suppose each row sum and each column sum of A is zero. Show that every submatrix of A of order $(n - 1) \times (n - 1)$ is nonsingular.

10. Let A be an $n \times n$ matrix of rank 1. Show that the determinant of $(I + A)$ equals $1 + $ trace A.

11. Show that rank$(A'AB)$ = rank(AB) = rank(ABB').

12. Let V be an $n \times n$ positive semidefinite matrix and let A be $n \times n$. Show that rank(AV) = rank$(AV^{\frac{1}{2}})$.

13. Let A be an $m \times n$ matrix. Show that rank $A = r$ if and only if A can be expressed as a sum of r, but not fewer than r, matrices of rank 1.

14. Let A, G be matrices of order $m \times n$, $n \times m$ respectively. Show that G is a g-inverse of A if and only if AG is idempotent and rank A = rank(AG). Similarly, show that G is a g-inverse of A if and only if GA is idempotent and rank A = rank(GA).

R.B. Bapat, *Linear Algebra and Linear Models*, Universitext,
DOI 10.1007/978-1-4471-2739-0_11, © Springer-Verlag London Limited 2012

15. Let A and B be matrices such that rank $A = \text{rank}(AB)$. Let $G = B(AB)^-$. Show that G is a g-inverse of A and that B^-G is a g-inverse of AB.

16. Let A be a matrix with n columns and let B be a matrix with n rows. Show that

$$\text{rank}\begin{bmatrix} 0 & A \\ B & I_n \end{bmatrix} = \text{rank}\,A + \text{rank}(B, I_n - A^-A)$$

$$= \text{rank}\begin{bmatrix} A \\ I_n - BB^- \end{bmatrix} + \text{rank}\,B.$$

17. Let A, B be matrices of order $m \times n, n \times q$ respectively. Show that

$$\text{rank}(AB) = \text{rank}\,B - \dim \mathcal{N}(A) \cap \mathcal{C}(B).$$

18. Show that $\text{rank}(B, I_n - AA^-) = \text{rank}\,B + \text{rank}(I_n - BB^-)(I_n - A^-A)$.

19. Show that

$$\text{rank}\begin{bmatrix} 0 & A \\ B & I_n \end{bmatrix} = n + \text{rank}(AB).$$

20. Show that $\text{rank}(AB) = \text{rank}\,A$ if and only if $(B, I_n - A^-A)$ has full row rank. Similarly, show that rank $AB = \text{rank}\,B$ if and only if $\begin{bmatrix} A \\ I_n - BB^- \end{bmatrix}$ has full column rank.

21. Let A be a matrix with n columns and let B be a matrix with n rows. Show that $\text{rank}(AB) \geq \text{rank}\,A + \text{rank}\,B - n$, with equality if and only if $(I_n - BB^-)(I_n - A^-A) = 0$.

22. Let A, B be $n \times n$ matrices such that $AB = 0$. Show that rank $A + \text{rank}\,B \leq n$.

23. Show that

$$\text{rank}\begin{bmatrix} 0 & AB \\ BC & B \end{bmatrix} = \text{rank}(AB) + \text{rank}(BC) + \text{rank}\,L$$

$$= \text{rank}\,B + \text{rank}(ABC),$$

where $L = (I - (BC)(BC)^-)B(I - (AB)^-(AB))$.

24. Show that $\text{rank}(ABC) \geq \text{rank}(AB) + \text{rank}(BC) - \text{rank}\,B$, with equality if and only if $(I - (BC)(BC)^-)B(I - (AB)(AB)^-) = 0$.

25. Let A, B be $m \times n$ matrices. Suppose $AB' = 0$ and $A'B = 0$. Show that $\text{rank}(A + B) = \text{rank}\,A + \text{rank}\,B$.

26. Let A, B be $n \times n$ matrices such that A is idempotent and suppose that $AB = BA = 0$. Show that $\text{rank}(A + B) = \text{rank}\,A + \text{rank}\,B$.

27. Let A, B be $n \times n$ matrices and suppose $AB = BA$. Show that $\text{rank}(A + B) \leq \text{rank}\,A + \text{rank}\,B - \text{rank}(AB)$.

28. Let A, B be $m \times n$ matrices. Let G be a g-inverse of A and let $B = UV$ be a rank factorization. Show that if $\text{rank}(A - B) = \text{rank}\,A - \text{rank}\,B$, then $U = AGU$ and $V = VGA$.

29. Let A, B be $n \times n$ matrices. Show that $\text{rank}\begin{bmatrix} A & I \\ I & B \end{bmatrix} = n$ if and only if $B = A^{-1}$.

30. Let A be an $n \times n$ matrix. If $\text{rank}\,A = \text{rank}\,A^2$, then show that $\text{rank}\,A = \text{rank}\,A^\ell$ for all $\ell \geq 1$.

31. Let A be an $n \times n$ matrix and let rank $A = 1$. Show that $\text{rank}\,A^2 = 1$ if and only if trace $A \neq 0$.

32. Let A, B be an $n \times n$ matrix. Show that $\text{rank}(AB - I) \leq \text{rank}(A - I) + \text{rank}(B - I)$.

33. Let A be an $n \times n$ matrix and let $A = BC$ be a rank factorization. Show that $\text{rank}\, A = \text{rank}\, A^2$ if and only if CB is nonsingular.

34. Let A be an $n \times n$ matrix. Show that $A = A^2$ if and only if $\text{rank}\, A + \text{rank}(I - A) = n$.

35. Let A be an $n \times n$ matrix. Show that $\text{rank}\, A = \text{rank}\, A^2$ if and only if $\mathbb{R}^n$ is a direct sum of $\mathscr{C}(A)$ and $\mathscr{N}(A)$.

36. Let A be an $n \times n$ matrix. Show that $\text{rank}\, A + \text{rank}(I - A) = n + \text{rank}(A - A^2)$. Conclude that A is idempotent if and only if $\text{rank}\, A + \text{rank}(I - A) = n$.

37. Let A be an $n \times n$ matrix such that $A^2 = I$. Show that $\text{rank}(I - A) + \text{rank}(I + A) = n$.

38. Let A be an $n \times n$ matrix. Show that A is *tripotent*, i.e., $A^3 = A$, if and only if $\text{rank}\, A = \text{rank}(A + A^2) + \text{rank}(A - A^2)$.

39. Let A, G be matrices of order $m \times n$, $n \times m$ respectively. Show that G is a g-inverse of A if and only if $\text{rank}\, A + \text{rank}(I - GA) = n$.

40. Let A be an $n \times n$ matrix such that $\text{rank}\, A = \text{rank}\, A^2$ and suppose $A^2 = A^3$. Show that $A = A^2$.

41. Let A be an $m \times n$ matrix and let $x \in \mathbb{R}^m$, $y \in \mathbb{R}^n$ be such that $\text{rank}(A + xy') > \text{rank}\, A$. Show that for any choice of g-inverse, $y'(A + xy')^- x = 1$.

42. Let A be an $n \times n$ matrix. Show that $\text{rank}\, A = \text{rank}\, A^2$ if and only if there exists a matrix G such that $AGA = A$, $GAG = G$ and $AG = GA$. Furthermore, show that G, when it exists, is unique. (The matrix G is known as the group inverse of A.)

43. Let A be an $n \times n$ matrix and let $\text{rank}\, A = r$. Show that $\text{rank}\, A^2 = r$ if and only if the sum of the $r \times r$ principal minors of A is nonzero.

44. Let A be an $n \times n$ matrix. Show that $\text{rank}\, A^k - \text{rank}\, A^{k+1}$ is nonincreasing in $k = 1, 2, \dots$.

45. Let A, B be $n \times n$ matrices and suppose $AB = BA$. If $\text{rank}\, A = \text{rank}\, A^2$ and $\text{rank}\, B = \text{rank}\, B^2$, then show that $\text{rank}(AB) = \text{rank}(AB)^2$.

46. Let A be an $n \times n$ matrix. Suppose $\mathscr{C}(A) = \mathscr{C}(A')$. Show that $\text{rank}\, A = \text{rank}\, A^2$.

47. Let A be an $m \times n$ matrix and let $\text{rank}\, A = r$. Show that an $r \times r$ submatrix of A is nonsingular if and only if the corresponding rows of A are linearly independent and the corresponding columns of A are linearly independent.

48. Let A be an $n \times n$ symmetric matrix. Show that if $\text{rank}\, A = r$ then A has a principal, nonsingular $r \times r$ submatrix.

49. Let A, B be $n \times n$ positive semidefinite matrices and suppose $A - B$ is positive semidefinite. Show that $\text{rank}\, A \geq \text{rank}\, B$.

50. Let A be an $n \times n$ positive semidefinite matrix and suppose A is partitioned as $A = \begin{bmatrix} B & C \\ C' & D \end{bmatrix}$. Show that $\text{rank}\, A = \text{rank}\, B + \text{rank}(D - C'B^-C)$.

51. Let A, B, C be matrices of order $m \times n$, $m \times m$ and $n \times n$ respectively. Show that there exists an $n \times m$ matrix X such that $\text{rank}\begin{bmatrix} A & B \\ C & X \end{bmatrix} = \text{rank}\, A$ if and only if $\mathscr{C}(B) \subset \mathscr{C}(A)$ and $\mathscr{C}(C') \subset \mathscr{C}(A')$, in which case, $X = CA^-B$.

52. Let A be an $n \times n$ positive semidefinite matrix and suppose A is partitioned as $A = \begin{bmatrix} B & C \\ C' & D \end{bmatrix}$. Show that $\text{rank}\, A \leq \text{rank}\, B + \text{rank}\, D$.

53. Let A be an $m \times n$ matrix and let B be a $p \times q$ submatrix of A. Show that $p + q - \operatorname{rank} B \leq m + n - \operatorname{rank} A$. In particular, if A is an $n \times n$ nonsingular matrix and if B is a $p \times q$ submatrix of A, then show that $p + q - \operatorname{rank} B \leq n$.

54. Let B be a $p \times q$ matrix. Show that B can be embedded in an $m \times n$ matrix A of rank r if and only if $p \leq m$, $q \leq n$ and $p + q - \operatorname{rank} B \leq m + n - r$. In particular, if B is $p \times q$ and if $n \geq \max\{p, q\}$, show that B can be completed to a nonsingular $n \times n$ matrix if and only if $p + q - \operatorname{rank} B \leq n$.

55. Let A be an $n \times n$ nonsingular matrix and let $B = A^{-1}$. Suppose A and B are partitioned as

$$A = \begin{bmatrix} A_{11} & A_{12} \\ A_{21} & A_{22} \end{bmatrix}, \qquad B = \begin{bmatrix} B_{11} & B_{12} \\ B_{21} & B_{22} \end{bmatrix},$$

where A_{11} and B_{11}' are both $p \times q$. Show that $q - \operatorname{rank} A_{11} = n - p - \operatorname{rank} B_{22}$. (This result, which says that A_{11} and B_{22} have the same nullity, is known as the Nullity Theorem.)

56. Let A be an $n \times n$ nonsingular matrix, let $B = A^{-1}$, and suppose $a_{11} = 0$. Show that the submatrix of B obtained by deleting the first row and column has rank $n - 2$.

57. Let A be an $n \times n$ tridiagonal matrix, i.e., $a_{ij} = 0$ if $|i - j| > 1$. Suppose A is nonsingular and let $B = A^{-1}$. Show that any submatrix of B located on or above the main diagonal has rank at most 1. (The submatrix formed by rows $i_1, \ldots, i_p$ and columns $j_1, \ldots, j_q$ is located on or above the main diagonal if $\max\{i_1, \ldots, i_p\} \leq \min\{j_1, \ldots, j_q\}$.)

58. Let A, B be $n \times n$ positive semidefinite matrices and suppose $A - B$ is positive semidefinite. Show that $B^+ - A^+$ is positive semidefinite if and only if $\operatorname{rank} A = \operatorname{rank} B$.

59. Let A be an $m \times n$ matrix of rank r and let $C_r(A)$ be the r-th compound matrix of A. Show that $\operatorname{rank} C_r(A) = 1$.

60. Let A be a skew-symmetric matrix, i.e. $A' = -A$. Show that $\operatorname{rank} A$ is even.

61. A square matrix is called a *tournament matrix* if it is skew-symmetric, each diagonal element is 0, and each off-diagonal element is ± 1. Show that the rank of an $n \times n$ tournament matrix is n, if n is even, and $n - 1$, if n is odd.

62. Let A be an $m \times n$ matrix and let X_1, X_2 be outer inverses of A, that is, they satisfy $X_1 A X_1 = X_1$, $X_2 A X_2 = X_2$. Show that

$$\operatorname{rank}(X_1 - X_2) = \operatorname{rank} \begin{bmatrix} X_1 \\ X_2 \end{bmatrix} + \operatorname{rank} \begin{bmatrix} X_1 & X_2 \end{bmatrix} - \operatorname{rank} X_1 - \operatorname{rank} X_2.$$

63. Let A be an $m \times n$ matrix and let X be an outer inverse of A. Show that

$$\operatorname{rank}(A - AXA) = \operatorname{rank} A - \operatorname{rank}(AXA).$$

64. Let A be an $n \times n$ matrix such that $A^2 = 0$. Show that $\operatorname{rank}(A + A') = 2 \operatorname{rank} A$.

65. Let A be an $m \times n$ matrix. Show that the following statements are equivalent:
    (i) the rank remains unchanged if any row or any column of A is deleted;
    (ii) the rank remains unchanged if any row and any column of A are deleted.

66. Let A be an $n \times n$ matrix such that each entry is positive and that $A^2 = A$. Show that $\operatorname{rank} A = 1$.

67. Let A be an $n \times n$ positive semidefinite matrix. Show that

$$\text{rank } A \leq (\text{trace } A)(\text{trace } A^+).$$

68. Let A be positive semidefinite, let $B = A^2$, and suppose A and B are conformally partitioned as

$$A = \begin{bmatrix} A_{11} & A_{12} \\ A_{21} & A_{22} \end{bmatrix}, \qquad B = \begin{bmatrix} B_{11} & B_{12} \\ B_{21} & B_{22} \end{bmatrix},$$

where A_{11} (and B_{11}) are square. Show that $\text{rank}(A_{11}) = \text{rank}(B_{11})$.

69. Let M be an $n \times n$ symmetric, idempotent matrix partitioned as $M = \begin{bmatrix} A & B \\ B' & D \end{bmatrix}$. Show that $\text{rank } M = \text{rank } A + \text{rank } D - \text{rank } B$.

70. Let $A = \begin{bmatrix} B & C \\ D & 0 \end{bmatrix}$ satisfy $\text{rank } A = \text{rank } B + \text{rank } C + \text{rank } D$, and let $G = \begin{bmatrix} E & F \\ H & X \end{bmatrix}$ be a g-inverse of A, partitioned conformally with A'. Show that E, F and H are g-inverses of B, D and C, respectively. Are there any other conditions that E, F and G must satisfy?

71. Let A, B be $n \times n$ idempotent matrices. Show that

$$\text{rank}(AB - BA) = \text{rank}(A - B) + \text{rank}(I - A - B) - n.$$

72. Let A, B be matrices of order $m \times n$, $n \times p$ respectively such that $\text{rank}(AB) = \text{rank } A + \text{rank } B - n$. Show that $B^- A^-$ is a g-inverse of AB for any choice of g-inverses B^-, A^-.

73. Let A be an $m \times n$ matrix. If $S \subset \{1, \ldots, n\}$, then let $\rho(S)$ be the rank of the submatrix of A formed by the columns in S. We set $\rho(\phi) = 0$. Show that for $S, T \subset \{1, \ldots, n\}$,

$$\rho(S) + \rho(T) \geq \rho(S \cup T) + \rho(S \cap T).$$

74. Let A be an $m \times n$ matrix. If $S \subset \{1, \ldots, m\}$, $T \subset \{1, \ldots, n\}$, then let $\rho(S, T)$ be the rank of the submatrix of A formed by the rows in S and the columns in T. If S or T is empty, we set $\rho(S, T) = 0$. Show that for $S_1, S_2 \subset \{1, \ldots, m\}$, $T_1, T_2 \subset \{1, \ldots, n\}$,

$$\rho(S_1, T_1) + \rho(S_2, T_2) \geq \rho(S_1 \cup S_2, T_1 \cap T_2) + \rho(S_1 \cap S_2, T_1 \cup T_2).$$

75. Show that $\text{rank} \begin{bmatrix} A & B \\ C & D \end{bmatrix} \geq \text{rank} \begin{bmatrix} C & D \end{bmatrix} + \text{rank} \begin{bmatrix} B \\ D \end{bmatrix} - \text{rank } D$.

76. Let A be an $m \times n$ matrix partitioned as

$$A = \begin{bmatrix} A_{11} & A_{12} & A_{13} \\ A_{21} & A_{22} & A_{23} \\ A_{31} & A_{32} & A_{33} \end{bmatrix}.$$

Show that

$$\text{rank} \begin{bmatrix} A_{11} & A_{12} \\ A_{21} & A_{22} \end{bmatrix} + \text{rank} \begin{bmatrix} A_{22} & A_{23} \\ A_{32} & A_{33} \end{bmatrix}$$

$$\geq \text{rank} \begin{bmatrix} A_{21} & A_{22} & A_{23} \end{bmatrix} + \text{rank} \begin{bmatrix} A_{12} \\ A_{22} \\ A_{32} \end{bmatrix}.$$

77. Let A be an $n \times n$ positive semidefinite matrix and suppose A is partitioned as

$$A = \begin{bmatrix} A_{11} & A_{12} & A_{13} \\ A_{21} & A_{22} & A_{23} \\ A_{31} & A_{32} & A_{33} \end{bmatrix},$$

where the diagonal blocks are square. Show that

$$\text{rank } A \leq \text{rank} \begin{bmatrix} A_{11} & A_{12} \\ A_{21} & A_{22} \end{bmatrix} + \text{rank} \begin{bmatrix} A_{22} & A_{23} \\ A_{32} & A_{33} \end{bmatrix} - \text{rank}(A_{22}).$$

Chapter 12
Hints and Solutions to Selected Exercises

Chapter 1

1. Consider a triangular matrix with zero diagonal entries.
2. Let B be obtained by setting b_{ij} equal to 0 or 1 according as a_{ij} is even or odd respectively. Then $|A|$ and $|B|$ have the same parity.
3. What is the trace of $XY - YX$?
5. $|A| = \frac{n(n+1)(2n+1)}{6}$.
6. Consider Laplace expansion of the determinant along the r rows corresponding to the zero submatrix.
10. trace $A'A$ equals the sum of squares of the entries of A.
11. Let $B = A' - A$. Then A is symmetric if and only if $B = 0$, which, by the preceding exercise, happens if and only if trace $B'B = 0$. Expand trace $B'B$.
12. Let $x = A'\mathbf{1} - \mathbf{1}$, where $\mathbf{1}$ denotes the vector of all ones. We must show that $x = 0$, and for this it is sufficient to show $x'x = 0$. Now $x'x$ equals, by expansion, $\mathbf{1}'AA'\mathbf{1} - \mathbf{1}'A\mathbf{1} - \mathbf{1}'A'\mathbf{1} + \mathbf{1}'\mathbf{1}$. This is seen to be zero since $AA' = A'A$ and each row sum of A is 1.
17. The dimension is $n^2 - 1$.
18. Clearly $S + T$ is a subspace since it is closed under addition and scalar multiplication. Similarly, $S \cap T$ is a subspace. Let $x_1, \ldots, x_p$ be a basis for $S \cap T$. Then there exists a basis

$$x_1, \ldots, x_p, y_1, \ldots, y_q$$

for S, and a basis

$$x_1, \ldots, x_p, z_1, \ldots, z_r$$

for T. We show that

$$x_1, \ldots, x_p, y_1, \ldots, y_q, z_1, \ldots, z_r$$

is a basis for $S + T$, and this will complete the proof. Obviously, the set spans $S + T$. We now show that the set is linearly independent. Suppose

$$u_1 x_1 + \cdots + u_p x_p + v_1 y_1 + \cdots + v_q y_q + w_1 z_1 + \cdots + w_r z_r = 0. \quad (12.1)$$

R.B. Bapat, *Linear Algebra and Linear Models*, Universitext,
DOI 10.1007/978-1-4471-2739-0_12, © Springer-Verlag London Limited 2012

Thus $w_1z_1 + \cdots + w_rz_r$, which belongs to T, can be expressed as a linear combination of $x_1, \ldots, x_p, y_1, \ldots, y_q$, and hence it belongs to $S \cap T$. Thus there exist $\alpha_1, \ldots, \alpha_p$ such that $w_1z_1 + \cdots + w_rz_r + \alpha_1x_1 + \cdots + \alpha_px_p = 0$. Since $x_1, \ldots, x_p, z_1, \ldots, z_r$ are linearly independent, it follows that $w_1 = \cdots = w_r = 0$. We can similarly show that $v_1 = \cdots = v_q = 0$, and then it follows from (12.1) that $u_1 = \cdots = u_p = 0$. Hence the vectors $x_1, \ldots, x_p$, $y_1, \ldots, y_q, z_1, \ldots, z_r$ are linearly independent and the proof is complete.

Chapter 2

1. The rank is 2 if $\alpha = -7$ and is 3 otherwise.
2. Let A, B be matrices with columns

$$\{x_1, \ldots, x_p\}, \qquad \{y_1, \ldots, y_q\}$$

respectively. If $\{x_1, \ldots, x_p, y_i\}$ is linearly dependent for each i, then each y_i is a linear combination of $\{x_1, \ldots, x_p\}$, and hence $B = AC$ for some matrix C. Now $q = \operatorname{rank} B \leq \operatorname{rank} A = p$, which is a contradiction.
4. We may assume $k \leq \min\{m, n\}$, for otherwise the result is trivial. Let $C = B - A$. Then C has at most k nonzero entries and thus $\operatorname{rank} C \leq k$. (To see this, note that a set of s rows of C, where $s > k$, must have a zero row and hence is linearly dependent.) Since $\operatorname{rank} B = \operatorname{rank}(A + C) \leq \operatorname{rank} A + \operatorname{rank} C \leq \operatorname{rank} A + k$, we get the second inequality in the exercise. The first one follows similarly.
7. If A, B, C, D are all singular, the result is trivial. So assume, without loss of generality, that A is nonsingular. Then the rank of A as well as that of the partitioned matrix being n, the last n columns are linear combinations of the first n. Thus there exists an $n \times n$ matrix X such that $B = AX, D = CX$. Then $|AD| = |A||C||X| = |BC|$.
8. Only (ii) defines an inner product.
16. The equation $AXB = 0$ consists of 27 homogeneous linear equations in 28 unknowns.
17. Let $X = UV$ be a rank factorization. Then $AXB = (AU)(VB)$. Now deduce the result from the Frobenius inequality.
18. Perform the following row operations on the matrix: Premultiply the top block by CA^{-1} and subtract from the lower block. Then we have

$$\begin{vmatrix} A & B \\ C & D \end{vmatrix} = \begin{vmatrix} A & B \\ 0 & D - CA^{-1}B \end{vmatrix} = |A||D - CA^{-1}B| = |AD - ACA^{-1}B|$$
$$= |AD - CB|,$$

using $AC = CA$.

Chapter 3

1. Note that α is an eigenvalue since the vector of all ones is an eigenvector for it. The eigenvalues of $A = \beta J$ are given by $\alpha + n\beta, \alpha_2, \ldots, \alpha_n$. This can be seen using the Spectral Theorem and the fact that the eigenvalues of A for $\alpha_2, \ldots, \alpha_n$ can be taken to be orthogonal to the vector of all ones.

2. The eigenvalues are $a + (n-1)b$ and $a - b$ with multiplicities $1, n-1$ respectively.

7. The following "proof" which is often given is incomplete. If λ is an eigenvalue of A, then $Ax = \lambda x$ for some nonzero (complex) vector x. Then $A^2 x = \lambda^2 x$. Hence λ^2 is an eigenvalue of A^2. Thus we have proved that if λ is an eigenvalue of A, then λ^2 is an eigenvalue of A^2. However, this does not rule out the possibility of, for example, A of order 3×3, having eigenvalues $1, 1, -1$ and A^2 having eigenvalues $1, 1, 4$. The proof is valid if A has distinct eigenvalues. We now give a proof, in general. We have $|A - \lambda I| = (\lambda_1 - \lambda) \cdots (\lambda_n - \lambda)$ and hence, replacing λ by $-\lambda$, $|A + \lambda I| = (\lambda_1 + \lambda) \cdots (\lambda_n + \lambda)$. Multiplying these equations we get, setting $\lambda^2 = \mu$,

$$\left| A^2 - \mu I \right| = \left(\lambda^2 - \mu \right) \cdots \left(\lambda_n^2 - \mu \right)$$

and the result follows.

8. If A is nonsingular, then

$$\left| AB - \lambda I \right| = \left| A^{-1}(AB - \lambda I)A \right| = \left| BA - \lambda I \right|.$$

Thus AB, BA have the same characteristic polynomial and hence the same eigenvalues. To settle the general case, first observe that if a sequence of matrices X_k converges (entrywise) to the matrix X, then the eigenvalues of X_k can be labeled, say $\lambda_1^k, \ldots, \lambda_n^k$ so that λ_i^k approaches λ_i, $i = 1, \ldots, n$ where λ_i, $i = 1, \ldots, n$ are the eigenvalues of X. This follows from the more general fact that the roots of a polynomial are continuous functions of its coefficients. Now if A is singular, we may construct a sequence of nonsingular matrices with limit A and use a continuity argument. See the next exercise for a different proof.

11. Use the Spectral Theorem to deduce the general case from the diagonal case.

14. If $Ax = 0$, then $x'A' = 0$, and hence $x'(A + A')x = 0$. Since $A + A'$ is positive definite, $x = 0$. It follows that A is nonsingular.

16. Equate the coefficient of λ^{n-k} on either side of the equation

$$|A - \lambda I| = (\lambda_1 - \lambda) \cdots (\lambda_n - \lambda).$$

17. By the Spectral Theorem, there exists an orthogonal matrix P such that $P'AP = \text{diag}(\lambda_1, \ldots, \lambda_n) = D$, say, where $\lambda_1, \ldots, \lambda_n$ are the eigenvalues of A. Since A is positive definite, $\lambda_i > 0$, $i = 1, \ldots, n$ and $D^{-\frac{1}{2}}$ is well-defined. Then $D^{-\frac{1}{2}} P'APD^{-\frac{1}{2}} = I$. The matrix $D^{-\frac{1}{2}} P'BPD^{-\frac{1}{2}}$ is symmetric and again by the Spectral Theorem, there exists an orthogonal matrix Q such that $Q'D^{-\frac{1}{2}} P'BPD^{-\frac{1}{2}} Q$ is a diagonal matrix. Set $E = PD^{-\frac{1}{2}}Q$. Then E is nonsingular, $E'AE = I$ and $E'BE$ is diagonal.

18. By Exercise 8, $AB = AB^{\frac{1}{2}} B^{\frac{1}{2}}$ has the same eigenvalues as $B^{\frac{1}{2}} AB^{\frac{1}{2}}$, but the latter matrix is symmetric and hence has only real eigenvalues. If A is positive semidefinite, then so is $B^{\frac{1}{2}} AB^{\frac{1}{2}}$, and has only nonnegative eigenvalues.

24. First suppose B has rank one. Then there exist $u_1, \ldots, u_n$ such that $b_{ij} = u_i u_j$, $i, j = 1, \ldots, n$. Then $C = UAU$ where $U = \text{diag}(u_1, \ldots, u_n)$ and hence C is positive semidefinite. The general case is obtained using the spectral decomposition of B.

25. For $t > 0$, the $n \times n$ matrix $(t^{x_i+x_j})$ is positive semidefinite. Now use the fact that $\frac{1}{x_i+x_j} = \int_0^1 t^{x_i+x_j-1}\, dt$.

26. Using the Spectral Theorem we may assume, without loss of generality, that $X = \mathrm{diag}(x_1, \ldots, x_n)$. Let $XY + YX = Z$. Then $y_{ij}(x_i + x_j) = z_{ij}$ and hence $y_{ij} = \frac{z_{ij}}{x_i+x_j}$ for all i, j. Now use the preceding two exercises.

27. Let $X = (A^{\frac{1}{2}} + B^{\frac{1}{2}}), Y = (A^{\frac{1}{2}} - B^{\frac{1}{2}})$. Then $XY + YX = 2(A - B)$, which is positive semidefinite. Now use the preceding exercise.

Chapter 4

3. It is easily verified that $G + (I - GA)U + V(I - AG)$ is a g-inverse of A for any U, V. Conversely, if H is a g-inverse of A, then set $U = HAG, V = H - G$ and verify that $G + (I - GA)U + V(I - AG) = H$.

5. There exist nonsingular matrices P, Q such that

$$A = P \begin{bmatrix} I_r & 0 \\ 0 & 0 \end{bmatrix} Q.$$

Let

$$G = Q^{-1} \begin{bmatrix} I_r & 0 & 0 \\ 0 & I_{k-r} & 0 \\ 0 & 0 & 0 \end{bmatrix} P^{-1}$$

be an $n \times m$ matrix. Then G is a g-inverse of A of rank k.

9. Let $P = I - X(X'X)^- X'$. Then it can be verified that $(I - P)y \in \mathscr{C}(X)$ and $(I-P)y$ is orthogonal to Py. Since $y = (I-P)y + Py$, it follows that $(I-P)y$ is the orthogonal projection of y onto $\mathscr{C}(X)$.

12. If G is a minimum norm g-inverse, then $GAA' = (GA)'A' = A'G'A' = A'$. Conversely, if $GAA' = A'$, then $AGAA' = AA'$, and it follows (for example, using the previous exercise) that $AGA = A$. Also, $GAA' = A'$ implies $A'G' = GAA'G'$, which is symmetric.

13. We may assume that A_{11} is nonsingular as the general case then follows by a continuity argument. If rank $A = r$ and A_{11} is $r \times r$, nonsingular, we can first show that $A_{22} = A_{21}A_{11}^{-1}A_{12}$. Now the result follows by multiplying $A\begin{bmatrix} \mathrm{adj}\,A_{11} & 0 \\ 0 & 0 \end{bmatrix}A$ out and using the fact that $A(\mathrm{adj}\,A_{11}) = (\mathrm{adj}\,A_{11}) = |A|I$.

14. Let $B_1, \ldots, B_s$ be $r \times r$ submatrices of A such that $\sum_{i=1}^s \alpha_i |B_i| = 1$, for some integers $\alpha_1, \ldots, \alpha_s$. First using the previous exercise, we may obtain integer matrices $G_1, \ldots, G_s$ such that

$$AG_i A = |B_i|A, \quad i = 1, \ldots, s.$$

Then $\sum_{i=1}^s \alpha_i G_i$ is the required integer g-inverse of A.

Chapter 5

4. The sum of the squares of the singular values of A equals $\mathrm{trace}(AA')$, which is the sum of the squares of the entries of A.

10. Let k be an integer, $1 \leq k \leq n$, and let X be a subset of some k players. The sum of the scores of the players in X is at least as much as the sum of their scores in the games played only against players within X. This latter sum is in fact the total of all scores in a subtournament of k players, and hence equals $\frac{k(k-1)}{2}$. Thus we have shown that the sum of any k scores in the tournament is at least $\frac{k(k-1)}{2}$.

12. Note that $\|A\|_F = (\sum_i \sigma_i^2(A))^{\frac{1}{2}}$. Thus the first part of the result follows from **5.19**. We give another, easier argument. Since $\|A\|_F = \|PAQ\|_F$ for orthogonal P, Q, we may assume, without loss of generality, that

$$A = \begin{bmatrix} \Sigma & 0 \\ 0 & 0 \end{bmatrix},$$

where $\Sigma = \mathrm{diag}(\sigma_1, \ldots, \sigma_r)$ and r is the rank of A. Then

$$G = \begin{bmatrix} \Sigma^{-1} & X \\ Y & Z \end{bmatrix}$$

for some X, Y, Z. Furthermore, $G = A^+$ precisely when X, Y, Z are zero. Clearly,

$$\|G\|_F^2 - \|A\|_F^2 = \sum_{i,j} x_{ij}^2 + \sum_{i,j} y_{ij}^2 + \sum_{i,j} z_{ij}^2$$

and the result, and the assertion about equality, follow.

13. The image of $\mathscr{C}$ is the parallelogram with vertices

$$\begin{bmatrix} 0 \\ 0 \\ 0 \end{bmatrix}, \quad \begin{bmatrix} 1 \\ 0 \\ 1 \end{bmatrix}, \quad \begin{bmatrix} 1 \\ -1 \\ 2 \end{bmatrix}, \quad \begin{bmatrix} 2 \\ -1 \\ 3 \end{bmatrix}.$$

The area of the parallelogram is $\sqrt{3}$, which equals $\mathrm{vol}(A)$.

15. Suppose σ_1 is the largest singular value of $A^{-1/2}CB^{-1/2}$. Then

$$\sigma_1^2 = \lambda_1 (A^{-1/2}CB^{-1}C'A^{-1/2}).$$

Thus $\sigma_1^2 < 1$ if and only if

$$I - A^{-1/2}CB^{-1}C'A^{-1/2}$$

is positive definite, or equivalently, $A - CB^{-1}C'$ is positive definite. Since B is positive definite, the partitioned matrix is positive definite if and only if the Schur complement $A - CB^{-1}C'$ is positive definite, and the result is proved.

17. Since $|A| = 0$, then 0 is an eigenvalue of A. If 0 has multiplicity greater than one, then by the interlacing principle, any $(n-1) \times (n-1)$ principal submatrix must have 0 as an eigenvalue and therefore has determinant zero. So suppose 0 has multiplicity one. Let B, C be principal submatrices of order $(n-1) \times (n-1)$. We must show $|B\|C| \geq 0$. This is trivial if either B or C is singular. So suppose B, C are nonsingular. Again by the interlacing principle it follows that the number of positive eigenvalues (and hence the number of negative eigenvalues) of B and C are the same. Hence $|B\|C| > 0$.

Chapter 6

1. Let $A = XX'$, $B = YY'$. Then $A + B = [X, Y][X, Y]'$ and thus the column space of B is contained in the column space of $A + B$, while the row space of A is contained in the row space of $A + B$. Thus A, B are parallel summable.

2. For any $S \subset \{1, \ldots, k\}$, we have

$$\text{rank } A \leq \text{rank}\left(\sum_{i \in S} A_i\right) + \text{rank}\left(\sum_{i \notin S} A_i\right) \leq \sum_{i=1}^{k} \text{rank}(A_i).$$

   Thus if $\text{rank } A = \sum_{i=1}^{k} \text{rank}(A_i)$, then equality must occur in the inequalities above, and the result is proved.

3. If $x \notin \mathscr{C}(A)$, then $\text{rank}(A + xx') = \text{rank } A + \text{rank}(xx')$ and thus any g-inverse of $A + xx'$ is a g-inverse of xx'. Thus $x'(A + xx')^- x = x'(xx')^- x = x'(xx')^+ x = 1$. If $x \in \mathscr{C}(A)$, then using the Spectral Theorem, we can reduce the problem to the case where A is positive definite. Then it is easily verified that

$$\left(A + xx'\right)^{-1} = A^{-1} - \frac{1}{1 + x'A^{-1}x}A^{-1}xx'A^{-1}.$$

   Using this identity we can simplify $x'(A + xx')^{-1}x$ and the result is proved.

4. Let $A^- = A^+ + X$. Then $AXA = 0$ and AX is symmetric. Therefore $X'A'A = 0$, and it follows that $AX = 0$. Since $\mathscr{R}(A^+) = \mathscr{R}(A')$, then $(A^+)'X = 0$. Thus

$$\left(A^-\right)'A^- = \left(A^+ + X\right)'\left(A^+ + X\right) = \left(A^+\right)'A^+ + X'X \geq \left(A^+\right)'A^+.$$

   Therefore $(A^+b)'A^+b \geq (A^-b)'(A^-b)$ and the proof is complete.

5. Clearly, for any V, $B^+ + V(I - BB^+)$ is a minimum norm g-inverse of B. Conversely, suppose G is a minimum norm g-inverse of B. Setting $V = B^+ + G$, we see that

$$B^+ + V\left(I - BB^+\right) = B^+ + G - GBB^+.$$

   Now, $GBB^+ = B'G'B^+$, which equals B^+, as can be seen using $\mathscr{C}(B^+) = \mathscr{C}(B')$.

6. Suppose $A <^* B$. Then by **6.4**, $AA^+ = BA^+$, $A^+A = A^+B$. Now $B^+(A^+)^+ = B^+A = (A^+ + (B - A)^+)A$ by **6.6**, which equals A^+A as observed in the proof of **6.7**. Similarly we can show $(A^+)^+B^+ = AA^+$ and hence $A^+ <^* B^+$. The converse is immediate.

   For solutions to Exercises 8–12 see the comments on Chap. 6 in Chap. 13.

Chapter 7

2. $c_1\beta_1 + c_2\beta_2 + c_3\beta_3 + c_4\beta_4$ is estimable if and only if $c_1 + c_2 + c_3 + c_4 = 0$.

3. The BLUE of $2\beta_1 + \beta_2$ is $\frac{1}{14}(9y_1 + 11y_2 + 8y_3)$ and has variance $\frac{19}{14}\sigma^2$, where σ^2 is the variance of each y_i.

4. $\alpha = -1$.

7. Using the Spectral Theorem we can reduce the problem to the case when A_{11}, A_{22} are diagonal matrices. Then use the Hadamard inequality.

9. If A is a Hadamard matrix, then so is $\begin{bmatrix} A & A \\ A & A \end{bmatrix}$.

10. $RSS = \frac{1}{3}(y_1 - y_2 + y_3)^2$.

11. $c\mu + d_1\alpha_1 + \cdots + d_k\alpha_k$ is estimable if and only if $c = d_1 + \cdots + d_k$. Since μ is not estimable, it is incorrect to say that $\bar{y}$ (or any linear function of y_{ij}) is an unbiased estimator of μ.

12. RSS subject to $\beta_1 = \beta_2$ is $\frac{1}{17}$ times

$$8y_1^2 + 13y_2^2 + 13y_3^2 - 12y_1y_2 - 12y_1y_3 - 8y_2y_3.$$

13. RSS subject to $\alpha_1 = \alpha_2$ is

$$\sum_{j=1}^{n_1}(y_{1j} - \bar{y}_{12.})^2 + \sum_{j=1}^{n_2}(y_{2j} - \bar{y}_{12.})^2 + \sum_{i=3}^{k}\sum_{j=1}^{n_1}(y_{ij} - \bar{y}_{i.})^2$$

where $\bar{y}_{12.} = \frac{n_1\bar{y}_{1.}+n_2\bar{y}_{2.}}{n_1+n_2}$.

Chapter 8

6. The F-statistic is $\frac{398/2}{138/9} = 12.97$. The Table value for $(2, 9)$ degrees of freedom and level of significance 0.01 is 8.02. Hence we reject the hypothesis that the means under the three methods are the same.

7. The error sum of squares is 92.5. The F-statistic for difference between the machines is 1.0216, which is not significant. The F-statistic for difference between the operators is 5.9027, which is significant.

8. RSS is $\frac{1}{3}$ times

$$y_1^2 + y_2^2 + y_3^2 - 2y_1y_2 - 2y_2y_3 + 2y_1y_3,$$

and $RSS_H = \frac{1}{2}(y_1 - y_2)^2 + y_3^2$. The test statistic is $(RSS_H - RSS)/RSS$, distributed as $F(1, 1)$.

9. $RSS = 153.86$. For the hypothesis $\beta_2 = 0$, $RSS_H = 158.89$ and $F = 0.12$, which is not significant. For the hypothesis $\beta_3 = 0$, $RSS_H = 2986.32$ and $F = 67.5$, which is significant.

10. The multiple correlation coefficient is $1/\sqrt{3}$.

11. $\hat{\beta}_0 = -58.398$, $\hat{\beta}_1 = 0.793$, $\hat{\beta}_2 = 1.111$, $\hat{\beta}_3 = -0.397$, $r = 0.971$. The value of the F-statistic for $\beta_1 = \beta_2 = \beta_3 = 0$ is 43.410. The Table value for the $F(3, 8)$ statistic at 1 percent level of significance is 7.59. Hence we reject the hypothesis.

12. The given hypotheses imply that CA^-B is invariant with respect to the choice of g-inverse. Also, $AA^-B = B$ and $CA^-A = C$. Let

$$U = \begin{bmatrix} I & 0 \\ -CA^- & I \end{bmatrix}, \qquad V = \begin{bmatrix} I & -A^-B \\ 0 & I \end{bmatrix}.$$

Then

$$UXV = \begin{bmatrix} A & 0 \\ 0 & D - CA^-B \end{bmatrix}.$$

Since U and V are nonsingular, rank $A = \text{rank}\, UXV = \text{rank}\, A + \text{rank}(D - CA^-B)$.

14. By the Spectral Theorem, we may write $\Sigma = P\begin{bmatrix} D & 0 \\ 0 & 0 \end{bmatrix}P'$, where P is orthogonal, and D is an $r \times r$ diagonal matrix with positive diagonal entries. Set $B = P\begin{bmatrix} D^{\frac{1}{2}} \\ 0 \end{bmatrix}$. Then $\Sigma = BB'$ and if $x \sim N(0, I_r)$, it can be seen that $y \sim N(0, \Sigma)$.

15. First make the transformation given in the previous exercise and then use **8.3**.

16. Since A is idempotent, all its eigenvalues are either 0 or 1. Using the Spectral Theorem we may assume, without loss of generality, that $A = \begin{bmatrix} I & 0 \\ 0 & 0 \end{bmatrix}$. Partition B conformally as $\begin{bmatrix} B_{11} & B_{12} \\ B_{21} & B_{22} \end{bmatrix}$. Since A, B and $A - B$ are all positive semidefinite, we see that $B_{22} = 0$. Then since B is positive semidefinite, it follows that B_{12}, B_{21} are both zero matrices. Also, B_{11} is idempotent and hence so is $I - B_{11}$. It follows that $A - B$ is idempotent. In terms of distribution of quadratic forms the result says the following: Suppose Q_1, Q_2 are quadratic forms in the vector $y \sim N(0, I)$, which are both distributed as chi-square. Then $Q_1 - Q_2$ is also distributed as chi-square if and only if $Q_1 - Q_2$ is nonnegative with probability one.

19. The conditional distribution is multivariate normal with mean 0 and dispersion matrix $I_n - \frac{1}{n}J_n$, where J_n is the $n \times n$ matrix of all ones.

23. The model is $y_i = \theta_i + \varepsilon_i$, $i = 1, 2, 3$, where ε_i, $i = 1, 2, 3$, are i.i.d. $N(0, 1)$ and $\theta_1 + \theta_2 + \theta_3 = \pi$. The test statistic for the hypothesis $\theta_1 = \theta_2 = \theta_3 \,(= \frac{\pi}{3})$ is

$$\frac{2(y_1 + y_2 + y_3)^2}{(y_1 + y_2 + y_3 - \pi)^2},$$

distributed as $F(1, 1)$.

24. (i)

$$1'\hat{y} = 1'\begin{bmatrix} 1 & X \end{bmatrix}\begin{bmatrix} \widehat{\beta_0} \\ \widehat{\beta_1} \\ \vdots \\ \widehat{\beta_p} \end{bmatrix}$$

$$= \begin{bmatrix} n & 1'X \end{bmatrix}\begin{bmatrix} n & 1'X \\ X'1 & X'X \end{bmatrix}^{-1}\begin{bmatrix} 1'y \\ X'y \end{bmatrix}$$

$$= \begin{bmatrix} 1 & 0 \end{bmatrix}\begin{bmatrix} 1'y \\ X'y \end{bmatrix}$$

$$= 1'y.$$

(ii)

$$(y - \hat{y})'\hat{y} = (y - \begin{bmatrix} 1 & X \end{bmatrix}\hat{\beta})'\begin{bmatrix} 1 & X \end{bmatrix}\hat{\beta}$$

$$= y'\begin{bmatrix} 1 & X \end{bmatrix}\hat{\beta} - \hat{\beta}'\begin{bmatrix} 1' \\ X' \end{bmatrix}\begin{bmatrix} 1 & X \end{bmatrix}\hat{\beta}$$

$$= y'[1 \quad X]\widehat{\beta} - \widehat{\beta}'\begin{bmatrix} 1' \\ X' \end{bmatrix} y$$

$$= 0.$$

(iii)

$$\sum_{i=1}^{n}(y_i - \overline{y})^2 = \sum_{i=1}^{n}(y_i - \widehat{y}_i + \widehat{y}_i - \overline{y})^2$$

$$= \sum_{i=1}^{n}(y_i - \widehat{y}_i)^2 + \sum_{i=1}^{n}(\widehat{y}_i - \overline{y})^2,$$

since the cross product term, $(y - \widehat{y})'(\widehat{y} - \overline{y}\mathbf{1})$, equals 0 by (i), (ii).

(iv) It follows from (ii) that

$$\sum_{i=1}^{n}(y_i - \overline{y})(\widehat{y}_i - \overline{y}) = \sum_{i=1}^{n}(\widehat{y}_i - \overline{y})^2.$$

Thus, since $\overline{y} = \overline{\widehat{y}}$ by (i), we have

$$r^2 = \frac{\sum_{i=1}^{n}(\widehat{y}_i - \overline{y})^2}{\sum_{i=1}^{n}(y_i - \overline{y})^2},$$

and hence, by (iii),

$$r^2 = \frac{\sum_{i=1}^{n}(\widehat{y}_i - \overline{y})^2}{\sum_{i=1}^{n}(y_i - \widehat{y}_i)^2 + \sum_{i=1}^{n}(\widehat{y}_i - \overline{y})^2}.$$

It follows that

$$\frac{r^2}{1 - r^2} = \frac{\sum_{i=1}^{n}(\widehat{y}_i - \overline{y})^2}{\sum_{i=1}^{n}(y_i - \widehat{y}_i)^2},$$

which equals

$$\frac{\sum_{i=1}^{n}(y_i - \overline{y})^2 - \sum_{i=1}^{n}(y_i - \widehat{y}_i)^2}{\sum_{i=1}^{n}(y_i - \widehat{y}_i)^2},$$

and the result is proved, in view of (8.20).

Chapter 9

1. Let $P = X(X'X)^{-1}X'$. If $VX = XQ$ for some Q, then $PVX = X(X'X)^{-1} \times X'VX = X(X'X)^{-1}X'XQ = XQ = VX$. Then $VP = VX(X'X)^{-1}X' = PVX(X'X)^{-1}X' = PVP$. Hence VP is symmetric and therefore $VP = (VP)' = PV$. It follows that $PV^{-1} = V^{-1}P$ and hence $PV^{-1}P = PV^{-1}$. This gives $X'V^{-1}P = X'PV^{-1} = X'V^{-1}$, since $X'P = X'$. Now

$$X(X'V^{-1}X)^{-1}X'V^{-1} = X(X'V^{-1}X)^{-1}X'V^{-1}P$$

$$= X(X'V^{-1}X)^{-1}X'V^{-1}X(X'X)^{-1}X' = X(X'X)^{-1}X'$$

and hence the OLSE and the BLUE coincide. The converse is proved similarly.

2. Verify the condition of the previous exercise.
6. We have SSA $= \sum_{i=1}^{k} n_i(\overline{y}_{i.} - \overline{y}_{..})^2$, SSE $= \sum_{i=1}^{k} \sum_{j=1}^{n_i} (y_{ij} - \overline{y}_{i.})^2$. Show that $E(\text{SSA}) = (n - \sum_{i=1}^{k} n_i^2/n)\sigma_1^2 + (k-1)\sigma^2$, $E(\text{SSE}) = (n-k)\sigma^2$. The estimates are $\hat{\sigma}^2 = \text{MSE}$, $\hat{\sigma}_1^2 = (\text{MSA} - \text{MSE})/\theta$, where MSA $= \text{SSA}/(k-1)$, MSE $= \text{SSE}/(n-k)$ and

$$\theta = \frac{1}{k-1}\left(n - \sum_{i=1}^{k} n_i^2/n\right).$$

8. The log likelihood function is given by

$$\log L(\mu, \sigma^2, \sigma_1^2; y) = -\frac{n}{2}\log(2\pi) - \frac{1}{2}(n-k)\log\sigma^2$$
$$- \frac{k}{2}\log(\sigma^2 + m\sigma_1^2) - \frac{1}{2\sigma^2}\sum_{i=1}^{k}\sum_{j=1}^{m}(y_{ij} - \mu)^2$$
$$+ \frac{\sigma_1^2}{2\sigma^2(\sigma^2 + m\sigma_1^2)}\sum_{i=1}^{k}(y_{i.} - m\mu)^2.$$

We have seen that the ML estimates are

$$\hat{\mu} = \overline{y}_{..}, \quad \hat{\sigma}^2 = \text{SSE}/(n-k), \quad \text{and} \quad \hat{\sigma}_1^2 = \frac{1}{n}\left(\text{SSA} - k\hat{\sigma}^2\right).$$

It can be seen, using the previous exercise, that

$$\log L(\hat{\mu}, \hat{\sigma}^2, \hat{\sigma}_1^2; y) = -\frac{n}{2}\log(2\pi) - \frac{n-k}{2}\log\text{MSE}$$
$$- \frac{k}{2}\log(\text{SSA}/k) - \frac{n-k}{2} - m.$$

When $\sigma_1^2 = 0$, the model reduces to $y_{ij} = \mu + \varepsilon_{ij}$ and clearly the ML estimate $\tilde{\mu}$ of μ remains the same ($\hat{\mu}$) while σ^2 is given by

$$\tilde{\sigma}^2 = \frac{\text{SSE} + \text{SSA}}{n}.$$

Now find $\log L(\tilde{\mu}, \tilde{\sigma}^2; y)$ and simplify $\log L(\tilde{\mu}, \tilde{\sigma}^2; y) - \log(\hat{\mu}, \hat{\sigma}^2, \hat{\sigma}_1^2; y)$.

9. Let K be the $(n-1) \times n$ matrix formed by taking the first $n-1$ rows of $I_n - \frac{1}{n}J_n$. Then $K\mathbf{1} = 0$. Let y be the $n \times 1$ vector with components $y_1, \ldots, y_n$. Show that the log likelihood of Ky is given by

$$-\frac{y'K'(KK')^{-1}Ky}{2\sigma^2} - \frac{1}{2}\log|KK'|^{\frac{1}{2}} - \frac{n-1}{2}\log\sigma^2.$$

Differentiating with respect to σ^2 and setting equal to zero, we get the REML estimator as $\frac{1}{n-1}y'K'(KK')^{-1}Ky$. Simplify $(KK')^{-1}$ and show that the estimate equals $\frac{1}{n-1}\sum_{i=1}^{n}(y_i - \overline{y})^2$.

10. For the confidence interval use the fact that $\frac{\text{MSA}}{\text{MSE}}\frac{\sigma^2}{\sigma^2 + m\sigma_1^2}$ is distributed as F with $k-1, n-k$ degrees of freedom to first find a confidence interval for σ_1^2/σ^2.

Chapter 10

1. The principal components are $\frac{1}{\sqrt{2}}(x_1 + x_2)$ and $\frac{1}{\sqrt{2}}(x_1 - x_2)$ with the corresponding variance 80 and 40 respectively.

2. The answer is given by 100 times the ratio of the least eigenvalue of the matrix and the trace, and is seen to be approximately 9.5 percent.

3. First canonical correlation: .9337.
   First pair of canonical variates: $.0957X_1 + .9954X_2$, $.6169X_3 + .7870X_4$.
   Second canonical correlation: .3054.
   Second pair of canonical variates: $.9954X_1 - .0957X_2$, $.7870X_3 - .6169X_4$.

4. Use the Schur complement formula for the determinant.

8. First show that the i-th diagonal entry of the C-matrix cannot be less than $\frac{k-1}{k}r_i$. The result follows since the largest eigenvalue of a symmetric matrix cannot be less than any diagonal element.

9. The eigenvalues of k times the C-matrix are, 0 with multiplicity 1, $m(\alpha - \beta) + \beta v$ with multiplicity $v - p$, and $m\beta(p - 1)$ with multiplicity $p - 1$.

11. By the previous exercise, the cofactors of C_d are all equal, let the common value be α. If J is the matrix of all ones, then $|C_d + J|$ can be seen to be the sum of all the cofactors of C_d, which is $n^2\alpha$. Also, the eigenvalues of $C_d + J$ are n, and $\mu_{1,d}, \ldots, \mu_{v-1,d}$. Hence $n^2\alpha = n \prod_{i=1}^{v-1} \mu_{i,d}$ and the result follows. (Another proof can be given using the fact that the sum of the $(v - 1) \times (v - 1)$ principal minors of C_d equals the sum of the products of the eigenvalues, taken $v - 1$ at a time.)

14. The C-matrices are given by

$$3C_{d_1} = \begin{bmatrix} 6 & -2 & -1 & -1 & -2 \\ -2 & 6 & -2 & -1 & -1 \\ -1 & -2 & 6 & -2 & -1 \\ -1 & -1 & -2 & 6 & -2 \\ -2 & -1 & -1 & -2 & 6 \end{bmatrix},$$

$$3C_{d_2} = \begin{bmatrix} 8 & -3 & -2 & -1 & -2 \\ -3 & 6 & -1 & -1 & -1 \\ -2 & -1 & 6 & -1 & -2 \\ -1 & -1 & -1 & 4 & -1 \\ -2 & -1 & -2 & -1 & 6 \end{bmatrix}.$$

The eigenvalues, rounded to four decimal places, are:

$$C_{d_1}: \quad 0, 2.1273, 2.1273, 2.8727, 2.8727,$$
$$C_{d_2}: \quad 0, 1.6667, 2.1461, 2.6667, 3.5205.$$

It can be verified that d_1 is better than d_2 according to each of the E-, A- and D-optimality criteria.

15. First show that the C-matrices of d, d' satisfy $C_d \geq C_{d'}$. Then use **5.10**.

16. (i) Let $d \in \mathcal{D}(v, b, k)$ and let the corresponding C-matrix C_d have eigenvalues $0 \leq \mu_{1,d} \leq \cdots \leq \mu_{v-1,d}$. Suppose there exists a BIBD, $d^* \in \mathcal{D}(v, b, k)$.

By **10.7**, all the nonzero eigenvalues of the corresponding C-matrix equal $\frac{v\lambda}{k}$. By **10.4**, we have

$$\text{trace}\, C_d \leq b(k-1) = \frac{\lambda v(v-1)}{k},$$

using (10.9), (10.10). Now, using the properties of ϕ, we get

$$\phi(\mu_{1,d}, \ldots, \mu_{v-1,d}) \leq \phi\left(\frac{\text{trace}\, C_d}{v-1}, \ldots, \frac{\text{trace}\, C_d}{v-1}\right) \leq \phi\left(\frac{\lambda v}{k}, \ldots, \frac{\lambda v}{k}\right)$$

and the result follows.

(ii) For E-, A-, and D-optimality, we set $-\phi(\mu_{1,d}, \ldots, \mu_{v-1,d})$ to be $\mu_{1,d}$, $\sum_{i=1}^{v-1} \frac{1}{\mu_{i,d}}$ and $\prod_{i=1}^{v-1} \mu_{i,d}$ respectively. It can be verified that each of these functions satisfies conditions (i), (ii), (iii).

Chapter 11

1. If $A = CBD$ where C and D are nonsingular, then rank $A =$ rank B, since multiplication by a nonsingular matrix does not change rank. Conversely, suppose rank $A =$ rank B. Let $A = XY$ and $B = UV$ be rank factorizations. Then $\mathscr{C}(U)$ and $\mathscr{C}(X)$ have the same dimension and are isomorphic. Thus $X = CU$ for some nonsingular C. Similarly, $\mathscr{R}(V)$ and $\mathscr{R}(Y)$ are isomorphic, and hence $Y = VD$ for some nonsingular D. Then $A = XY = CUVD = CBD$.

2. If $\mathscr{C}(B) = \mathscr{C}(C)$, then $B = CX$ for some X. Then rank$(AB) =$ rank$(ACX) \leq$ rank(AC). Similarly we can show that rank$(AC) \leq$ rank(AB) and hence rank$(AB) =$ rank(AC).

   Conversely, if $\mathscr{C}(B) \neq \mathscr{C}(C)$, then $\mathscr{C}(B)^\perp \neq \mathscr{C}(C)^\perp$. Then there exists a vector x such that exactly one of $x'B$ and $x'C$ is the zero vector. Setting $A = x'$ we see that rank$(AB) \neq$ rank(AC).

3. Since B has full column rank, there exists B^- such that $B^-B = I$. Then for any A, rank $A =$ rank$(B^-BA) \leq$ rank$(BA) \leq$ rank A. Hence rank$(BA) =$ rank A. The second part is similar.

4. First note that rank$(XA) =$ rank A implies $\mathscr{R}(XA) = \mathscr{R}(A)$, and hence $A = BXA$ for some B. Now rank$(AF) =$ rank$(BXAF) \leq$ rank$(XAF) \leq$ rank(AF) and hence rank$(XAF) =$ rank(AF) for every F.

5. Note that $\mathscr{N}(A) \subset \mathscr{N}(XA)$. If rank $A =$ rank(XA), then by the rank plus nullity theorem, $\dim \mathscr{N}(A) = \dim \mathscr{N}(XA)$, and hence $\mathscr{N}(A) = \mathscr{N}(XA)$. Then $XAG = XAH$ implies $XA(G-H) = 0$, which gives $A(G-H) = 0$.

6. We may reduce $\begin{bmatrix} A+B & A \\ A & A \end{bmatrix}$ first to $\begin{bmatrix} B & A \\ 0 & A \end{bmatrix}$ and then to $\begin{bmatrix} B & 0 \\ 0 & A \end{bmatrix}$ by row operations.

7. The inequality may be proved using the determinant definition of rank. The inequality is strict if $A = \begin{bmatrix} 0 & I \\ 0 & 0 \end{bmatrix}$.

8. $A - B = -B(A^{-1} - B^{-1})A$.

9. By Exercise 10, Chap. 10, the cofactors of A are all equal.

10. We may write $A = xy'$ where $x, y \in \mathbb{R}^n$. Then the only nonzero eigenvalue of A is $y'x$. Thus the eigenvalues of $I + A$ are $1 + y'x$ and 1 with multiplicity $n-1$. Then $|I + A| = 1 + y'x = 1 + \text{trace}\, A$.

11. Clearly, $A'ABx = 0 \Rightarrow x'B'A'ABx = 0 \Rightarrow ABx = 0$. Thus $\mathcal{N}(A'AB) \subset \mathcal{N}(AB)$. It follows by the rank plus nullity theorem that $\text{rank}(AB) \leq \text{rank}(A'AB)$. Since $\text{rank}(A'AB) \leq \text{rank}(AB)$ trivially holds, the first equality is proved. The second part is similar.

12. Use the second equality in the previous exercise, setting $B = V^{\frac{1}{2}}$.

13. If $\text{rank}\, A = r$, then there exist matrices X, Y of order $m \times r, r \times n$ respectively, such that $A = XY$. If $x_1, \ldots, x_r$ are the columns of X and $y_1', \ldots, y_r'$ are the rows of Y, then $A = x_1 y_1' + \cdots + x_r y_r'$ is the required representation of A as a sum of r matrices of rank 1. If $A = B_1 + \cdots + B_s$, then $\text{rank}\, A \leq \text{rank}(B_1) + \cdots + \text{rank}(B_s)$, and hence if $\text{rank}(B_i) = 1$, $i = 1, \ldots, s$, then $r \leq s$.

14. If $\text{rank}\, A = \text{rank}(AG)$, then $\mathscr{C}(A) = \mathscr{C}(AG)$ and hence $A = AGX$ for some matrix X. If AG is idempotent, it follows that $AGA = AGAGX = AGX = A$.

15. Since $\text{rank}\, A = \text{rank}(AB)$, we may write $A = ABX$ for some matrix X. Then $AGA = AB(AB)^- A = AB(AB)^- ABX = ABX = A$. The second part is similar.

16. In $\begin{bmatrix} 0 & A \\ B & I_n \end{bmatrix}$, premultiply the top block by A^- and subtract from the bottom block. Then

$$
\text{rank} \begin{bmatrix} 0 & A \\ B & I_n \end{bmatrix} = \text{rank} \begin{bmatrix} 0 & A \\ B & I_n - A^- A \end{bmatrix}
$$

$$
= \dim \mathscr{R} \begin{bmatrix} 0 & A \\ B & I_n - A^- A \end{bmatrix}
$$

$$
= \dim\left(\mathscr{R}[0, A] + \mathscr{R}[B, I_n - A^- A]\right)
$$

$$
= \dim \mathscr{R}(A) + \dim \mathscr{R}[B, I_n - A^- A]
$$

$$
- \dim\{\mathscr{R}[0, A] \cap \mathscr{R}[B, I_n - A^- A]\}.
$$

Thus the first equality in the exercise will follow if we show that $\mathscr{R}[0, A] \cap \mathscr{R}[B, I_n - A^- A] = \{0\}$. For this, it is sufficient to show that $\mathscr{R}(A) \cap \mathscr{R}(I_n - A^- A) = \{0\}$. This is clear since $x'A = y'(I_n - A^- A) \Rightarrow x'AA^- A = y'(I_n - A^- A)A^- A = 0 \Rightarrow x'A = 0$. The second part is similar.

17. We may assume, without loss of generality, that $B = \begin{bmatrix} I_r & 0 \\ 0 & 0 \end{bmatrix}$, where $\text{rank}\, B = r$. Partition $A = \begin{bmatrix} A_{11} & A_{12} \\ A_{21} & A_{22} \end{bmatrix}$ conformally. Then $AB = \begin{bmatrix} A_{11} & 0 \\ A_{21} & 0 \end{bmatrix}$. By the rank plus nullity theorem,

$$
\text{rank}(AB) = \text{rank} \begin{bmatrix} A_{11} \\ A_{21} \end{bmatrix} = r - \dim \mathcal{N} \begin{bmatrix} A_{11} \\ A_{21} \end{bmatrix}. \tag{12.2}
$$

The result follows if we observe that $\mathcal{N} \begin{bmatrix} A_{11} \\ A_{21} \end{bmatrix} = \mathcal{N}(A) \cap \mathscr{C}(B)$ and use (12.2).

18. We have

$$
\text{rank}[B, I_n - A^- A]
$$

$$
= \dim \mathscr{C}(B) + \dim \mathscr{C}(I_n - A^- A) - \dim \mathscr{C}(B) \cap \mathscr{C}(I_n - A^- A)
$$

$$
= \text{rank}\, B + \text{rank}(I_n - A^- A) - \dim \mathscr{C}(B) \cap \mathscr{C}(I_n - A^- A). \tag{12.3}
$$

Furthermore, by the previous exercise,

$$\text{rank}(I_n - BB^-)(I_n - A^-A)$$
$$= \text{rank}(I_n - A^-A) - \dim \mathcal{N}(I_n - BB^-) \cap \mathcal{C}(I_n - A^-A). \quad (12.4)$$

Since $\mathcal{C}(B) = \mathcal{N}(I_n - BB^-)$, it follows from (12.4) that

$$\text{rank}(I_n - BB^-)(I_n - A^-A)$$
$$= \text{rank}(I_n - A^-A) - \dim \mathcal{C}(B) \cap \mathcal{C}(I_n - A^-A). \quad (12.5)$$

The result is proved by substituting (12.5) in (12.3).

19. By the Schur complement formula for rank,

$$\text{rank} \begin{bmatrix} 0 & A \\ B & I_n \end{bmatrix} = \text{rank} \, I_n + \text{rank}(0 - A(I_n)^{-1}B) = n + \text{rank}(AB).$$

20. This follows from Exercises 16 and 19.
21. This follows from Exercises 16, 18 and 19.
22. This follows from Exercise 21.
23. The proof is similar to that of Exercises 16, 18, 19.
24. The proof is similar to that of Exercise 21.
25. It is sufficient to show that $\mathcal{C}(A) \cap \mathcal{C}(B) = \{0\}$ and $\mathcal{R}(A) \cap \mathcal{R}(B) = \{0\}$. Suppose $z = Ax = By$. Then $A'Ax = A'By = 0$. It follows that $z = Ax = 0$. Thus $\mathcal{C}(A) \cap \mathcal{C}(B) = \{0\}$. Similarly it can be shown that $\mathcal{R}(A) \cap \mathcal{R}(B) = \{0\}$.
26. It is sufficient to show that $\mathcal{C}(A) \cap \mathcal{C}(B) = \{0\}$ and $\mathcal{R}(A) \cap \mathcal{R}(B) = \{0\}$.
27. If $AB = BA$, then $\mathcal{C}(AB) \subset \mathcal{C}(A) \cap \mathcal{C}(B)$. Now use

$$\text{rank}(A + B) \leq \dim(\mathcal{C}(A) + \mathcal{C}(B)) = \text{rank} \, A + \text{rank} \, B - \dim(\mathcal{C}(A) \cap \mathcal{C}(B)).$$

28. Since $\text{rank} \, A = \text{rank} \, B + \text{rank}(A - B)$ then $(A - B)GB = 0$ and $BGB = B$. Hence $AGB = B$. Thus $AGUV = UV$ and since V admits a right inverse, it follows that $AGU = U$. Similarly, $VGA = V$.
29. If A is nonsingular and $B = A^{-1}$, then by the Schur complement formula for the rank,

$$\text{rank} \begin{bmatrix} A & I \\ I & B \end{bmatrix} = \text{rank} \, A + \text{rank}(B - A^{-1}) = n.$$

Conversely, if $\text{rank} \begin{bmatrix} A & I \\ I & B \end{bmatrix} = n$, then the lower block should linearly depend on the top block, which has rank n. It follows that $BA = I$.

30. If $\text{rank} \, A = \text{rank} \, A^2$, then $\mathcal{C}(A) = \mathcal{C}(A^2)$ and hence $A = A^2X$ for some matrix X. Then $A^2 = A^3X$ and it can be seen that $\text{rank} \, A^2 = \text{rank} \, A^3$. Thus $\text{rank} \, A^3 = \text{rank} \, A$. Similarly $A^\ell = A^{\ell+1}X, \ell \geq 3$.
31. If $\text{rank} \, A = 1$, then $A = xy'$ for some $x, y \in \mathbb{R}^n$. Then $A^2 = x(y'x)y'$ which is nonzero if and only if $y'x = \text{trace} \, A \neq 0$.
32. $AB - I = (A - I)B + (B - I)$.
33. First suppose $\text{rank} \, A = \text{rank} \, A^2 = r$. Then B is $n \times r$, C is $r \times n$. There exists X such that $A = A^2X$. Then $BC = BCBCX$. Let B^-, C^- be a left inverse of B and a right inverse of C respectively. Then $B^-BCC^- = B^-BCBCXC^-$

and hence $CBCXC^- = I_r$. Therefore CB is nonsingular. Conversely, if CB is nonsingular, then

$$A^2 B(CB)^{-2} C = BCBCB(CB)^{-2} C = BC = A$$

and hence rank $A = $ rank A^2.

34. If $A = A^2$ then $I - A$ is also idempotent and rank $A + \text{rank}(I - A) = \text{trace } A + \text{trace}(I - A) = \text{trace}(A + I - A) = \text{trace } I = n$. The converse can be proved in many ways. For example, since $I = A + (I - A)$, if rank $A + \text{rank}(I - A) = n$, then by the results on rank additivity, every g-inverse of I is a g-inverse of A. It follows that $A^2 = A$. The next two exercises give different approaches to this problem.

35. Use rank $A^2 = $ rank $A - \dim(\mathcal{N}(A) \cap \mathcal{C}(A))$.

36. We get the result by evaluating the rank of $\begin{bmatrix} I & A \\ A & A \end{bmatrix}$ in two different ways, once by the Schur complement formula and then by the generalized Schur complement formula (see Exercise 12 in Chap. 8).

37. Since $2I = (I - A) + (I + A)$, we get $n \le \text{rank}(I - A) + \text{rank}(I + A)$. Also by the Frobenius inequality, $\text{rank}(I - A)(I + A) \ge \text{rank}(I - A) + \text{rank}(I + A) - n$.

38. First suppose that rank $A = \text{rank}(A + A^2) + \text{rank}(A - A^2)$. Then rank additivity holds in $2A = (A + A^2) + (A - A^2)$ and hence any g-inverse A^- of A satisfies $(A + A^2)A^-(A - A^2) = 0$. It follows that $A^3 = A$. Conversely, let $A^3 = A$. Using the generalized Frobenius inequality,

$$\text{rank}\big((A + A^2)A(A - A^2)\big) \ge \text{rank}\big((A + A^2)A\big) + \text{rank}\big(A(A - A^2)\big) - \text{rank } A$$

$$= \text{rank}(A + A^2) + \text{rank}(A - A^2) - \text{rank } A.$$

Since $(A + A^2)A(A - A^2) = 0$, it follows that

$$0 \ge \text{rank}(A + A^2) + \text{rank}(A - A^2) - \text{rank } A. \qquad (12.6)$$

Also,

$$\text{rank } A = \text{rank}(2A) = \text{rank}(A + A^2 + A - A^2)$$
$$\le \text{rank}(A + A^2) + \text{rank}(A - A^2). \qquad (12.7)$$

It follows from (12.6), (12.7) that rank $A = \text{rank}(A + A^2) + \text{rank}(A - A^2)$.

39. If G is a g-inverse of A, then GA is idempotent and rank $A = \text{rank}(GA)$. It follows that

$$\text{rank } A + \text{rank}(I - GA) = \text{rank}(GA) + \text{rank}(I - GA)$$
$$= \text{trace}(GA) + \text{trace}(I - GA)$$
$$= \text{trace}(GA + I - GA)$$
$$= n.$$

Conversely, suppose rank $A + \text{rank}(I - GA) = n$. Then

$$\text{rank}(GA) + \text{rank}(I - GA) \le \text{rank } A + \text{rank}(I - GA) = n.$$

Also, trivially, $\mathrm{rank}(GA) + \mathrm{rank}(I - GA) \geq \mathrm{rank}(GA + I - GA) = n$. So $\mathrm{rank}(GA) + \mathrm{rank}(I - GA) = n$ and $\mathrm{rank}\,A = \mathrm{rank}(GA)$. By Exercise 34, GA is idempotent. Since $\mathrm{rank}\,A = \mathrm{rank}(GA)$, we may write $A = XGA$ for some X. Then $AGA = XGAGA = XGA = A$ and G is a g-inverse of A.

40. Since $\mathrm{rank}\,A = \mathrm{rank}\,A^2$, we may write $A = A^2 X$ for some X. Then $A^2 = A^3 X = A^2 X = A$.

41. If $\mathrm{rank}(A + xy') > \mathrm{rank}\,A$, then $\mathrm{rank}(A + xy') = \mathrm{rank}\,A + 1 = \mathrm{rank}\,A + \mathrm{rank}(xy')$. Thus rank additivity holds and hence any g-inverse of $A + xy'$ is a g-inverse of xy'. Thus $xy'(A + xy')^- xy' = xy'$. Clearly, x, y must be nonzero vectors and hence $y'(A + xy')^- x = 1$.

42. Let $A = BC$ be a rank factorization. If $\mathrm{rank}\,A = \mathrm{rank}\,A^2$, then by Exercise 33, CB is nonsingular. Set $G = B(CB)^{-2}C$ and verify that $AGA = A$, $GAG = G$ and $AG = GA$. Conversely if there exists G such that $AGA = A$, $GAG = G$ and $AG = GA$, then $A = AGA = A^2 G$ and it follows that $\mathrm{rank}\,A = \mathrm{rank}\,A^2$. Now suppose G_1, G_2 satisfy $AG_1A = A$, $G_1AG_1 = G_1$, $AG_1 = G_1A$ and $AG_2A = A$, $G_2AG_2 = G_2$, $AG_2 = G_2A$. Then

$$G_1 = G_1AG_1 = G_1AG_2AG_1 = AG_1AG_2G_1 = AG_2G_1 = G_2AG_1.$$

Also,

$$G_2 = G_2AG_2 = G_2AG_1AG_2 = G_2G_1AG_2A = G_2G_1A = G_2AG_1$$

and it follows that $G_1 = G_2$.

43. Let $\mathrm{rank}\,A = r$ and let $A = BC$ be a rank factorization. By Exercise 33, $\mathrm{rank}\,A = \mathrm{rank}\,A^2 = r$ if and only if CB is nonsingular. It can be seen by the Cauchy–Binet formula that the sum of the $r \times r$ principal minors of A equals $|CB|$ and the result follows.

44. By the generalized Frobenius inequality,

$$\mathrm{rank}\,A^{k+2} = \mathrm{rank}\,A(A^k)A \geq \mathrm{rank}\,A^{k+1} + \mathrm{rank}\,A^{k+1} - \mathrm{rank}\,A^k.$$

Hence

$$\mathrm{rank}\,A^k - \mathrm{rank}\,A^{k+1} \geq \mathrm{rank}\,A^{k+1} - \mathrm{rank}\,A^{k+2}, \quad k = 1, 2, \ldots$$

and the result is proved.

45. By Exercise 35, we know that $\mathscr{C}(A) \cap \mathscr{N}(A) = \{0\}$ and $\mathscr{C}(B) \cap \mathscr{N}(B) = \{0\}$. It is sufficient to prove that $\mathscr{C}(AB) \cap \mathscr{N}(AB) = \{0\}$. Let $y = ABx \in \mathscr{C}(AB) \cap \mathscr{N}(AB)$. Then $ABy = 0 \Rightarrow ABABx = 0 \Rightarrow A^2B^2x = 0 \Rightarrow AB^2x = 0 \Rightarrow BABx = 0 \Rightarrow ABx = 0$. Thus $y = 0$ and hence $\mathscr{C}(AB) \cap \mathscr{N}(AB) = \{0\}$.

46. By Exercise 35, it is sufficient to show that $\mathscr{C}(A) \cap \mathscr{N}(A) = \{0\}$. Let $y \in \mathscr{C}(A) \cap \mathscr{N}(A)$. Then $y \in \mathscr{C}(A')$ and hence $y = A'z$ for some z. Then $Ay = 0 \Rightarrow AA'z = 0 \Rightarrow A'z = 0 \Rightarrow y = 0$. Thus $\mathscr{C}(A) \cap \mathscr{N}(A) = \{0\}$ and the proof is complete.

47. If an $r \times r$ submatrix is nonsingular, then clearly the corresponding rows of A are linearly independent and the corresponding columns of A are linearly independent. The converse can be proved using rank factorization. Let $A = BC$ be a rank factorization. For simplicity, suppose the first r rows of A are linearly

independent and the first r columns of A are linearly independent. Let B_1 be the submatrix of B formed by the first r rows of B and let C_1 be the submatrix of C formed by the first r columns of C. Then B_1, C_1 must be $r \times r$ nonsingular matrices. The submatrix of A formed by the first r rows and the first r columns of A equals $B_1 C_1$, which must also be nonsingular.

48. Use the previous exercise.

49. It is sufficient to show that $\mathcal{N}(A) \subset \mathcal{N}(B)$. If $x \in \mathcal{N}(A)$, then $x'Ax = 0$. Also, $x'(A - B)x \geq 0$ and it follows that $x'Bx = 0$. It can be concluded that $Bx = 0$ and hence $x \in \mathcal{N}(B)$.

50. It will be sufficient to show that $\mathscr{C}(C) \subset \mathscr{C}(B)$, for then, the result follows by the generalized Schur complement formula for rank. Let $A = XX'$ and partition $X = \begin{bmatrix} X_1 \\ X_2 \end{bmatrix}$ so that X_1 has the same number of rows as B. Then $B = X_1 X_1'$ and $C = X_1 X_2'$. Now $\mathscr{C}(C) = \mathscr{C}(X_1 X_2') \subset \mathscr{C}(X_1) = \mathscr{C}(X_1 X_1') = \mathscr{C}(B)$.

51. First suppose that $\mathscr{C}(B) \subset \mathscr{C}(A)$ and $\mathscr{C}(C') \subset \mathscr{C}(A')$. Set $X = CA^-B$. By the generalized Schur complement formula for rank,

$$\text{rank}\begin{bmatrix} A & B \\ C & X \end{bmatrix} = \text{rank}\, A + \text{rank}(X - CA^-B) = \text{rank}\, A.$$

Conversely, suppose there exists X such that $\text{rank}\begin{bmatrix} A & B \\ C & X \end{bmatrix} = \text{rank}\, A$. Then the block $\begin{bmatrix} B \\ X \end{bmatrix}$ depends linearly on the block $\begin{bmatrix} A \\ C \end{bmatrix}$ and hence $\mathscr{C}(B) \subset \mathscr{C}(A)$. Similarly it can be shown that $\mathscr{C}(C') \subset \mathscr{C}(A')$. It then follows by the generalized Schur complement formula for rank, that $X = CA^-B$.

52. Let $A = XX'$ and partition $X = \begin{bmatrix} X_1 \\ X_2 \end{bmatrix}$ so that X_1 has the same number of rows as B. Then $B = X_1 X_1'$ and $D = X_2 X_2'$. Now

$$\begin{aligned}
\text{rank}\, A &= \text{rank}\begin{bmatrix} X_1 \\ X_2 \end{bmatrix} \\
&\leq \text{rank}\, X_1 + \text{rank}\, X_2 \\
&= \text{rank}(X_1 X_1') + \text{rank}(X_2 X_2') \\
&= \text{rank}\, C + \text{rank}\, D.
\end{aligned}$$

53. We assume, without loss of generality, that $A = \begin{bmatrix} B & C \\ D & E \end{bmatrix}$. Then

$$\begin{aligned}
\text{rank}\, A &\leq \text{rank}\begin{bmatrix} B & C \end{bmatrix} + \text{rank}\begin{bmatrix} D & E \end{bmatrix} \\
&\leq \text{rank}\, B + \text{rank}\, C + (m - p) \\
&\leq \text{rank}\, B + (n - q) + (m - p).
\end{aligned}$$

It follows that $p + q - \text{rank}\, B \leq m + n - \text{rank}\, A$. In particular, if A is $n \times n$ and nonsingular, then $p + q - \text{rank}\, B \leq n$.

54. If B can be embedded in an $m \times n$ matrix of rank r, then it follows by Exercise 53 that $p + q - \text{rank}\, B \leq m + n - r$. Conversely, suppose B is a $p \times q$ matrix, $p \leq m$, $q \leq n$ and $p + q - \text{rank}\, B \leq m + n - r$. First show that B can be augmented by either a row or a column so that the rank increases by 1. Then use induction to show that B can be embedded in an $m \times n$ matrix of rank r.

55. We have the equations

$$A_{11}B_{12} + A_{12}B_{22} = 0, \tag{12.8}$$

$$A_{21}B_{12} + A_{22}B_{22} = I. \tag{12.9}$$

Let X be a matrix whose columns form a basis for $\mathcal{N}(B_{22})$. From (12.8), (12.9) we have, after post-multiplying by X, the equations $A_{11}B_{12}X = 0$, $A_{21}B_{12}X = X$. From these equations we get

$$q - \operatorname{rank} A_{11} \geq \operatorname{rank}(B_{12}X) \geq \operatorname{rank}(A_{21}B_{12}X) = \operatorname{rank} X = n - p - \operatorname{rank} B_{22}.$$

Similarly we can show that $n - p - \operatorname{rank} B_{22} \geq q - \operatorname{rank} A_{11}$.

56. Use the Nullity Theorem.

57. Use the Nullity Theorem.

58. Let A, B be positive semidefinite matrices. If $A - B$ is positive semidefinite, then $\mathscr{C}(B) \subset \mathscr{C}(A)$ and hence $\operatorname{rank} A \geq \operatorname{rank} B$. If $B^+ - A^+$ is also positive semidefinite, then

$$\operatorname{rank} B = \operatorname{rank} B^+ \geq \operatorname{rank} A^+ = \operatorname{rank} A.$$

Thus if $A - B$ and $B^+ - A^+$ are both positive semidefinite, then $\operatorname{rank} A = \operatorname{rank} B$. We now sketch the proof of the fact that if $A - B$ is positive semidefinite and $\operatorname{rank} A = \operatorname{rank} B$, then $B^+ - A^+$ is positive semidefinite. The following result can be proved using techniques similar to those used in Sect. 5.1. If C is an $n \times n$ positive semidefinite matrix, then for any $x \in \mathbb{R}^n$,

$$x'C^+x = \sup_{0 \neq y \in \mathscr{C}(C)} \frac{(y'x)^2}{y'Cy}. \tag{12.10}$$

Note that if $A - B$ is positive semidefinite and $\operatorname{rank} A = \operatorname{rank} B$, then $\mathscr{C}(A) = \mathscr{C}(B)$. Using this fact, (12.10) and that $A - B$ is positive semidefinite, we get

$$x'A^+x = \sup_{0 \neq y \in \mathscr{C}(A)} \frac{(y'x)^2}{y'Ay}$$

$$\leq \sup_{0 \neq y \in \mathscr{C}(A)} \frac{(y'x)^2}{y'By}$$

$$= \sup_{0 \neq y \in \mathscr{C}(B)} \frac{(y'x)^2}{y'By}$$

$$= x'B^+x$$

for any $x \in \mathbb{R}^n$. Hence $B^+ - A^+$ is positive semidefinite.

59. Let $A = BC$ be a rank factorization. Then $C_r(A) = C_r(B)C_r(C)$. Note that $C_r(B)$ is a nonzero column vector while $C_r(C)$ is a nonzero row vector. Hence the rank of $C_r(A)$ is 1.

60. Suppose $\operatorname{rank} A = r$ and let rows $i_1, \ldots, i_r$ of A be linearly independent. Then, since $A' = -A$, columns $i_1, \ldots, i_r$ are also linearly independent. Let B be the

submatrix of A formed by rows $i_1, \ldots, i_r$ and columns $i_1, \ldots, i_r$. By Exercise 47, B is nonsingular. Note that $B' = -B$ and hence $|B| = |B'| = (-1)^r |B|$. Since $|B| \neq 0$, r must be even.

61. Let X be the $n \times n$ matrix with each diagonal entry equal to 0 and each off-diagonal entry equal to 1. It can be seen that $|X| = (-1)^{n-1}(n-1)$. Let A be an $n \times n$ tournament matrix. Note that A and X are either both even or both odd, since changing a 1 to a -1 does not alter the parity of the determinant when the entries are all 0 or ± 1. If n is even, then $|X|$ is odd. Thus $|A|$ is also odd, in particular, nonzero. Thus A is nonsingular if n is even. If n is odd, then since A is skew-symmetric, its rank must be even and hence it cannot be n. However if we delete a row and the corresponding column, the resulting matrix must be nonsingular by the first part. Thus the rank of A is $n-1$ in this case.

62. Let $M = \begin{bmatrix} -X_1 & 0 & X_1 \\ 0 & X_2 & X_2 \\ X_1 & X_2 & 0 \end{bmatrix}$. It can be seen by elementary row operations that

$$\text{rank } M = \text{rank} \begin{bmatrix} -X_1 & 0 & 0 \\ 0 & X_2 & 0 \\ 0 & 0 & X_1 - X_2 \end{bmatrix}$$
$$= \text{rank } X_1 + \text{rank } X_2 + \text{rank}(X_1 - X_2). \tag{12.11}$$

Also,

$$\begin{bmatrix} I_n & 0 & X_1 A \\ 0 & I_n & 0 \\ 0 & 0 & I_n \end{bmatrix} M \begin{bmatrix} I_m & 0 & 0 \\ 0 & I_m & 0 \\ 0 & -AX_2 & I_m \end{bmatrix} = \begin{bmatrix} 0 & 0 & X_1 \\ 0 & 0 & X_2 \\ X_1 & X_2 & 0 \end{bmatrix},$$

and hence

$$\text{rank } M = \text{rank} \begin{bmatrix} X_1 \\ X_2 \end{bmatrix} + \text{rank} \begin{bmatrix} X_1 & X_2 \end{bmatrix}. \tag{12.12}$$

The result follows from (12.11), (12.12).

63. Note that A and AXA are both outer inverses of A^+. It follows from the previous exercise that

$$\text{rank}(A - AXA) = \text{rank} \begin{bmatrix} A \\ AXA \end{bmatrix} + \text{rank} \begin{bmatrix} A & AXA \end{bmatrix} - \text{rank } A - \text{rank}(AXA)$$
$$= \text{rank } A - \text{rank}(AXA).$$

64. We first claim that $\mathscr{C}(A) \cap \mathscr{C}(A') = \{0\}$. Suppose $y = Ax = A'z$. Then $Ay = A^2 x = 0$. Thus $AA'z = 0$ and it follows that $y = A'z = 0$. Hence the claim is proved. Now by rank additivity we have $\text{rank}(A + A') = \text{rank } A + \text{rank } A' = 2\,\text{rank } A$.

65. The proof of (ii) $\Rightarrow$ (i) is easy. To show (i) $\Rightarrow$ (ii), suppose A is partitioned as $A = \begin{bmatrix} a_{11} & x' \\ x & B \end{bmatrix}$. Since the rank of A is unchanged if the first column is deleted, x must be a linear combination of columns of B. Thus the rank of B is the same as the rank of $[x, B]$, which must then be the same as the rank of A, by assumption. Hence the rank of A is unchanged if the first row and the first column are deleted. The proof is similar in the case when any row and any column are deleted.

66. Let x, y be the first two columns of A. Then $A^2 = A$ implies that $Ax = x$ and
    $Ay = y$. If x and y are not linearly dependent, then there exists $\alpha > 0$ such
    that $z = x - \alpha y$ is a nonzero vector with at least one zero coordinate. However
    $Az = z$ and z must have all coordinates positive, which is a contradiction. Hence
    x and y are linearly dependent. We can similarly show that any two columns of
    A are linearly dependent and hence rank $A = 1$.

67. If the rank of A is r, then A has r positive eigenvalues, say, $\lambda_1, \ldots, \lambda_r$. Then
    A^+ has eigenvalues $\frac{1}{\lambda_1}, \ldots, \frac{1}{\lambda_r}$.

68. Note that

$$B_{11} = \begin{bmatrix} A_{11} & A_{12} \end{bmatrix} \begin{bmatrix} A_{11} \\ A_{21} \end{bmatrix}.$$

Since A is positive semidefinite, $\mathscr{C}(A_{12}) \subset \mathscr{C}(A_{11})$ (see the solution to Exercise 50). Thus the rank of B_{11}, which equals rank$[A_{11}\ A_{12}]$ in view of the above expression, is the same as rank(A_{11}).

69. Using $M = M^2 = M'$, we get $A = A'$, $D = D'$, and

$$A(I - A) = BB', \qquad D(I - D) = B'B,$$
$$B'(I - A) = DB', \qquad (I - A)BD = BD. \tag{12.13}$$

Since $A(I - A) = BB'$, then $\mathscr{C}(B) = \mathscr{C}(BB') \subset \mathscr{C}(A)$. Therefore by the generalized Schur complement formula for rank,

$$\text{rank } M = \text{rank } A + \text{rank}(D - B'A^+B). \tag{12.14}$$

Since M is symmetric, idempotent, it is positive semidefinite and hence, so is A.
Then A^+ is also positive semidefinite. Therefore

$$\text{rank}(B'A^+B) = \text{rank}(B'(A^+)^{\frac{1}{2}}(A^+)^{\frac{1}{2}}B) = \text{rank}((A^+)^{\frac{1}{2}}B). \tag{12.15}$$

We claim that rank$((A^+)^{\frac{1}{2}}B) = \text{rank } B$. Note that $B = AX$ for some X. Thus
$B = AX = AA^+AX = A(A^+)^{\frac{1}{2}}(A^+)^{\frac{1}{2}}B$ and hence rank $B \leq \text{rank}((A^+)^{\frac{1}{2}}B)$.
Also rank$((A^+)^{\frac{1}{2}}B) \leq \text{rank } B$ and the claim is proved. It can be verified using
(12.13) that $(D - B'A^+B)B'A^+B = 0$. Thus the column spaces of $D - B'A^+B$
and $B'A^+B$ are virtually disjoint (have only the zero vector in their intersection)
and hence

$$\text{rank } D = \text{rank}(D - B'A^+B) + \text{rank}(B'A^+B)$$
$$= \text{rank}(D - B'A^+B) + \text{rank } B. \tag{12.16}$$

The result follows from (12.14) and (12.16).

70. Since

$$\text{rank} \begin{bmatrix} B & C \\ D & 0 \end{bmatrix} \leq \text{rank} \begin{bmatrix} B & C \\ 0 & 0 \end{bmatrix} + \text{rank} \begin{bmatrix} 0 & 0 \\ D & 0 \end{bmatrix}$$
$$\leq \text{rank} \begin{bmatrix} B & 0 \\ 0 & 0 \end{bmatrix} + \text{rank} \begin{bmatrix} 0 & C \\ 0 & 0 \end{bmatrix} + \text{rank} \begin{bmatrix} 0 & 0 \\ D & 0 \end{bmatrix},$$

if rank $A = $ rank $B + $ rank $C + $ rank D, then by rank additivity, we see that G must be a g-inverse of each of the matrices in the above expression. This gives rise to several conditions involving E, F, H and g-inverses of B, D, C.

71. Since $AB - BA = (A - B)(A + B - I)$, by the Schur complement formula for the rank,

$$\text{rank}(AB - BA) = \text{rank}\begin{bmatrix} I & A+B-I \\ A-B & 0 \end{bmatrix} - n. \qquad (12.17)$$

Also, it can be verified by elementary row operations, that

$$\text{rank}\begin{bmatrix} I & A+B-I \\ A-B & 0 \end{bmatrix} = \text{rank}(A-B) + \text{rank}(I-A-B). \qquad (12.18)$$

The result follows from (12.17) and (12.18).

72. We have (see Exercise 17)

$$\text{rank}(AB) = \text{rank } B - \dim \mathscr{N}(A) \cap \mathscr{C}(B)$$
$$\geq \text{rank } B - \dim \mathscr{N}(A)$$
$$= \text{rank } B + \text{rank } A - n.$$

Thus if $\text{rank}(AB) = \text{rank } A + \text{rank } B - n$, then $\mathscr{N}(A) \subset \mathscr{C}(B)$. Since $\mathscr{C}(I - A^-A) = \mathscr{N}(A)$, there exists a matrix X such that $I - A^-A = BX$. Hence $A^-A = I - BX$. Now

$$ABB^-A^-AB = ABB^-(I - BX)B = ABB^-B - ABB^-BXB = AB$$

and hence B^-A^- is a g-inverse of AB.

73. If $U \subset \{1, \ldots, n\}$, then let $A(U)$ be the submatrix of A formed by the columns indexed by U. Note that $\mathscr{C}(A(S \cup T)) \subset \mathscr{C}(A(S)) + \mathscr{C}(A(T))$. Hence by the modular law,

$$\text{rank}(A(S \cup T)) \leq \dim(\mathscr{C}(A(S)) + \mathscr{C}(A(T))$$
$$= \dim \mathscr{C}(A(S)) + \dim \mathscr{C}(A(T))$$
$$- \dim(\mathscr{C}(A(S)) \cap \mathscr{C}(A(T))). \qquad (12.19)$$

Note that $\mathscr{C}(A(S \cap T)) \subset \mathscr{C}(A(S)) \cap \mathscr{C}(A(T))$ and hence

$$\dim(\mathscr{C}(A(S \cap T))) \leq \dim(\mathscr{C}(A(S)) \cap \mathscr{C}(A(T))). \qquad (12.20)$$

The result follows from (12.19), (12.20).

74. Define the augmented matrix $B = [A, I_m]$. Note that if $S \subset \{1, \ldots, m\}$, $T \subset \{1, \ldots, n\}$, then $\rho(S, T)$ equals the rank of the submatrix of B indexed by the columns in $T \cup \{n+1, \ldots, n+m\}$ minus $(m - |T|)$. Thus the result follows by applying Exercise 73 to B.

75. The result follows from Exercise 74 by making appropriate choice of S_1, S_2, T_1, T_2.

76. The result follows from Exercise 74 by making appropriate choice of S_1, S_2, T_1, T_2.

77. Let $A = BB'$ and partition $B = \begin{bmatrix} B_1 \\ B_2 \\ B_3 \end{bmatrix}$ conformally with A. Note that rank $A =$ rank B', rank$(A_{22}) =$ rank B_2', while

$$\text{rank} \begin{bmatrix} A_{11} & A_{12} \\ A_{21} & A_{22} \end{bmatrix} = \text{rank} \begin{bmatrix} B_1' & B_2' \end{bmatrix},$$

$$\text{rank} \begin{bmatrix} A_{22} & A_{23} \\ A_{32} & A_{33} \end{bmatrix} = \text{rank} \begin{bmatrix} B_2' & B_3' \end{bmatrix}.$$

The result follows by an application of Exercise 73.

Chapter 13
Notes

Chapter 1 From among the numerous books dealing with linear algebra and matrix theory we particularly mention Horn and Johnson (1985), Mehta (1989), Mirsky (1955), Rao and Rao (1998), and Strang (1980). Several problems complementing the material in this chapter are found in Zhang (1996).

Chapter 2 The proof of **2.1** is taken from Bhimasankaram (1988); this paper contains several applications of rank factorization as well.

Chapter 3 The proof of **3.5** is based on an idea suggested by N. Ekambaram. Some readers may find the development in this and the preceding sections a bit unusual. But this approach seems necessary if one wants to avoid the use of complex vector spaces and lead toward the spectral theorem.

The item "Schur complement" was coined by E. Haynsworth (1968) (see also Carlson 1986).

Chapter 4 The books by Rao and Mitra (1971), Ben-Israel and Greville (1974), and Campbell and Meyer (1979) contain a vast amount of material on the generalized inverse.

The development in Sect. 4.2 follows the treatment in Rao (1973, pp. 48–50).

Exercises 13, 14 are based on Bhaskara Rao (1983). Bapat et al. (1990) and Prasad et al. (1991) constitute a generalization of this work.

Chapter 5 Most of the material in the first four sections of this chapter has been treated in greater detail in Horn and Johnson (1985), where more inequalities on singular values and eigenvalues can be found.

The proof of **5.10** given here is due to Ikebe et al. (1987), where some related inequalities are proved using the same technique.

The standard reference for majorization is Marshall and Olkin (1979). Arnold (1987) is another entertaining book on the subject.

Section 5.5 is based on Bapat and Ben-Israel (1995); the notion of volume was introduced in Ben-Israel (1992).

R.B. Bapat, *Linear Algebra and Linear Models*, Universitext,
DOI 10.1007/978-1-4471-2739-0_13,

Chapter 6   Many of the conditions in **6.2** are contained in the papers due to S.K. Mitra and his coauthors. We refer to Carlson (1987) and Mitra (1991) for more information.

The definition of the minus partial order is attributed to Hartwig (1980) and Nambooripad (1980). Several extensions of this order have been considered; see Mitra (1991) for a unified treatment.

The star order was introduced by Drazin (1978). The result in **6.7** is due to Mitra (1986).

Exercise 8 and further properties of the parallel sum can be found in Rao and Mitra (1971). Exercise 9 and related results are in Anderson and Styan (1982). Exercises 10, 11 are based on Mitra (1986) and Mitra and Puri (1983), respectively. A solution to Exercise 12 is found in Rao (1973, p. 28).

Chapter 7   For some inequalities related to the Hadamard inequality, see Bapat and Raghavan (1997).

For a survey of Hadamard matrices we refer to Hedayat and Wallis (1978).

Christensen (1987) is a nice book emphasizing the projections approach. Sen and Srivastava (1990) is highly recommended for an account of applications of linear models.

Result **7.9** is part of the "inverse partitioned matrix method"; see Rao (1973, p. 294). The proof given here, using rank additivity, is due to Mitra (1982). Results **7.10–7.12** can be found in Rao (1973, p. 298).

Chapter 8   We refer to Muirhead (1982) for a relatively modern treatment of multivariate analysis.

There are numerous results in the literature on the distributions of quadratic forms; see the discussion in Searle (1971), Anderson and Styan (1982), and the references contained therein.

The proof of Cochran's theorem given here is not widely known.

Our treatment in this as well as the previous chapter is clearly influenced by the books by Searle (1971), Seber (1977), and Rao (1973, Chap. 4). In deriving the F-test for a linear hypothesis we have adopted a slightly different method.

For some optimal properties of the F-statistic used in one-way and two-way classifications we refer to the discussion in Scheffe (1959, Chap. 2).

Chapter 9   Linear mixed models is a vast and complex topic with several practical applications. We have outlined only some basic aspects. Our treatment primarily draws upon the books by McCulloch et al. (2008), Ravishankar and Dey (2002) and Rencher and Schaalje (2008).

Chapter 10   We refer to the books by Dey (1986), Joshi (1987), and John (1971), where much more material on block designs and further references can be found.

Exercise 14 is essentially taken from Constantine (1987), which is recommended for a readable account of optimality.

Chapter 11   Exercises 16–24 are based on the classical paper Marsaglia and Styan (1974). These results have become standard tools and the paper has influenced much of the subsequent work in the area.

The group inverse, introduced in Exercise 42, finds important applications in several areas, particularly in the theory of Markov chains; see Berman and Plemmons (1994). The group inverse of a matrix over an integral domain is studied in Prasad et al. (1991).

The Nullity Theorem in Exercise 55 is attributed to Fiedler and Markham (1986). For related results and applications see Vandebril et al. (2008). An extension to generalized inverses is given in Bapat (2003, 2007).

For more applications of generalized Schur complement and for several results related to Exercise 58, see Nordström (1989).

Exercise 64 is from Herman (2010). It is in fact true that $A + A'$ has r positive and r negative eigenvalues.

Exercises 62, 63 are from Tian (2001). The work of Yongge Tian contains significant contributions to the area of rank equalities.

Exercise 67 is from Baksalary and Trenkler (2006).

Exercise 69 is from Tian (2000).

Exercise 70 is from Bapat and Bing (2003).

Exercise 71 is from Tian and Styan (2001).

The converse of the result in Exercise 72 is true, if we assume that $AB \neq 0$, see, for example, Werner (1994). This result is an example of a "reverse order law" for generalized inverses, a topic on which there is extensive work.

Exercises 73, 74 hold in the more general set up of a matroid and a bimatroid respectively, see Murota (2000).

References

Anderson, T. W., & Styan, G. P. H. (1982). Cochran's theorem, rank additivity and tripotent matrices. In G. Kallianpur, P. R. Krishnaiah & J. K. Ghosh (Eds.), *Statistics and probability: essays in honor of C. R. Rao* (pp. 1–23). Amsterdam: North-Holland.

Arnold, B. C. (1987). *Majorization and the Lorentz order: a brief introduction*. Berlin: Springer.

Baksalary, O. M., & Trenkler, G. (2006). Rank of a nonnegative definite matrix, Problem 37-3. *IMAGE: The Bulletin of the International Linear Algebra Society, 37*, 32.

Bapat, R. B. (2003). Outer inverses: Jacobi type identities and nullities of submatrices. *Linear Algebra and Its Applications, 361*, 107–120.

Bapat, R. B. (2007). On generalized inverses of banded matrices. *The Electronic Journal of Linear Algebra, 16*, 284–290.

Bapat, R. B., & Ben-Israel, A. (1995). Singular values and maximum rank minors of generalized inverses. *Linear and Multilinear Algebra, 40*, 153–161.

Bapat, R. B., & Bing, Z. (2003). Generalized inverses of bordered matrices. *The Electronic Journal of Linear Algebra, 10*, 16–30.

Bapat, R. B., & Raghavan, T. E. S. (1997). *Nonnegative matrices and applications. Encyclopedia of mathematical sciences* (Vol. 64). Cambridge: Cambridge University Press.

Bapat, R. B., Bhaskara Rao, K. P. S., & Prasad, K. M. (1990). Generalized inverses over integral domains. *Linear Algebra Its Applications, 140*, 181–196.

Ben-Israel, A. (1992). A volume associated with $m \times n$ matrices. *Linear Algebra and Its Applications, 167*, 87–111.

Ben-Israel, A., & Greville, T. N. E. (1974). *Generalized inverses: theory and applications*. New York: Wiley-Interscience.

Berman, A., & Plemmons, R. J. (1994). *Nonnegative matrices in the mathematical sciences*. Philadelphia: SIAM.

Bhaskara Rao, K. P. S. (1983). On generalized inverses of matrices over integral domains. *Linear Algebra and Its Applications, 40*, 179–189.

Bhimasankaram, P. (1988). Rank factorization of a matrix and its applications. *The Mathematical Scientist, 13*, 4–14.

Campbell, S. L., & Meyer, C. D. Jr. (1979). *Generalized inverses of linear transformations*. London: Pitman.

Carlson, D. (1986). What are Schur complements anyway? *Linear Algebra and Its Applications, 74*, 257–275.

Carlson, D. (1987). Generalized inverse invariance, partial orders, and rank minimization problems for matrices. In F. Uhlig & R. Groine (Eds.), *Current trends in matrix theory* (pp. 81–87). New York: Elsevier.

Christensen, R. (1987). *Plane answers to complex questions: the theory of linear models*. Berlin: Springer.

Constantine, G. M. (1987). *Combinatorial theory and statistical design*. New York: Wiley.

Dey, A. (1986). *Theory of block designs*. New Delhi: Wiley Eastern.

Drazin, M. P. (1978). Natural structures on semigroups with involutions. *Bulletin of the American Mathematical Society, 84*, 139–141.

Fiedler, M., & Markham, T. L. (1986). Completing a matrix when certain entries of its inverse are specified. *Linear Algebra and Its Applications, 74*, 225–237.

Hartwig, R. E. (1980). How to order regular elements? *Mathematica Japonica, 25*, 1–13.

Haynsworth, E. V. (1968). Determination of the inertia of a partitioned Hermitian matrix. *Linear Algebra and Its Applications, 1*, 73–82.

Hedayat, A., & Wallis, W. D. (1978). Hadamard matrices and their applications. *Annals of Statistics, 6*, 1184–1238.

Herman, E. A. (2010). Square-nilpotent matrix, Problem 44-4. *IMAGE: The Bulletin of the International Linear Algebra Society, 44*, 44.

Horn, R. A., & Johnson, C. R. (1985). *Matrix analysis*. Cambridge: Cambridge University Press.

Ikebe, Y., Inagaki, T., & Miyamoto, S. (1987). The monotonicity theorem, Cauchy interlace theorem and the Courant–Fischer theorem. *The American Mathematical Monthly, 94*(4), 352–354.

John, P. W. M. (1971). *Statistical design and analysis of experiments*. New York: Macmillan.

Joshi, D. D. (1987). *Linear estimation and design of experiments*. New Delhi: Wiley Eastern.

Marsaglia, G., & Styan, G. P. H. (1974). Equalities and inequalities for ranks of matrices. *Linear and Multilinear Algebra, 2*, 269–292.

Marshall, A. W., & Olkin, I. (1979). *Inequalities: theory of majorization and its applications*. New York: Academic Press.

McCulloch, C. E., Searle, S. R., & Neuhaus, J. M. (2008). *Generalized, linear, and mixed models* (2nd ed.). New York: Wiley.

Mehta, M. L. (1989). *Matrix theory: selected topics and useful results* (enlarged re-ed.). Delhi: Hindustan Publishing Corporation.

Mirsky, L. (1955). *An introduction to linear algebra*. London: Oxford University Press.

Mitra, S. K. (1982). Simultaneous diagonalization of rectangular matrices. *Linear Algebra and Its Applications, 47*, 139–150.

Mitra, S. K. (1986). The minus partial order and the shorted matrix. *Linear Algebra and Its Applications, 83*, 1–27.

Mitra, S. K. (1991). Matrix partial orders through generalized inverses: unified theory. *Linear Algebra and Its Applications, 148*, 237–263.

Mitra, S. K., & Puri, M. L. (1983). The fundamental bordered matrix of linear estimation and the Duffin–Morley general linear electromechanical system. *Applicable Analysis, 14*, 241–258.

Muirhead, R. J. (1982). *Aspects of multivariate statistical theory*. New York: Wiley.

Murota, K. (2000). *Matrices and matroids for systems analysis. Algorithms and combinatorics* (Vol. 20). Berlin: Springer.

Nambooripad, K. S. S. (1980). The natural partial order on a regular semigroup. *Proceedings of the Edinburgh Mathematical Society, 23*, 249–260.

Nordström, K. (1989). Some further aspects of the Löwner-ordering antitonicity of the Moore–Penrose inverse. *Communications in Statistics—Theory and Methods, 18*(12), 4471–4489.

Prasad, K. M., Bhaskara Rao, K. P. S., & Bapat, R. B. (1991). Generalized inverses over integral domains II. Group inverses and Drazin inverses. *Linear Algebra and Its Applications, 146*, 31–47.

Rao, C. R. (1973). *Linear statistical inference and its applications* (2nd ed.). New York: Wiley.

Rao, C. R., & Mitra, S. K. (1971). *Generalized inverse of matrices and its applications*. New York: Wiley.

Rao, C. R., & Rao, M. B. (1998). *Matrix algebra and its applications to statistics and econometrics*. Singapore: World Scientific.

Ravishankar, N., & Dey, D. K. (2002). *A first course in linear model theory*. London/Boca Raton: Chapman & Hall/CRC.

Rencher, A. C., & Schaalje, G. B. (2008). *Linear models in statistics* (2nd ed.). New York: Wiley.

Scheffe, H. (1959). *The analysis of variance*. New York: Wiley.

Searle, S. R. (1971). *Linear models*. New York: Wiley.

Seber, G. A. F. (1977). *Linear regression analysis*. New York: Wiley.

Sen, A., & Srivastava, M. (1990). *Regression analysis: theory, methods and applications*. New York: Springer.

Strang, G. (1980). *Linear algebra and its applications* (2nd ed.). New York: Academic Press.

Tian, Y. (2000). Two rank equalities associated with blocks of an orthogonal projector, Problem 25-4. *IMAGE: The Bulletin of the International Linear Algebra Society, 25*, 16.

Tian, Y. (2001). Rank equalities related to outer inverses of matrices and applications. *Linear and Multilinear Algebra, 49*(4), 269–288.

Tian, Y., & Styan, G. P. H. (2001). Rank equalities for idempotent and involutory matrices. *Linear Algebra and Its Applications, 335*, 01-117.

Vandebril, R., Van Barel, M., & Mastronardi, N. (2008). *Matrix computations and semiseparable matrices* (Vol. 1). Baltimore: Johns Hopkins University Press.

Werner, H. J. (1994). When is $B^- A^-$ a generalized inverse of AB? *Linear Algebra and Its Applications, 210*, 255–263.

Zhang, F. (1996). *Linear algebra, challenging problems for students*. Baltimore and London: Johns Hopkins University Press.

Index